CW00427942

WHERE THE OUTBACK DROVERS RIDE

WHERE THE OUTBACK DROVERS RIDE

STORIES, POEMS AND YARNS FROM THE BUSH

BRUCE SIMPSON

ABC
Books

BOOKS BY THE SAME AUTHOR

The Territory Rouseabout and Other Humorous Verses
In Leichhardt's Footsteps
Chilla's Apprentice
Co-editor of *A Thousand Campfires*
Songs of the Droving Season
Where the Dead Men Lie

Aboriginal and Torres Strait Islander readers are warned that this book may contain images of deceased persons.

This book is a compilation of two earlier titles by Bruce Simpson: *Packhorse Drover*, first published 1996 and *Hell, Highwater and Hard Cases*, first published 1999.

Published by ABC Books for the
AUSTRALIAN BROADCASTING CORPORATION
GPO Box 9994 Sydney NSW 2001

Copyright © Bruce Simpson 2005

This edition first published 2005
Reprinted December 2005
Reprinted December 2007

All rights reserved. No part of this publication may be reproduced, stored in a retrieval system or transmitted in any form or by any means electronic, mechanical, photocopying, recording or otherwise, without the prior written permission of the Australian Broadcasting Corporation.

ISBN 0 7333 1699 9

Cover photo by Getty Images. All other photos are by the author unless otherwise credited.
Designed by Christabella Designs
Set in 10.5/14 pt Sabon by Midland Typesetters, Maryborough, Victoria
Printed by Shannon Books, Victoria

5 4 3

This book is dedicated to the memory of all those tough characters and hard cases who helped tame the outback but also, most especially, to my father Donald Forbes Simpson, pioneer bushman, and my mother, who faced the wilderness with him.

The author, Bruce Forbes Simpson.

AUTHOR'S NOTE

I WAS FORTUNATE enough to be part of the droving game at a time when it was much the same as in the days of Nat Buchanan. When change did come, it came with a rush. Within a few short years the sound of motors had replaced the music of horsebells, and the day of the packhorse drover had passed into history. In this book I have tried to give the reader an insight into a way of life that is now part of our great cultural heritage.

The men who opened up the Northern Territory to cattle were of heroic mould. It is true that the time and circumstances helped them to achieve greatness, but the spirit to dare and the will to endure were theirs alone. We must never forget them, for their ilk will not pass this way again.

ACKNOWLEDGMENTS

THERE ARE MANY people who I would like to thank for their help and encouragement. My sincere thanks to the following: Jack Cunningham of Brisbane, Qld; Mrs Lola Rowe of Mildura, Vic; Cecil Teece of Normanton, Qld; Peter Treloar of Delaney Creek, Qld; Peter Knowls of Winton, Qld; Rod Bellette of Patterson Lakes, Vic; Kerry Kendall of Middlemount, Qld; Jim 'Ringer' Edwards of Gin Gin, WA; Jim Pearson of Gatton, Qld; Merv Rogers of Charters Towers, Qld; Luke McCall of Batlow, NSW; Roy Hulbert of Bangalow, NSW; Bob Isles of Redcliffe, Qld; Lucky Forrester of Strathpine, Qld; Barry Desailly of North Ward, Qld; Les Huddy of Mt Isa, Qld; Gordon Gaffney of Tamworth, NSW; Ray Webster of Landsborough, Qld; George Booth Jnr of Port Douglas, Qld; Alf Chambers of Taroom, Qld; Darell Lewis of Canberra, ACT; Mick Bailey of Broken Hill, NSW; Tidly Treffett of Charters Towers, Qld; Frank Uhr of Finch Hatton, Qld; Alex Logan of Kumbia, Qld; Ernie McCarthy of Pine Creek, NT; Eddie Hackman of Rockhampton, Qld; Herb Huemiller of Barcaldine, Qld; Ian Tait of Koumala, Qld; Jack Gardner of Caloundra, Qld; Bob Kirk of Herbert Downs, Qld; Mal Debney of Glenormiston Station, Qld; Walter Lloyd of Boulia, Qld; Bob Howard of Caboolture, Qld; Ross Ratcliffe of The Willows, Qld; Jeff Simpson of Stanthorpe, Qld; Merv Thomas of Landsborough, Qld; Mick Thomas of Barcaldine, Qld; Noel Thompson of D'Aguilar, Qld; Eugene Costin, of Brunette Downs, NT; Barney Bellford of Eukey, Qld; Bobby McDonald of Barcaldine, Qld; Tony Roberts of Canberra, ACT; Gilbert Macintosh of Mt Isa; Qld; Tom Cusack of Mittiebah Station, NT; Noel 'Pic' Willetts of Camooweal, Qld; Rodney Mosted of Camooweal, Qld; John Chaplain of Cloncurry, Qld; Jack Drake of Eukey, Qld; Ab Teece of Cloncurry, Qld; Mrs Ada Devereaux of Brisbane, Qld; Ron Easey of Petrie, Qld; Chris Gladwell and Jim Cuming of the Stockmen's Hall of Fame office, Brisbane, Qld; Colin Campbell of Mitchell, Qld; Sam Fuller Jnr of Mitchell, Qld; Bill Alexander of Marian Downs, Qld; Blue Ellis of Bankstown, NSW; Ray Gillham of Suttor Creek Station, Qld; Lyn Craig of Eton, Qld; Laurie Hansen of Finch Hatton, Qld; the staff of the John Oxley and State Library, Brisbane, Qld; Steve Millard of the NAPCO office, Brisbane, Qld; Jim Kennedy of Brisbane, Qld; Graham Murchie of Stanthorpe, Qld; Lloyd Linson-Smith of Oakey, Qld; Ian Tinney of Brisbane, Qld; Keith Haughton of Narangba, Qld; Bob Nash of Pinnacle, Qld; Peter Isles of Redcliffe, Qld; Fred Holm of Winton, Qld; Larry Holm of Townsville, Qld; Brian Holm of Winton, Qld; Bill Moore of Redcliffe, Qld; Mick Cheadle, now of Millungera Station, Qld; Graham McKerrow of Weona Station, Winton, Qld; Matt Masterson of Mareeba, Qld; Alex Long of Caboolture, Qld; Bobbie Buchanan of Berry Springs, NT; Ron Bates of Gatton, Qld; Tim Butler of the ABC; Ted Egan of Alice Springs; Alf Chambers of Taroom; Cec Watts of Rockhampton; Bob Gordon of Roma; Jack Charlton of Scone; Dick Scobie of Charters Towers; Peter Treloar of Delaney's Creek; Ced Teece of Rockhampton; Mrs Jeff Hill of 'Glencovie', Munna Creek; Jim Pola of the staff of the *North Queensland Register*; and lastly my son Ranald for his technical help in producing the manuscript for *Hell, Highwater & Hard Cases* and my daughter Fiona who did the original typing of *Packhorse Drover*.

All poems in the book with the exception of 'Where the Pelican Builds' are by the author.

The poems in this book have appeared in various papers and periodicals including Sydney *Bulletin*, the *North Queensland Register*, *Hoofs and Horns*, the *North Queensland Monthly* and the *Longreach Leader*. Many have appeared in the *Bronze Swagman Book of Verse* and other books of collected verse.

CONTENTS

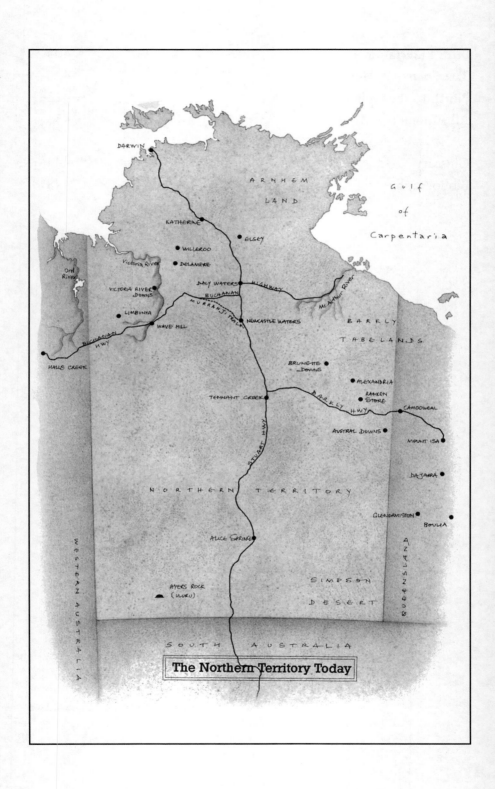

DARWIN

ARNHEM

LAND

Gulf

of

Carpentaria

KATHERINE

ELSEY

WILLEROO

Victoria River

DELAMERE

Ord
River

DALY WATERS

HIGHWAY

VICTORIA RIVER
DOWNS

BUCHANAN

McArthur River

LIMBUNNA

MURRANJI TRACK

NEWCASTLE WATERS

BARKLY

WAVE HILL

TABELANDS

BUCHANAN
HWY

HALLS CREEK

BRUNETTE
DOWNS

ALEXANDRIA

RANKEN
STORE

TENNANT CREEK

BARKLY

HWY

CAMOOWEAL

STUART HWY

AUSTRAL DOWNS

MOUNT ISA

DAJARRA

NORTHERN   TERRITORY

GLENORMISTON

BOULIA

ALICE SPRINGS

WESTERN   AUSTRALIA

AYERS ROCK
(ULURU)

SIMPSON

DESERT

QUEENSLAND

SOUTH   AUSTRALIA

The Northern Territory Today

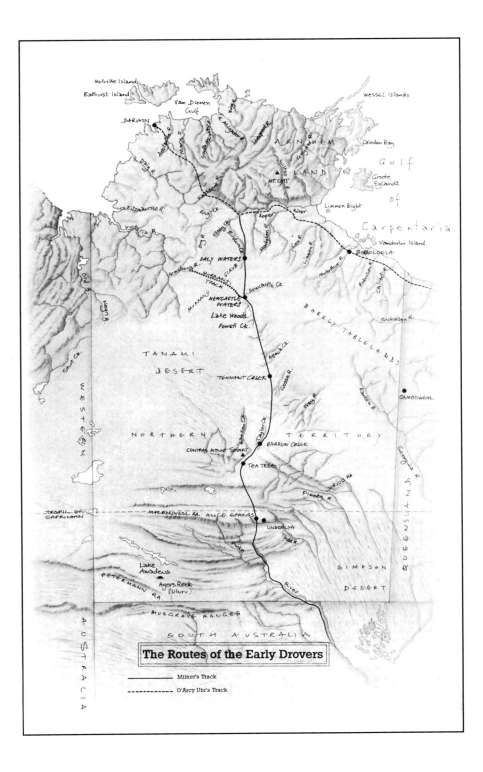

The Routes of the Early Drovers

——————— Milner's Track

- - - - - - - - - D'Arcy Uhr's Track

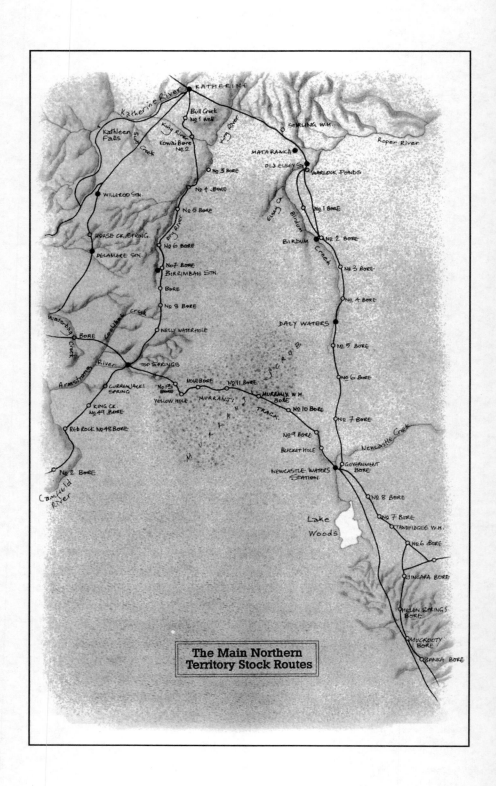

The Main Northern Territory Stock Routes

FOREWORD

BRUCE SIMPSON IS a unique man. He joins the likes of 'Breaker' Morant and, latterly, Bert Facey and Tom Cole as a true bushman sufficiently articulate and eloquent to relate his personal experiences in literary form. And he covers a unique part of Australia's lifestyle— 'the droving game'. Much has been written about droving: largely the personal experiences of others, related via the pens of professional writers like Mary Durack and Keith Willey. Bruce Simpson tells it in the first person.

Bruce Simpson was a drover—and a 'packhorse drover' at that—right up to the 1960s when road trains were introduced to perform the long hauls of cattle to market. Droving is a bit like the Man from Snowy River legend: every second person's grandfather was either the 'stripling on a small and weedy beast' or a famous drover. On closer questioning, you perhaps find that grand-dad walked 100 sheep 50 miles (80 kilometres). But, year after year, Simpson walked a mob of Territory cattle—usually 1000 to 1200 in the mob—over 1000 miles (1600 kilometres) to either the railhead at Dajarra or to the fattening properties 'inside' (as drovers would put it) in Queensland.

They would be months on the road, experiencing incredible privations of heat and cold, living in 'cigarette' swags on a diet of beef, damper and tea, and taking incredible responsibility for a pittance in payment as they battled with this harsh continent. Many of the drovers became callous brutes and the best of them were tough and uncompromising. As Bruce Simpson says, 'You looked after the cattle, the horses, and the men—in that order'.

Yes, Bruce Forbes Simpson is tough and uncompromising. He is a proud, determined man, proud of his Celtic (Scottish in his case) ancestry, and proud of the role played by Celts in the pioneering of the land. He is aggressively determined to retain 'old fashioned' values in this country, and asserts that meticulous effort and the work ethic are the best means of keeping the country sound. He would not use words like 'enthnocentric' himself, but would probably not mind that adjective being used to describe him. He is fiercely nationalistic and deplores any moves by Australians to imitate Americans or English, either in speech, dress, habit or use of equipment. He fairly bristles if he hears Australians sing in half-baked Yankee accents, or use words like cowboy, ranch, corral or stampede. At the same time he was delighted to represent Australia at the Cowboy Poetry Gathering at Elko, Nevada, in 1990, where he had a great time swapping yarns and poetry, and talking horses and cattle with the real cowboys—the ones with huge horny hands, from places like Wyoming, where they still ride horses as they work their ranches.

There have been many wonderful observers of bush life and the 'outback ethos' and many Australians, living in the cities, yearn for and speak nostalgically of 'the vision splendid of the sunlit plains extended'. Thanks to Lawson, Mackellar, Ogilvie, Paterson, Gilmore, Wright and others, Australians can live in suburbia yet turn to the open plains, the dust, the sunsets and the sunrises, and the bellow of cattle and the smell of gum leaves via their literary works. If we want the bush on a more scholarly level, we read McAuley, Hope, Murray, Stewart and Neilson. If you want it straight from the bushman himself, you will enjoy this book.

Bruce Simpson's poems have often been attributed to other people, or to that ubiquitous poet 'Anon'. I published 'The Drover's Life' and attributed it, incorrectly, to Wally Dowling when in fact it was written by Simpson. This is understandable if you know how the 'literary thing' worked in the bush in earlier days. Books like *Such is Life* tell us that itinerants always had a 'borrow book' or a 'swap book' in their swags. You possessed the book until perhaps you knew the content 'by heart'; then you 'swapped' it. It was thus that the bush library operated and people educated themselves. Another habit was to write out in longhand in an 'exercise book' any poems that one sought to learn or liked to recite. Under these circumstances, it often became easier to accept the plaudits on a personal level than explain that somebody else had written the poem. Perhaps a line would be changed or a reference personalised. When Wally Dowling, the Canning Stockroute drover, died, books of poems were found in his saddlebags and it was assumed he had written them. In this way, many of Bruce Simpson's poems have been 'borrowed'; typically, he has 'copped' this as 'one of those things that happen in the bush'.

It has been a thrill and a privilege for me to have assisted in a minor way in having Bruce Simpson's many fine poems recognised and published in this book. Equally, it is wonderful that he has recorded the detail of a droving tradition developed in Australia and unparalleled in the world. Australians, especially schoolchildren, need to be told that the world's biggest movements of stock did not take place in Brazil, or Mexico, or the United States, or Canada or Africa. They took place in Australia.

It is important to note that as a 'packhorse drover', Bruce Simpson carried on the exact traditions, techniques and skills used by the incomparable Nat Buchanan in the 1880s. Sadly, there's no more singing on watch, for 'silent drivers ride the night' as their huge trucks speed over the landscape. Nor are there any more of the monumental drinking sprees in Dajarra, Camooweal, Boulia or 'at the six-mile in Wyndham' as the drovers cut out their cheques. It is no wonder they drank, for it was tough, boring relentless work. Yet they did it, hundreds of them, and never thought of themselves as being clever, or special, or unique.

So why do I think Bruce Simpson is unique? Because not only did he 'go a droving' for so many years, he can speak with absolute authority about the period with the expressive ability of a self-educated man. And because he can write (in respect of his much-loved horse, Actor) poetry like this:

Actor farewell! Till your last long sleep,
May never the creeks run dry,
May the grass be whispering fetlock deep,
Forever, Old Chap, Goodbye.

Ted Egan

Bruce Simpson, left, *with Jimmy Charles,* right,
with Sam Fuller's plant in 1951.

Ian Tinney

The Drover's Statue in the Memorial Park of Newcastle Waters.

THE PACKHORSE DROVER

Oh the droving life is a life that's free,
On the unfenced routes of the back country,
And a packhorse camp is the place to be,
When they're bringing the store mobs over;
Oh life is happy with not a care,
With the bush smells strong on the balmy air,
For a whiff of the cook would curl your hair,
In the camp of the packhorse drover.

Now the drover's bed is a couch to please,
On the stony ground mid the Bogan fleas,
Or in mud that is up to a horse's knees,
When the wintry rains drift over;
But life is happy and life is sweet,
Tho' there's never enough for a man to eat,
And losing weight is a simple feat,
In the camp of a packhorse drover.

The sky is grey with a hint of rain,
While the wind blows chill o'er the Rankine plain,
And a ringer swears that he'll drove again,
When the ceiling of Hell frosts over;
But life is happy and life is good,
'Round a cow dung fire when there is no wood,
When the damper tastes as it never should,
In the camp of a packhorse drover.

We watch the mob and we sing the blues,
And we'd sell our souls for a nip of booze,
As the hours drag by on their leaden shoes,
And the Southern Cross turns over;
It's a rugged life but we never whine,
For the mateship found in the bush is fine,
Tho' the boss of course is a hungry swine,
And a typical packhorse drover.

*Packing a mule with water canteens.
A windbreak for the nighthorses can
be seen in the background.*

NIGHT WATCH ON THE DRY RIVER ROUTE

THE NIGHTHORSE I was riding picked his way carefully around the sleeping bullocks. As I whistled tunelessly, I looked over the mob of big, aged, store-conditioned bullocks bred in the rough country south-west of Katherine. There was no moon and the Southern Cross was dipping towards the horizon. It was possible to see quite clearly, however, for it is never really dark in the Australian bush, except when there are low, heavy clouds.

Actor walked steadily around the camped cattle with no guidance from me. He was one of those unique nighthorses that knew as much as any man. The camp was not a good one, but it was the best available. The area was in light timber country with scattered antbeds and some fallen timber. As I rode around the tightly packed bullocks, I could see their big arching horns gleaming softly in the starlight. They were a bad mob; during the week since I had taken delivery of them they had exploded off the night camp in a maddened rush no less than four times. So far we had managed to hold them without loss, but I knew there was no cause for complacency, for when mobs like this rushed, they roared off the camp in a bovine avalanche that crashed over and through everything in its path. It was my first droving trip as a boss drover and with me I had three Aboriginal ringers, a white cook, and my young brother Jeff, who, at the time, was relatively inexperienced. We still had to face the Murranji scrub, but I was confident that we would get the mob through despite the trouble we'd had.

I passed the camp and was riding towards the back of the mob when somewhere behind me a bullock stood on a dry stick. In a split second the mob was on its feet and galloping. I stood up in the stirrups and bellowed, 'Whoa bullocks, whoa bullocks'. To my surprise and relief, the mob wheeled sharply and started to ring madly around, just off the cattle camp. The thundering hoofs of the tightly massed beasts stirred up a maelstrom of dust and flying debris. As I called out to the mob to calm them, I could feel the thudding of Actor's heart through the saddle flaps and was aware of my own racing pulse. The surge of adrenalin that triggered a sharpening of the reflexes and an enhancement of the senses was not unfamiliar to me, and I thanked God that the mob had not rushed.

The bullocks were owned by Vestey's, an English company with a string of stations across the Territory and the East Kimberley region. As I rode and sang to the mob, I wondered if the company's directors had any inkling of the problems and perils faced by the men who moved cattle to market. Slowly the mob settled down and my thoughts turned to the train of events that had resulted in me becoming a boss drover.

THE EARLY YEARS

IT IS PROBABLY true to say that the bush is in my blood. Looking back at my childhood, it is difficult to see how my life could have unfolded differently. I was reared with my brothers on a small selection, one of a number cut off old Pinnacle Station, west of Mackay. The unimproved block was virgin tropical scrub and forest when taken up by my father in 1923, the year I was born.

My parents were no strangers to the bush, although before she was married my mother had led a relatively sheltered life as a station governess in the Mundubbera area. She was a member of a well-known pioneering family, her grandfather John Connolly having been one of the first settlers on the Burnett. He was known as the father of Gayndah and must have been a tough character, for he lived to one hundred and three. My mother told me he smoked a pipe and chopped wood to the very end. My father was born in Australia and was an only child. His father was Scottish, and although his mother was born of Scottish parents, she first saw the light of day in Calcutta, in 1857, the year of the Indian mutiny.

On finishing his education at Maryborough Grammar, my father, against the wishes of his parents, went bush. He worked on cattle stations in the Dawson Valley and on Cape York Peninsula. When World War I broke out, he was managing Bonny Downs, a mixed cattle and sheep property in the Muttaburra district. He enlisted early in 1915, and soon after sailed for France. He won his sergeant's stripes at the front, but late in the war was badly gassed. In 1919 he returned to Australia and married my mother, to whom he had become engaged before sailing.

After my parents' marriage, my father managed Gowan Hills in the Blackall area until he drew the block. My elder brother Keith was born during this period, and in 1923 my mother and he travelled to Brisbane to await my arrival—while my father went to Mackay to take up the selection. The block was far too small to run cattle alone; in North Queensland the talk then was all of sugar growing and the country had been cut up with that in mind.

My father arrived on the selection with one saddle horse and a packhorse. That night as he unrolled his swag under the tall gums, it must have seemed to him like the fulfilment of a dream. For years he had worked on other people's properties; now at last he had his own place. He was not to know that in a few short years the Great Depression would almost destroy that dream.

My father's first task was to fence the selection. He set to cutting and splitting the posts from the giant bloodwood trees that grew in the open forest country. The fencing done, he bought a few head of cattle and a team of horses. The best land for sugar growing was on the creek flats; the deep, rich soil there was covered in rainforest, a tangled thicket of vines, palms and huge trees. Working on his own with a block and tackle, my father cleared enough to plant his first crop.

By the middle of 1923 I had put in an appearance, and my father, keen to re-unite the family, ordered the material for a house and contracted a teamster to bring the load out to the selection. After paying for the building material there was enough money left to purchase a light wagon, a buggy and the necessary farm machinery, but the bank would have to carry the place until the first crop was harvested. It was at that point that unkind fate stepped in. The teamster bringing the load out had an accident as the wagon was negotiating a jump-up. He was taken to Mackay hospital, and the building material was off-loaded on the spot.

It was a few days before my father heard of the mishap. He rode over to find that the whole load had been stolen, not a stick of timber or a nail remained. Cursing his luck, my father, who was now forced to improvise, started on the job with little more than a crosscut saw and an axe. Out of bush timber, he erected a crude two-room house with an open front verandah. It had a dirt floor and a bark roof. My mother, who had been used to living in spacious homesteads, must have received a shock when we arrived. However, she made the best of things and somehow managed to cope. My father, toiling from dawn to dusk to make the selection viable, did what he could to help and knocked up a charcoal cooler to keep perishables from the heat and flies. Under my mother's influence, the rough dwelling soon developed the atmosphere of a home.

To keep the dust down, the dirt floor had to be sprinkled with water and swept each morning. The smell of damp earth still brings back memories of the old home to me. As water had to be carried up from the creek in buckets, my mother did the family wash at a shallow rocky stretch in the stream. Later when water was brought up in a 100 gallon (450 litre) tank on a horse-drawn slide, she used a wood-fired clothes boiler and tin tubs. With no phone or radio, my mother worried constantly about us children. During the Wet, we were sometimes cut off completely for weeks at a time as the normally placid creeks roared on their way to join the Pioneer River.

With the first crop harvested, things looked up a little and my father bought enough galvanised iron to cover the bark roof. This made the place a lot more weatherproof and quite cool.

During the wet season, however, the gap between the bark and the iron provided a snug haven for the green frogs that croaked all night and added to my mother's woes. The selection was lousy with snakes, which at times got into the roof chasing the frogs. I have a vivid recollection, when a child, of seeing a large snake with a frog in its mouth fall out of the roof onto the dinner table.

To beautify the home a little, my mother made hanging baskets for the verandah and filled them with ferns from the creek. She got my father to enclose the area with wire netting, then trained sweet peas to cover the mesh. My mother fussed endlessly over the sweet peas; I don't think any of us realised just how much they meant to her. When she won a box brownie in a competition run by the *Woman's Mirror*, one of the first photos taken was of the sweet peas.

The one thing our home did not lack was reading material. My maternal grandmother owned and ran a large lending library in Brisbane, and mindful of our isolation, she bundled up the books that became too dog-eared for circulation and sent them to us.

We received books of every description, from *Westward Ho* to *On Our Selection*, from *Tom Brown's Schooldays* to *Lasseter's Last Ride*. Long before my elder brother and I could read, our parents often read these books to us a chapter at a time. Later, when I could read myself, a copy of the *Bulletin Reciter* arrived in a parcel. I read it avidly and an enduring love of bush verse was born.

Before the arrival of my two younger brothers, my father added two extra rooms plus a back verandah to the home and put down a wooden floor throughout. The place had been built as a temporary dwelling only; now it was taking on the appearance of a permanent residence. My mother, however, had her own ideas about its future and my father promised her he would build her the home she wanted as soon as he could afford it.

My mother cooked on an old wood stove with a hot water fountain fixed to its side. On cold winter evenings it became the centre of the family's social life. We would all sit around the stoked-up stove while my elder brother and I pressed our father to tell us of his experiences in the outback. We would listen spellbound as he spoke in a quiet voice of cattle duffing, buckjumpers, Aboriginal culture, and epic feats of endurance. He also told stories of Bully Hayes, the notorious blackbirder who shanghaied natives from the Pacific Islands and brought them back in his ship to sell as cheap labour to the early Queensland sugar growers. It was heady stuff to a youngster growing up in the bush and I went to sleep each night dreaming of the time when I would be old enough to seek adventure for myself. The valley in which we lived was surrounded on three sides by mountains. As a young boy I often looked at those hills and promised myself that one day I would find out what lay beyond them.

If those early days were a constant trial to my mother, they were a delight to my brothers and me. The selection teemed with wildlife of every description; there was either a koala or a possum in every tree, sugar gliders feasted on the blossoms of bloodwood and gum trees, while bandicoots, rat kangaroos and wallabies all shared the bush with us. As youngsters we had just about every kind of bush creature imaginable as a pet. Our mother suffered them all, although our echidna sometimes got us into trouble because of its habit of digging holes everywhere.

Beatrice Creek meandered through the property, running clear and cool between the tropical rainforest that lined its banks. The creek teemed with fish, harboured a number of water rats and was home to a family of platypuses. During the summer months we swam in its palm-fringed swimming holes, made crude boats to play at blackbirding, and dived to the sandy bottom to gather imaginary pearl shell. All in all, it was an idyllic lifestyle and I dare say we were as close to nature as it is possible to get.

As we grew older we gave our mother grey hairs by wandering further afield with a mate who knew more about bush tucker than the Bush Tucker Man himself. By the time we were of school age we were virtually capable of living off the land. One of our favourite sports was snake hunting. We would arm ourselves with green sticks about 6 feet (2 metres) long, then whistling to the dogs, we would set out into the bush to do battle with our sworn enemies.

We had two dogs that were expert snake killers. Working as a team, they could deal with any snake, including the king browns and the big red-bellied blacks that in the summer months seemed to be everywhere. The dogs' technique was simple, but very effective—as one teased the snake, the other would dash in and, grasping the reptile in its jaws, would shake it violently, breaking its back. If the snake was a very large one, they would take turns doing this until they had it completely immobilised. We would then move in and administer the coup de grace with our waddies.

We went on these expeditions with bare legs and feet. Looking back, I suppose there was some risk, but we were bushwise kids aware of the dangers. A neighbour's son in our age group was bitten by a snake and died. My mother was appalled by the tragedy, but it did little to dampen our enthusiasm for the hunt. Years later it was discovered that the area was a taipan habitat. By today's enlightened standards there is no doubt that our activities would be classed as environmental vandalism. However, back in those days, when medical help was virtually out of reach, the only good snake was deemed to be a dead one.

The best snake dog we ever had was Pincer. Right from the time my elder brother Keith and I were toddlers she was our constant companion. Pincer was not all that good with stock, but because she was so protective of us, Mother thought the world of her. While out hunting on her own one day, Pincer met the fate of most snake dogs. I don't know what type of snake killed her, but it must have been a bad one, for in her efforts to get home, she crawled only 20 yards from the log under which she had been scratching. We carried her body home and gave her a solemn burial. My mother wept openly, while Keith and I stood silently with constricted throats and dry eyes. Boys did not cry those days.

Each year we travelled to Mackay twice, once just before Christmas, and on Anzac Day. The first part of the trip was made in our buggy, pulled by Dolly, a reliable grey mare. At the railway siding she would be tied up with a nosebag on, until we returned that night.

Christmas was of course always something we looked forward to with relish, for it was the only time we had ham and soft drink. The ham arrived packed in oat husks and stockinet. It was carefully unwrapped and cooked with due ceremony in the cleaned-out clothes boiler. The soft drink was home-brewed ginger beer and a type of hop beer called horehound. The brew was started well before the big day, and usually all went well. There were times, however, when the silence of the bush night was shattered by the sounds of exploding bottles. When this happened, it was panic stations until the remaining bottles had been uncorked. I suppose it was a bit like disarming live bombs, but, then, soft drink in those days was not the everyday thirst quencher it is today.

My mother decorated the house with native plants and gum tips that we gathered for her. The pièce de résistance on the Christmas dinner table was always her great boiled plumduff. We would hoe into it in the hope of finding the threepenny bits she had secreted among the fruit and nuts. Later, in the outback, I had some rather lean Christmases, and looked back with nostalgia at those early Christmas dinners.

Anzac Day was quite different. Although my father never spoke of his time at the front, the Great War—as it was called—exerted a subtle yet powerful influence over the families of all who fought in it. We always arrived in Mackay in time to watch the march. My father, however, never marched himself and wore no medals, just his returned soldiers' badge. After the march he always attended the reunion lunch, then met us in the park, where we would picnic with the families of other returned men.

As a returned soldier my father never received or asked to receive any privileges other than those accorded to an ordinary citizen. Only once did I hear him address in a rather derogatory manner a man who had not enlisted. The incident occurred during a wharf lumpers' strike in the depression years. As the stockpile of unshipped sugar built up, the mills stopped crushing and the industry ground to a halt.

A man who was trying to organise the growers into a strike-breaking gang rode over to enlist the help of my father. When he had finished putting his case, my father looked up at the rider and said, 'Are you asking me to go in and scab on the men I fought with?'

'Well,' replied the visitor. 'We have to keep the home fires burning, you know.'

There was a touch of cold anger in my father's voice as he dismissed the man. 'I'll leave the home fires to you. After all, you got a lot of practice stoking them when we were fighting in France.'

As the would-be strike breaker rode off, I felt very proud of my father.

When my elder brother reached school age, my mother decided to teach him by correspondence until I was old enough to ride to school with him. The nearest school was built beside a road some miles from the nearest township. To shorten the route to the school, my father blazed a track through the bush for us to follow. In time the bridle track became a well-used road. Riding there was not a problem as we had been taught to ride almost as soon as we could walk. Paddy, our first pony, had died, so it was on Playboy that we rode to school, bareback and double-bank; saddles were out, as my father contended that the only way to learn to ride was bareback. Playboy was a bay horse of about 15 hands. We mounted him by putting our toes in his knee and swinging up from there.

As we were old enough to go to school, it was decided that we should help around the place. Each morning before riding to school we had to muster the work horses and the milkers, then milk the cows, and separate the milk so that my mother could make butter. After a quick swim in the creek, it was off to school for the three Rs, interposed with a bit of mayhem. After school we helped unharness and feed the horses, chopped wood for the stove and generally made ourselves useful. What homework we had was done by the light of a hurricane lamp.

As the 1920s ended, sugar prices fell, banks crashed and credit became unobtainable. As unemployment grew, men carried their swags in search of work. I remember clearly the sad procession of down-at-heel swagmen, many of them returned soldiers, who called at our place in the hope of getting a job or a handout. None went away empty-handed, for although we had little money, we were close to being self-sufficient as far as food went. As the depression deepened, despair and hopelessness seemed to be everywhere and my mother saw her cherished plans for a new home, together with her ambition to send us to boarding school, fade into the realm of impossible dreams.

Despite the depression, I managed to acquire a horse of my own, although I still did not have a saddle. The gelding was a smart-looking chestnut about five years old. He had been kept as a stallion for some time and bore the impressive name of Robert Dean. I shortened his name to Bobby and felt 10 feet tall when I rode him about the district. Before long I found that by touching him on the rump, I could get him to kick up with both hind feet. I regarded this as great fun, and soon had him kicking up so high that the only way I could stay on him was to lean back while jamming my bare feet under his front legs.

My father jumped on him one day to go after some stock; Bobby went into his act and nearly unseated him. Later I was taken to task.

'You've been teaching that horse tricks, haven't you?'

There was little sense in denying it. 'Well, I want to work on stations later and I've got to learn to ride.'

'I see. If I were you, I'd be careful the horse doesn't learn faster than you do.'

I caught the hint of a smile as my father walked away.

One of my more pleasant tasks was to ride into the township of Pinnacle every Saturday to pick up mail and any rations we needed. My father allowed me to use his saddle for the trip, as it made it easier to carry a split bag. A split bag is made by sewing up the open end of a sack bag then cutting one side across the middle; the resulting split bag is thrown over the back of the saddle to provide a roomy pocket on each side. I usually took a short cut to the township, fording Cattle Creek, then crossing the Pinnacle plains past the grave of a young stockman who had been killed in a fall from a horse. I always saluted the headstone as I cantered past on Bobby.

Once upon returning with the mail, I left the saddle on the ground up against a post rather than hanging it up. A cattle pup that I had just acquired got stuck into the lining, tearing it to pieces. My father gave me two options: get rid of the pup or repair the saddle myself. To me, the choice was simple. I cadged some curtain material from my mother and, at a very tender age, was to line my first saddle.

At times stockmen would bring mobs of draughthorses from Charters Towers to sell to the farmers. Whenever I got the chance, I rode around with them. They would yarn about life over the range, and as I listened, I became more determined to see it all for myself.

NORTH TO THE TERRITORY

I HAD ALWAYS wanted to work in the Northern Territory, and finally I got the chance. But when I threw my gear onto the Northern mail train one night early in 1944, I had little idea of the problems that lay ahead of me. Before leaving Brisbane I had dropped in to the office of the North Australian Pastoral Company and talked to D.M. Fraser, the company's managing director. He greeted me in a friendly manner and listened to my story; he appeared to me to be a man who took a fatherly interest in the staff of all the NAPC's stations. Before I left the office, he told me there was a job as stockman on Alexandria waiting for me and wished me well.

I arrived in Mt Isa three days after leaving Brisbane. I left the train with some relief, and stretched my legs as I looked the place over. Mt Isa, those days, had the raw dusty look of most mining towns in the early years of development. I rolled a smoke and considered a plan of action. The first thing was to find out when, and with whom, I could get a ride out to Alexandria. As the railway station was on the mine side, well away from the town, I decided to leave my gear on one of the seats on the platform. I had less than five pounds to my name; if the worst came to the worst, I could always camp on the platform. I was just walking off when I heard a bellow.

'Is this gear yours?'

I turned to see a railway employee glaring at me.

'Yes. Why?'

'Well, get it out of here before I call the cops.'

'Christ,' I thought to myself. 'Welcome to Mt Isa.'

What I did not realise was that the police had alerted every government employee to be on the lookout for soldiers who were AWL and heading for the Territory.

I picked up my swag and headed for the town. As I crossed the low causeway across the Leichhardt River, I saw ahead of me the friendly facade of the Argent Hotel. Bush pubs are always a good source of information and I needed a drink badly. I pushed open the swinging doors, threw my swag in the corner and headed for the bar. The man behind the bar wandered over in a rather uninterested manner.

'Any chance of a beer?'

'Nope, not until the shift finishes at four o'clock.'

'Any rum?'

He looked at me as if I'd just arrived from Mars. 'There's a war on, you know.'

'So they tell me. What the hell have you got?'

'There's lolly water.'

'Well, that'll do.'

I watched him pour some locally made soft drink into a glass. He pushed it over to me.

'That'll be a bob.'

I gave him a shilling and took a drink of the sickly stuff, then asked him, 'Who runs the mail or loading out to Alexandria?'

'Trying to get to the Territory, are you?' He looked me over. 'We'll, you'd better see Les Peak.'

I finished the drink. 'Where do I find him?'

He told me, and as I was walking out, called me back.

'Don't leave your swag there. These bloody miners will kick it to pieces trying to get to the bar. Leave it by the office.'

I took his advice, and after a couple of minutes walking I found Peak's yard. There were a number of trucks parked, with a couple being serviced. A chap pulled his head out from under a bonnet as I asked, 'Where will I find Les Peak?'

Without answering, he jerked his thumb in the direction of a shed that I could see doubled as an office.

Les Peak greeted me affably and asked what he could do for me.

'I've got a job on Alexandria. When is your next trip out there?'

'Won't be 'till Sunday. It'll cost you two quid.'

'Fair enough. I'll pay you now—the way I'm going, I won't have it later.'

Les scratched me out a receipt, then looked up. 'You'll need a permit.'

'What do you mean?'

He laughed at my apparent innocence. 'The Territory is under martial law. You can't get in without a permit.'

'Well, where do I get a blasted permit?'

'At the manpower office. It's just across from the Argent on the left before you go over the river.'

I thanked him, saying I'd see him on Sunday, and left.

As I walked back to the pub, I realised I had a problem. The permit should not be difficult to obtain, but Sunday was four days away and I had just over two pounds in my pocket. Camping on the river was out, I decided. It was likely that anyone found camping there would be thrown into gaol for life. I came to the conclusion that the sensible thing to do was to see the publican. The permit could wait until the morrow.

When I got back to the Argent I found the area around the bar chock-a-block with thirsty miners struggling to get a drink. It looked like something between a riot and a rugby union ruck. I gave it a wide berth and went to the office, where I found Stewart Summerville, the licensee. I introduced myself and told him everything. He looked at me appraisingly.

'You're not AWL?'

'No, I'm not.'

I unrolled my swag, pulled out a small writing case and set his mind at rest.

'You say you've got a job in the Alexandria camp?'

I nodded. 'You can ring Brisbane and verify it if you wish.'

'That's all right. There's a bed on the verandah, and I'll stand you board. Send in a cheque as soon as you can.'

I thanked him, and with my faith in human nature restored, I took my swag upstairs.

The next morning at ten o'clock I strolled over to the manpower office. I had had a hearty breakfast and was feeling on top of the world. I entered the office and stood at the counter. A middle-aged clerk saw me, but went back to writing something or other at his desk. After a couple of minutes I knocked on the counter. The clerk looked at me as though I'd just broken wind, but grudgingly came over.

'What do you want?'

I was determined to be pleasant.

'I'd like a permit to enter the Territory, please.'

'Do you? For what reason?'

'I've got a job to go to on Alexandria.'

'Have you? Do you have a clearance from manpower?'

I looked at him stupidly. 'A what?'

'A clearance. You just can't go where you please these days. We tell you where you will work.'

'Well, can you organise it? They expect me out there on the first truck.'

'I don't think you heard me. We tell you where you can work. Now, where did you work last, and for whom?'

I thought for a while, then told him, trying not to lose patience.

'Well, you will have to go back there.'

I looked at him incredulously. 'What the hell do you mean?'

'You will have to go back and work where you worked last.'

'Look, I'll say it again. I've got a job. Ring up the North Australian Pastoral Company if you don't believe me.'

'You will have to go back and see the manpower office where you last worked.'

He was beginning to sound like a broken gramophone record. I forced myself to reason with him.

'I've paid my fare out to Alexandria, but I've only got a few shillings left. I can't go anywhere.'

He looked at me sternly. 'That puts you in the same category as a vagrant.'

'No, it puts you in the same category as a bloody cretin. Are you going to pay my fare back and give Summerville the week's board I owe him?'

It was a calculated bluff. For all I knew he may have been able to write out a rail warrant on the spot, but it shook him.

'I'll have to confer with Brisbane on this. You'll have to come back tomorrow.'

I turned and walked out. As I went through the door, he bleated, 'I didn't get your name and particulars.'

I kept walking. Over at the pub, reassured now that I was a house guest, the barman reached under the counter for the rum bottle. A ruddy-faced character in the almost empty bar nodded to me and drifted over.

'Mind if I join you? A man shouldn't drink on his own.'

'No, I'm glad of the company. I've just been trying to talk sense to that dictatorial bastard over at the manpower office.'

'You're wasting your time. Those blokes make Hitler look like Tinker Bell, but they don't worry me—I'm a yard builder and I go where I like, and when I like. I just slip out of town at night and I've got them rooted. That mob couldn't find their arse in two grabs.'

I bought him a rum and thought about what he had said.

That night after dinner I decided to go for a stroll. When I got outside I found that it was drizzling rain so went back upstairs and put on the only coat I had, an army tunic. I wandered up the main street, then returned to stand under the verandah awning in front of the bar. I thought about a drink, but decided against it as the clamour within indicated a full house. I lent up against a post and rolled a smoke. As I lit it, a character in a snap brim hat sauntered up to me.

'A stranger in town?' he said.

I took him to be a bit of a spiv, but nodded agreement.

'I see. Where did you get that tunic?'

'Who the hell wants to know?'

He pulled something from his shirt pocket. 'I do. I'm a demon with the local CIB. Now about that tunic?'

I tried to make myself heard above the growing din. 'It was issued to me.'

'What?'

'It was bloody well issued to me.'

'Have you got your discharge on you?'

'No, not on me.'

'You'd better come up to the station with me.'

'Look, if I was AWL, I wouldn't be stupid enough to wear this in public.'

At that moment the swinging doors of the bar burst open and a struggling mass of humanity almost knocked us both over. I left the local Dick Tracy to sort things out and went up to bed. My sense of humour was being steadily eroded.

The next morning I fronted up at the manpower office again, to be told that no decision had been made—I should return after lunch when my fate would be known. The clerk wanted my name and so on and to keep him happy I obliged, then wandered back to the pub. Over lunch I thought about what the yard builder had said. I was determined to get to the Territory by whatever means, and I would not be sorry to see the last of Mt Isa.

The clerk in the manpower office greeted me enthusiastically when I returned at three o'clock. 'Well, we've solved your problem.'

'Great. I can get a permit?'

'No, you will start work at the Mt Isa mines smelter at eight o'clock on Monday morning. You can work there until you have enough money to pay your fare and clear your debts, then we'll be sending you back.'

He spoke triumphantly, with a gleam in his eye reminiscent of a fox in a fowl yard. If he expected a reaction, he was disappointed. My mind was already made up, I was going to the Territory. Life is full of uncertainties, but as I left that building, I was absolutely sure I would not be reporting for work at the smelters on Monday morning.

I made a beeline for Peak's yard, where I asked the first chap I saw who would be taking the loading out to Alexandria. He told me that Clayton Ewart was doing the trip and pointed to a part-Aboriginal driver standing by an International truck. I walked over and introduced myself.

He shook hands and said, 'Les told me I'd have a passenger. We'll be leaving at daylight.'

'Well, I don't have a permit. If you've got a tarp on the back, I'll crawl under it—you don't have to know I'm there.'

Clayton laughed. 'Like that, is it? You'll be right in front. I've never been inspected yet, and anyway, you'll be out before they miss you.'

I thanked him and walked back to the Argent, feeling that the world was not a bad place after all.

On Sunday morning everything went according to plan and we drove across the forbidden border without a hitch. For me, it was the start of a new life. I was to spend the next 17 years on the stations and stockroutes of the North-West. I finally left the outback in 1981, taking my family to Toowoomba.

ALEXANDRIA

I ARRIVED AT Alexandria to learn that the stockcamp was out mustering the headwaters of the Rankine River and that the manager, Harry Barns, was back in Mt Isa hospital with a broken arm—the result of a fall from a horse. His son Henry, who was the station bookkeeper, made me welcome. He told me to throw my swag in the quarters as it would be three days before a truck went out to the camp.

After tossing the swag on a greenhide-laced bunk, I had a look around. The station complex was on the bank of the Playford River and consisted of the homestead with its own kitchen, a men's kitchen and the ringers' quarters; other buildings were a thatch-roofed meat house, a blacksmith's shop, a work shed and a vehicle shed. A couple of hundred yards away was the blacks' camp. Its rough shelters housed over a hundred men, women and children. I was told that only about 20 per cent of the Aborigines were employed in the stockcamp and around the station.

Alexandria Station is located on the Barkly Tableland in the eastern part of the Northern Territory. Today the property is still owned by the North Australian Pastoral Company. Over the years the run has been greatly improved by additional bores, paddocks and station buildings. Despite being reduced in area to 16 000 square kilometres through land resumption, Alexandria still has a carrying capacity of over 50 000 head of cattle. When I worked there Alexandria was one of the biggest, if not the biggest, cattle properties in the world. It covered 11 800 square miles (30 560 square kilometres), 25 square miles (65 square kilometres) larger than Belgium. The place was said to carry 80 000 head, but on huge unfenced runs like Alexandria estimates of stock numbers were at best an educated guess. The place was worked by three stockcamps, one at the head station, and one at both Gallipoli and Sudan, the two outstations.

At morning smoko I met Deal Adams. I soon learnt that Deal was a rather extraordinary individual. He was a jack of all trades, and master of them all—a good ringer, capable saddler and a builder of horse-drawn vehicles.

After smoko I strolled over to the blacksmith shop where Deal was busy with an electric welder. I watched him for a while, then when he pushed the mask up to inspect a weld, my curiosity got the better of me.

'What's this going to be, Deal?'

Aboriginal stockman riding a buckjumper
in the yards at Alexandria Station.

'This,' said Deal, grinning at me. 'This is going to be a rubber-tyred wagonette for the stockcamp.'

I was impressed, and showed it.

'What are they using at present?'

'They're carting the gear around on a big dray I made for 'em.'

'You made it. What about the wheels?'

He looked surprised. 'I made them too, but it's a bit heavy to pull; this will be as light as a feather. Sweeny will handle it, though.'

He looked at me hard and changed the subject. 'You're going into the stockcamp, eh?'

I nodded.

'Can you hang up?'

'I can ride a bit.'

'Well, be careful how you say that to Cammy Cleary. He's the best man on a bad horse I've seen and he'll try you out.'

When I arrived at the stockcamp several days later I was greeted warily by the four whites and with unabashed curiosity by the Aboriginal ringers, Wilson, Johnny, Limerick, Frank, Alec and the others. Cammy Cleary, the head stockman, was a taciturn type of chap, as was Reg Winton, an experienced ringer aged about thirty. Cecil Rose, the other white ringer, was about my age. He was known as 'Yarra', and once he got to know me, he talked quite a lot. He was from Tocumwal, on the Murray River in central southern New South Wales, and one day confided in me that he had not been in touch with his family for years as he could not read or write. I volunteered to write a letter for him and until Cecil left Alexandria I wrote to his mother on his behalf.

The camp cook was Ted Sweeny. He had a very large set of loose dentures that clicked like castanets as he talked. When listening to Sweeny, I half expected him to leap in the air and dance a lively fandango. He always brought smoko up to us when we were branding in the bronco yard; his stock in trade was what Reg Winton called 'Sweeny's jamless jam rolls'.

I was disappointed with the first string of horses allocated to me; the five I had were bits of plonkers with very little spirit. Cleary advised me with a quiet smile that a complete change of horses was due in two weeks. When the 100-odd fresh mounts came out from the station, he gave me five that shut me up. To his chagrin, none of them threw me, although a couple of times it was touch and go. Despite the head stockman's desire to teach me a lesson, I felt I had won his grudging respect, and for the first time felt I was accepted in the camp.

It was about this time that I saw Cammy Cleary ride a station outlaw called Rickety Kate and I marvelled at the ease with which he rode her. He rode long—that is, with long stirrups—his legs swinging with the bucks and only the toe of his boot in the irons. One moment he would reach back and tickle the mare in the flank, the next he would be slapping her on the shoulder. I knew then that his reputation as one of the Territory's best buckjump riders was well earned. He was magnificent on a bad horse, but he was not the best all-round horseman I would work with.

I was intrigued by two fat horses that nobody ever rode. They ran with the plant unworked until the next change was due. I asked Cecil about them, to be told they were supposed to be ridden by the Aboriginals, who had bailed up and refused to ride them. One was a yellow bay horse named Yallaman, a horse that bucked backwards, Cecil informed me. The other was a nuggety black gelding with a white blaze. Coola (wild) Paddy, as he was called, had earlier killed an Aboriginal stockman on Sudan, one of the outstations.

When the two horses arrived in the camp the following year, I worked them both. I found Yallaman to be a top stockhorse; with a bit of encouragement, he gave all his bad habits away and settled down. Coola Paddy, however, was, as they say, a horse of a different colour; he probably should have been shot, for he was hard to catch, difficult to mount, and had to be thrown to be shod. He only threw me once, but he was just as bad at the end of the change as he had been at the beginning.

After I left Alexandria, Coola Paddy put Chuckler, a top horseman, in Alice Springs hospital. He was one of the worst horses I ever struck.

I worked under three head stockmen on Alexandria, Cammy Cleary, Doug Harris and Jack Britt. Early in 1946 I left to work on Nutwood, a Vestey station. Some time before leaving, a bay mare called Cockroach bucked over with me down the bank of the Rankine River, badly injuring my lower spine. I was unconscious for two days, then I went on working. It was an injury that was to play merry hell with me later.

The Number 6 Team at Alexandria Station.

THE CATTLE RUNS

IN THE DAYS before the motorised revolution, cattle work in the North-West was done exclusively with horses. Cattle runs ranged from the vast company stations carrying up to 60 000 head to the 'poddy-dodging' blocks tucked away in the rough hills of the Top End.

The work was hard, with long hours and few days off, but it was never dull. In rough country, the job was fast, challenging, and sometimes dangerous, and young men who had escaped the drudgery of city or farm work took to the life like ducks to water. They relished the opportunity to gain their 'spurs' in an occupation where respect was gained solely on the grounds of personal ability. It was a time when top cattlemen and fine horsemen could be found in every stockcamp.

The mustering of wild cattle in scrub country was the most exciting work on the station. This was done by tracking the cattle until the riders got close enough for the mad gallop through the timber to wheel them, then driving the scrubbers back to the waiting quiet cattle held some distance behind. Often beasts broke away from the galloping mob, and these had to be thrown and tied down until the quiet cattle could be brought up. As these breakaways were often scrub bulls, a great deal of skill and guts was needed to pull them down.

In scrub country, throwing was done on foot: after jumping from his horse, the stockman grabbed the beast's tail, throwing it by pulling the tail to the side as the beast turned to charge. In open country, throwing was usually done from the stockhorse.

Branding in the Territory and the Channel Country was done by 'broncoing', but in most of the Gulf and the coastal hinterland of Queensland the calf-pen method was preferred when branding. Broncoing was introduced into Australia from Mexico around the turn of the century. It entailed catching cleanskins with a greenhide rope that was attached to a harness that fitted over a stock saddle. Straps connected this harness to a collar or breastplate on the bronco horse.

All drafting was done in open camps. The cattle was held on an open flat while the selected beasts were worked out of the mob by the camprider on a camphorse. Once clear of the main mob, the selected beast was controlled by ringers called 'face of the camp men'. These men took the selected beast a short distance to where other cattle were held. Camphorses, like nighthorses, were picked mounts of outstanding intelligence and ability.

As the huge cattle stations of those days were unfenced, neighbouring runs sent stockmen to attend the muster. These men drafted out their cattle, kept them in hand, and drove them back to their respective stations at the end of the muster.

Stockcamp gear was transported by packhorse or wagonette, and some East Kimberley stations used pack camels. Stockmen slept in swags on the ground. The food was plain, mostly beef, or beef dishes such as stews and curries.

Stockcamps were run by head stockmen—older experienced men skilled in every facet of stockwork—and camps ranged in size from six or eight men up to 20 in a big camp. The ratio of Aboriginal stockmen to whites was at times four to one in the Territory.

The changes that revolutionised droving also impacted on station work. Old methods changed, and today stations use aerial mustering and portable yards, and catch scrub bulls with vehicles. Progress finally caught up with one of Australia's last frontiers, and no doubt living conditions have improved in the Territory, but I wonder if the quality of life is as rich and rewarding as it was before the change.

Plant horses at a trough on the Barkly Tableland.

PADDY LENNIE'S BRUMBIES

PADDY LENNIE WAS the epitome of the wild Irishman: raw boned, bearded, and anti-social to the point where he could not even fit in with the free and easy ways of the Territory. Paddy was a horse crank who thought far more of his horses than he did of his fellow man. After working on stations on the Barkly Tableland, including Alexandria in the 1930s, he settled on Lorne Creek (a part of Alexandria) with his horses and lived the life of a recluse, shunning human company. Paddy visited the Rankine occasionally for stores, but he avoided setting up a permanent camp and had plants of tucker and rough yards hidden over a large area round Lorne Creek, which he came to regard as his own.

As time passed, Lennie's horses multiplied and began to get out of hand; fewer and fewer carried his 44L brand, and young ungelded colts cut out smaller mobs of mares and began to range over a large area of the station. All Paddy's horses were fine stamps of stockhorses, but interested horse buyers, who offered good prices for his Waler-type mounts, were given short shrift by the Hermit of Lorne Creek. Finally C.A.Y. Johnson, the manager of Alexandria, had had enough. He sought the help of the law and a police muster of the wild mobs of horses was carried out. With the majority of them safely in the Rankine dip yard, the heavy gate was made fast with a chain and padlock, and that, thought the powers that be, was that.

Paddy was a renowned grass fighter and that evening everyone was careful to stay clear of the disgruntled Irishman. But Paddy had other ideas of retribution; when daylight broke, the yard had been broached and Paddy and his horses were back in the fastness of Lorne Creek. Paddy died with most of his beloved horses still free. He passed away at Dunmara, on his way to front the court in Darwin.

When I worked on Alexandria some years later the progeny of Paddy Lennie's horses still roamed the Lorne Creek area. When mustering the bottom end of the Rankine, the stockcamp camped and mustered from the gidgees, on the Rankine River. Cammy Cleary, one of the best roughriders in the Territory, was head stockman, and on this occasion Barney Smyth and an Aboriginal stockman from Avon Downs were attending the muster also, bringing the camp's complement to six whites and 13 Aborigines.

One morning the full camp headed out in the direction of Lorne Creek to muster back to the gidgees, a camp that boasted a rather frail wire bronco yard. When mustering, it was always the custom to ride out behind the cattle then split up and muster back, driving the cattle towards the selected spot.

We had ridden out about 4 miles (about 6 kilometres) when, coming over a rise in the downs, we saw spread out in the hollow before us some 200 brumbies scattered about in small mobs. We were downwind from the horses and they had not spotted us, so we reined in our mounts and sat admiring the spectacle. There were many fine-looking types in the mobs, obviously descendants of Paddy Lennie's stallions and mares. We looked at Cleary. He was rolling a smoke, the reins in the crock of his elbow. Suddenly he looked up at us and grinned: 'To hell with the cattle, let's have a crack at yarding this lot'.

The idea was greeted with quiet enthusiasm by all; who would want to muster cattle when there were brumbies to run? We were all well mounted, as Alexandria, like most cattle stations those days, had magnificent stockhorses. I was riding a big bay gelding by Spaza, a stallion renowned as a station sire. My mount had somehow picked up our restrained excitement and was rearing to go.

Riding back down the ridge, we rode in a great circle to get around behind the horse mob. Our whole group was almost in position when the brumbies got wind of us; then ahead of us and to our left we saw the flying manes and tails of galloping horses making back towards Lorne Creek. As one, we gave our mounts their heads, and the chase was on. I doubt if there is anything as exhilarating for both horse and rider as the wild gallop after brumbies; stones flew from under the shod hooves of our horses and men shouted and urged their mounts on, for there was now no need for stealth.

It was Barney Smyth who finally wheeled them, with Cleary, myself and Reg Winton close behind; but that was only the first round. For the next hour it was one mad gallop after another as stallions broke out of the mob with their mares. It grew ever harder to control them when they hit the timber, but the adrenalin was still flowing and the yard was not far away.

We were in sight of the yard when the mob finally beat us; had we had calico wings out from the gate, we would have got the lot, but as it was, we were lucky to yard some 15 head. Then out of the scrub came Barney Smyth to yard a fine chestnut mare in a remarkable feat of horsemanship; he had raced his horse up beside her as she broke away from the yard, then vaulted from his stockhorse on to her back, steering her back to the yard with his hat.

After unsaddling our horses, we looked over our catch. There was one young black stallion and eight good sorts of mares; the rest, however, were not worth keeping. As Barney was trying to put a horse plant together, it was agreed that he could have what he wanted out of the captive brumbies and we would bush the rest. Next morning, for a dare, I caught and rode the black stallion. Riding an unbroken and unmouthed brumby buck in a wire yard may seem like reckless stupidity, but to walk away from a challenge in the presence of men like Cleary and Smyth would have been unthinkable.

THE RANKINE STORE

THE RANKINE STORE, complete with bottle licence, was on the Rankine (or Ranken) River about 40 miles (65 kilometres) from the Alexandria homestead. It was always spelled Rankine by the drovers and the owners of the store but usually appears as Ranken on modern maps. As it was situated on country mustered by the stockcamp, the store proved, over the years, to be a headache to managers of the sprawling cattle property. Finally, bowing to the inevitable, tacit approval was given to the ringers to have a few days off whenever they mustered past the place.

One hears a lot about endurance riders these days. Once, for a bet, Cammy Cleary rode a horse from Alexandria to the Rankine and back, a round trip of 80 miles (130 kilometres) between sun-up and sundown. He took a bottle of Fowler's rum back as proof. Not bad for a grass-fed stockhorse.

In my time Jim Fowler and his good wife catered to the needs of the drovers and ringers. Jimmy had been head stockman on Alexandria and was a top roughrider who once rode a grey outlaw called The Snake. He was a bit of a showman, handy with his fists, and a real artist with a whip. I once saw a big young ringer challenge Jimmy to hop outside and put his fists up; after a moment's thought, Jimmy agreed, but on his way outside he made a detour through the kitchen, where he emptied one of his wife's pepper pots into his left fist. The bout was a brief one: Jimmy threw a straight left, opening his fist at the end of the punch; the right cross that followed flattened his half-blinded opponent.

Wason Byers, one of the Territory's rougher denizens, dropped into the Rankine one day when we were all there. He was after a couple of chaps, he told us, who he claimed had maligned him. He caught up with them in Mrs Fowler's kitchen, where a leg of goat was roasting for dinner. Wason dropped one of the alleged offenders, then grabbing the other, he sat the struggling ringer on the hot stove top and held him there. For a while it looked as though the night's menu of roast goat would be augmented by roast ringer.

One day at the Rankine, Reg Winton and I got into a debate on rushes. He contended any animals would rush, while I believed highly domesticated ones would not, despite the opinion of a drunken cook who kept relating how he'd seen 30 cats rush and take the side out of a meat

North Australian Pastoral Company

The Rankine Store in 1920.

house at McArthur River. The debate was an amicable one and I forgot about it until on the way back to the camp, Reg stopped beside Mrs Fowler's goat yard. Mrs Fowler had over 100 goats that provided meat and milk for the isolated settlement. They were penned every night in a large yard that had an iron-roofed shed in one corner for shelter.

'Now,' said Reg, 'let's settle this rush business.'

He climbed up the fence and then carefully made his way on to the roof of the shed. The goats camped around the yard took no notice of the intruder, until he suddenly leapt in the air, landing with a bellow in the middle of the iron roof. The result was instantaneous and devastating: the goats flattened one side of the compound and disappeared at high speed into the night. Reg made his point, but our reception at the store next day was decidedly frosty.

During those times when we were at the Rankine, we always camped at the one mile waterhole in the river just below the store. It was an easy walk sober, but for those of us who overdid it at Fowlers', it became something between a marathon and an army obstacle course. At one time we had in the camp a cook who earlier had made a fortune at Tennant Creek. He had blown it all in Sydney, with the exception of a top dental plate specially made for him from gold from his mine. One morning we awoke to find our babbler missing. He later staggered into camp, a hungover and heartbroken wreck, crying that he'd lost his fangs. He had apparently got lost and wandered around in circles most of the night. He had had a number of big spits during his drunken wanderings and no doubt his teeth had taken flight on one of these occasions.

After some merriment at the cook's expense, we poured a rum into him and all hands set out to track down the lost dentures. I could not help thinking of Jason and his search for the Golden Fleece, only this time it was the search for the Golden Teeth. Finally one of the group found the cook's last link with his affluent past. The relieved owner picked up his dentures and, after wiping them briefly on his trousers, popped them into his mouth and headed up to the store for another rum.

THE SHOOTING OF
PALMER BRUSHE

ONE DAY BEFORE going out to the Alexandria stockcamp I was having a yarn to Arthur Remfrey in his room at the men's quarters. I noticed a hole in the door and remarked, 'That looks like a bullet hole.'

'It's a bullet hole, all right,' he replied. 'In fact it's two bullet holes close together. This is the room where Palmer Brushe was shot.'

I was curious about the incident and pressed him for the details.

Sudden and violent death was not uncommon at one time in the Territory, but the shooting of Palmer Brushe was different; it was a tragic mistake. The man who pulled the trigger had murder on his mind, that is indisputable. The tragedy was that he shot the wrong man, a man who was in fact a good mate of his. The cause of the trouble was the old eternal triangle, at the apex of which was an Aboriginal girl on Alexandria. Cohabitation between whites and Aboriginal women did go on in the Territory; it was supposed to be illegal, but as long as there was no trouble, the authorities were prepared to turn a blind eye. Perhaps the fact that it went on in fairly high places also led to its tacit acceptance.

It must be understood that the men who settled and developed the Northern Territory were no saints; they were tough, hard-bitten and lusty characters who worked hard and played hard. There were few white women in the Territory those days, and the few who were there were married and of a very different class. There was a saying in the Top End: 'Necessity is the mother of invention and the father of all half-caste children.' The saying, offensive by today's standards, had more than an element of truth in it. It is true that in the early days of settlement rape and kidnapping of Aboriginal women did, for a while, take place. However, that disappeared when stations learnt to depend on Aboriginal labour and the Territory's mounted police gained control. The liaisons that developed later between white males and Aboriginal women were based on mutual agreement and were at times initiated by the women themselves.

It must also be clearly understood that not all Territorians indulged in promiscuity; many, like Palmer Brushe, did not. In the affair at Alexandria, he was an innocent victim. The main players in the tragedy were Snowy Baker, who in the mid-1930s was employed as a horse breaker on Alexandria; Matey Cotters and Frank Sweeny, who were also employed at the homestead; and of course, Palmer Brushe himself. A man named Johnson also played a small part.

Baker was a hard man and a typical Territorian; he got on well with Palmer Brushe, who was the windmill expert. Baker became infatuated with an Aboriginal girl on the station and this later developed into a full-blown liaison. Snowy Baker was intensely jealous of anyone who as much as looked at his girl, but there was one man who bided his time.

Baker left Alexandria to take up a block on the Robinson River with a partner. Later he brought cattle from the block back through Alexandria. Baker had a few days with the girl at the station, then drove his cattle on down the stockroute. It was then that Matey Cotters moved in; whether in fact he had been sleeping with the girl before is not known, but he lost no time when Snowy Baker left.

Johnson, who may have been asked by Baker to keep an eye on things, caught a horse after work the next day and rode with the news to Baker's camp on the Buchanan River. Snowy Baker, mad with jealousy, strapped on a revolver, caught a fast horse and headed back to the station. It was well after dark when he arrived and by that time he was in a murderous rage. He tied up his horse and strode to the quarters to settle his account with Cotters.

Snowy Baker always wore long-necked spurs that dragged on the ground and jingled as he walked. On that fateful night those spurs may well have sounded Palmer Brushe's death knell. Cotters, who had the girl in his room, heard and recognised the sound. He fled from his room, ran down the length of the barrack-style building and dived into Palmer Brushe's room at the far end. Palmer and Frank Sweeny were sitting on the bed yarning. They looked up in surprise as Cotters slammed the front door shut, gasped out, 'Baker's here', then raced out the back door.

Baker, who had witnessed the flight of his intended victim, approached the closed door roaring, 'Come out, you gutless dingo, or I'll shoot you through the door.'

Palmer jumped up as Frank cried a warning. 'Stay away from the door. He's mad, that bloke, he'll shoot you.'

'It's right. I'll talk to him and calm him down.'

As Palmer reached for the door handle, Baker fired two shots. The bullets crashed through the door, mortally wounding the windmill expert, who slumped backwards to the floor. As Frank Sweeny sat stunned, Baker kicked the door open and sprang into the room. He stopped short and reeled back when he saw the man on the floor.

'Oh God, Palmer, I've shot you,' he cried.

Without another word Snowy Baker wheeled around and walked up to the homestead. He handed the revolver to C.A.Y. Johnson, the manager, saying, 'For Christ's sake, take this. I've just shot my best mate.'

The next morning Baker was arrested and Cotters was found hiding in an old steam engine behind the quarters, where he had been cowering all night.

Snowy Baker stood trial in Darwin and was sentenced to a long term in Fanny Bay gaol. Cotters, who was reviled by many for having caused the tragedy, later left Alexandria and moved to Tennant Creek. When the Japs bombed Darwin in 1942 all prisoners, including Snowy Baker, were released. If Cotters believed that Baker now had two scores to settle with him, he did not wait around to find out. He headed south and dropped out of sight, as did Baker himself.

Palmer Brushe left a wife and family in Winton. Many years later I met them. I also met Palmer's brother Gaynor, who with his sons Ron and Stan had a plumbing business in Winton. All three became very good friends of mine.

The shooting of Palmer Brushe was one of those freakish incidents that should never have happened. It cost Palmer his life, Baker his freedom, and Cotters his reputation as a man.

THE RANKINE RACES

THE FIRST RACE meeting of the Alexandria, Brunette and Creswell Race Club was held at the Rankine in 1922. One of the prime movers in the establishment of the ABC Race Club was Jim Broadbridge, bookkeeper on Alexandria, and the club's first secretary. Other members of that first committee were Dick Holt, manager of Alexandria, Herbert Lloyd, manager of Avon Downs, George Watson, owner of the Rankine store, Bill Reilly, owner of the Landsborough Hotel in Camooweal, and Pat Synott, of Synott Murray and Scholes, who had stores in both Camooweal and Burketown.

A track was laid out near the Rankine store, and a tin shed was erected to act as a bar. Watson built a small dance hall close to his establishment, for George Watson was a good businessman, and race meetings meant money. The high hopes for the meeting were soon realised. Finding gallopers was never a problem, as all of the stations had thoroughbred stallions servicing the station mares, and the bloodlines of some of the stallions were as good as many standing at southern studs. The Territory was full of horsemen ready to ride, bet, drink and dance, so a race meeting was right up their alley. The Rankine races became an instant success and the meeting quickly became the main social event on the Barkly Tableland, with station staff and townspeople alike setting up elaborate camps along the one mile hole in the Rankine River. A piano was set up in the hall and the revellers danced well into the small hours.

There was, of course, a lot of high-spirited fun: I once saw Jimmy Carr throw a large goanna onto the middle of the dance floor during a quick step. The wildly thrashing reptile found it almost impossible to get traction on the highly polished surface, but the dancers had no such difficulty. The quick step turned into a rout, with the ladies leading the charge for the door.

Jimmy Carr was a jocular, rotund individual, with an infectious chuckle and a permanent twinkle in his eye; he was a natural comedian and the perpetrator of many outrageous jokes. Jimmy decided to go into business at one Rankine meeting. His plan was to set up a 'knock 'em down' stall, with himself as the target. He arrived early and purchased a bag of potatoes from Jimmy Fowler, the current owner of the Rankine store. These he boiled in a 44 gallon (200 litre) drum until nearly cooked. On race day he enlisted the aid of a helper whose job it was to hand out

North Australian Pastoral Company

The ABC Race Club Executive, July 1922. Left to Right: *George Watson, Herbert Lloyd, Pat Synnott, Richard Holt and Bill Reilly.* Front: *James Broadbridge, club secretary.*

the spuds at sixpence a throw. Setting the drum at about 20 paces, Jimmy stood behind it and invited all and sundry to have a go and win five bob with a direct hit.

The sixpences rolled in, the air became thick with flying potatoes, and Jimmy danced and dodged and chuckled behind the drum. Finally, the last potato was thrown and no one had managed to hit Jimmy, but this led to his undoing. He bought another bag of spuds, and confident of his ability to outwit the potato pelters, he saved time by not boiling the new projectiles. The sixpences continued to roll in, Jimmy dodged and chuckled, and the raw potatoes went bounding over the landscape.

All went well until a left-handed Aborigine faced his tormentor with a spud in each hand. Feinting with the right, he drove the left-hand potato at Jimmy like a bullet. It struck him fair between the eyes, knocking him unconscious and out of sight behind his drum. The Aborigine waited expectantly for a few minutes, then turned to Jimmy's assistant and said: 'Well I bin hit 'im all right, but he's a bloody long time paying me.'

After that Jimmy decided that being in business was not all it was cracked up to be and retired, with two black eyes, to Fowlers' to liquidate his accumulated capital. The Aborigines, meanwhile, gathered the scattered missiles for a blow out of potatoes cooked in the ashes.

A rather unusual wrestling match took place at the Rankine one race day. The manager of a Northern Territory cattle station, who was proud of his prowess as a wrestler, claimed he could break any hold that could be put on him and challenged all comers to try their skill. No one seemed all that interested until the heavily built policeman from Anthony's Lagoon was persuaded to take up the challenge. Although the station manager had been on the grog for a few days, he was prepared to back himself and money was wagered on the outcome. The policeman was allowed to apply the hold and then the battle commenced.

The two men grappled and struggled for a while, then both fell to the floor, where the station manager heaved and strained in his efforts to break the hold. It looked as if the policeman's grip would hold when the manager, in a last ditch attempt, gave a terrific heave and strained his hardest to break free. He failed to break the policeman's hold—what he did do, however, was to dirty his trousers thoroughly. The policeman sprang to his feet crying foul. He paid up, though, saying that the

Barney Smythe, a ringer, contemplates his
fortunes at dawn after the race meeting.

manager had perfected an unorthodox but very effective method of breaking a wrestling hold.

It was not all beer and skittles at the Rankine, for the race club has seen tragedy. When the horses lined up for the Cup in 1938, no one in the excited and expectant crowd could have had any inkling of the impending disaster. The track at the Rankine was a black soil one that was fire ploughed before each meeting, and the resulting surface was fairly good. There was no running rail in the straight, just a large post firmly set in the ground at the furlong mark.

The Cup had been reduced to a two-horse race, with most of the starters having been scratched, leaving the race to the two favourites in what had all the appearances of a match race. George Lewis, one of the Territory's best horsemen, was riding a grey gelding highly fancied by some to win the Cup. However, it was Wynowie, a black mare owned by Tommy Lewis Snr of Avon Downs, that was most fancied by the crowd. Wynowie was a well-bred mare by Brimstone, but she had one bad habit that at times made her difficult to ride. She sometimes threw her head and then reefed at the bit. Young Len Lloyd, her jockey, knew the mare, but in the saddling yard he was reminded to watch her.

The two horses lined up, the judge dropped the flag and the field for the 1938 Rankine Cup was away. For the first half of the race the two were neck and neck, then gradually the black mare inched ahead. With a little over a furlong to go, she looked a winner, then, as she came to the furlong post, Wynowie threw her head, then reefed her young rider half out of the saddle. His head struck the furlong post a sickening blow and the young jockey fell to the track.

I doubt if anyone saw Lewis win the Cup on the grey—all eyes were on the fallen jockey. Help was soon at his side, but little could be done. The young horseman died within a few minutes. The rest of the program was cancelled that afternoon, but at his father's request, racing resumed the following day. That, as his father said, was what young Len would have wanted.

In 1948 the race committee moved the meeting to a new venue on Brunette Downs.

RANKINE REVERIE

They'll be racing today where the Southerlies play
And the Rankine goes wandering by,
With the downs sweeping past undulating at last
To merge with the Territory sky.

From near and from far by packhorse and car
The bush crowd will gather once more,
There'll be laughter and song from the camps strung along
The one mile and down by the store.

From the furthest out runs they'll be there with the 'guns'
And maiden hacks trained for the fray,
Every track good or bad whether main road or pad
Will lead to the Rankine today.

Though I'm far from the scene with long miles in between
Old times as I muse reappear,
In my mind I'm again on the course on the plain
With the horsemen who rode yesteryear.

Oh! I mind well the ways of those old carefree days
All that came then we took for the best,
For we cared not the cost of a race won or lost
Though the 'Square A' nags seldom were pressed.

Game Searchlight was one and San-Simeon
And gallant old Tum Tum the grey,
Ah! no doubt there'll be few of those horses we knew
That carry the colours today.

Though I couldn't get back to the old Rankine track
To join in the bush revelry,
This day shall not pass ere I raise a charged glass
To the Rankine—a grand memory.

EQUIPMENT AND DRESS
OF THE RINGER

ALMOST ALL THE equipment used in the cattle industry had its origins in the British Isles and was adapted to local conditions and the demands of cattle work here in Australia. The one exception was bronco gear. Unlike the pioneering era in America, where the Spanish influence played a major role in the style of both saddlery and dress, there evolved in this country personal gear and equipment that was uniquely Australian.

The Australian stock saddle was based on the English park saddle, and for many years the Australian saddle, although a lot heavier than the park saddle, retained small knee pads placed low on the flaps. It was in Queensland that the stock poley saddle was developed. Saddle makers listened to the men who rode in their products and gradually changes took place. Saddles were produced with knee pads placed up nearer the pommel and at the right angle to allow the rider on a rough horse to 'get under the pads', as it were, if a horse started to buck unexpectedly miles from camp. There were no pick-up men in the bush and no ambulance standing by if someone was injured. The only disadvantage with these saddles was that they were harder to get clear of should a horse fall.

There were, and still are, many fine saddle makers in Queensland. Saddle makers in outback towns, who had the advantage of knowing many good horsemen personally, produced some of the best saddles made. Tim Carr of Charters Towers was probably the best known of these. He made a fairly light saddle with a narrow grip that was famous throughout the back country.

The Australian stockwhip, with its full- or half-plaited cane handle, is another piece of equipment unique to this country. A whip was essential on the road with cattle, as it was in most mustering camps. Whips for rough work were often plaited from greenhide or redhide, but it was the 12- or 16-strand 'roo hide beauties that were prized by cattlemen. The most famous of all whip makers was Alec Scobie. All his sons and daughters could plait fine whips, but Alec was the master. His whips were instantly recognisable as he used a hitch, which became known as the Scobie Hitch, rather than plaiting on his whip handles.

As there were four men at most with up to 1500 bullocks on the road, the mob had to be broken in to respond to the crack of a whip. If a mob

Glenormiston ringers, left to right, *Ross Ratcliffe, the late Bruce Hanson, Bruce Simpson and Charlie Trottman.*

was spreading out when travelling, the drover had only to ride out and crack his whip and the spreading bullocks would move back into position as one.

A bush sage once said, 'A drover without a whip is like a eunuch in a brothel—both are at a serious disadvantage due to a lack of essential equipment.'

Stockwhips evolved from the buggy or coach whip introduced from England, but later when whip makers established themselves in Australia, they responded to the needs of our pioneers and the stockwhip was born.

Spurs were not used on every horse. However, all ringers owned a pair. The length of the spur neck was usually two-and-a-half or three-and-a-half inches (6–9 centimetres) longer than the English Cavalry spur, because stockmen rode with longer stirrup leathers and with legs forward. Blacksmiths played an important role in outback life. The smithy who made the famous Condamine bells from old saw blades was one; Fred Gutte was another. Fred was employed by Vestey's as a blacksmith on Wave Hill station in the Northern Territory. In his spare time he made and sold the famous Wave Hill spurs—acclaimed by horsemen throughout the North-West as the best spur ever produced.

The humble quartpot played an important part in bush life, particularly on the road with cattle. As the cook and horsetailer went directly to the night camp, ringers with the mob boiled their quarts at dinner camp and ate the corned beef and damper cut that morning. Quarts were small oval billy cans with a deep lid that fitted inside and served as a mug.

To pass the time it was common practice for ringers to wager on whose quart would boil first. No one but a new chum, however, would bet against a Jenkins quart. Made in Charters Towers, the Jenkins quart was handmade in a flattened oval shape and was approximately 2 inches (5 centimetres) wide. Ringers who owned them boasted you could almost boil them with a lit match. I'm not sure if the Towers has an historical museum, but if it has, pride of place in it should go to the Tim Carr saddle and the Jenkins quart.

All ringers wore belts, not so much to keep their trousers up but to carry pouches. Every one had a knife pouch carried along the belt so as not to cause the wearer a mischief. Watch pouches were also common (wristwatches were regarded as being a bit effeminate those days). In addition, many ringers carried match box and tobacco tin pouches on their belts.

Ringers and other bush workers in Australia seldom, if ever, wore gloves or other protective clothing. Fencers and yard builders did the job with bare hands, as did stockmen when they worked in the branding yard.

Station work and droving in my day entailed long hours in dusty conditions—certainly not the environment for sartorial splendour. Clothing worn in the camps was plain and practical. When in town, ringers prided themselves on looking smart, and although there were a few characters who were regarded as flash, flamboyance in dress among white ringers was seldom seen. Despite this there was a great deal of individuality in dress in the cattle industry, quite unlike the clothing affected by the sheepmen, who dressed in a style that was almost a uniform. Ringers' hats came in all shapes and styles, from the 10 gallon to the 3 inch brim, and the bashes in these hats were just as varied. Shirts worn were of plain colours in flannel or cotton, some with two pockets and all with long sleeves. Trousers in the Territory and North-West Queensland were in stock-cut pattern, while other parts of Queensland favoured jodhpurs (called poop catchers in the Territory). Moleskin, gaberdine and riding twist were the materials used. Those days jeans were called dungarees and were worn only by shearers and navvies.

Scenes from a droving life.
A drover's wagonette and 'five in-hand' team.

A typical drover, Andy Zigenbine, a member
of a well-known droving family in the 1950s.

Leggings were mainly the light pull-on type, although the spring side and concertina styles were still worn. Johnson and Sons riding boots were the favoured brand. Their Kooreelah, Maranoa and Emperor boots were generally worn by cattlemen, until R.M. Williams produced his own well-known Cuban heel boot, which captured the market in a few short years.

The Tasmanian Bluey, an overcoat made from wool, was very popular with drovers and ex-army great coats were also worn a lot. The shorter leather coat or jacket was often seen in later years. There was a lot more wool used in clothing in those days. Wearers of the woollen flannel shirt used to say, 'No matter how wet and cold you are, you're always warm and dry in a flannel shirt'.

Aboriginal stockmen favoured a bit more colour in their clobber; there is an old story about the Aborigine who asked a storekeeper for a shirt and on being asked what colour he wanted, replied, 'Any colour, boss, so long as him red'.

Whether a ringer was droving or working in a stockcamp, his swag was his home. In it were all his worldly possessions apart from his saddlery. Swag covers were made from Birkmere and some were lined and had a pocket at the top for spare clothing that acted as a pillow. Most, however, were merely 8-by-10 tarpaulins in which the ringer rolled up his blankets. Two leather straps went round the rolled-up swag.

Boss drovers looked hard at a man's swag before employing him. If the swag was heavy, it was no job—a bulky swag would not fit well on a packhorse and the man would sleep too soundly and would be hard to wake to go on watch. The lighter the swag, the better chance of a job, and if a man's rolled-up swag could be passed between the spokes of a wagonette wheel, all was well.

Ringers, by and large, were drifters and when a man spoke of greasing the swag straps he really meant he was thinking of moving on.

Forty or so years ago revolvers were still carried by many North-West Queensland and Northern Territory stockmen. Few of these were licensed, but as the hand guns were never taken out of a work situation, no one seemed to worry too much. I had a Smith and Wesson .38-calibre revolver for many years.

Revolvers could be handy at times but were never as effective as a rifle. Looking back, I believe the revolver was as much a symbol as a necessity.

BULLS, PUMPERS AND
MIN MIN LIGHTS

EARLY IN 1945 Harry Barnes, the manager of Alexandria, asked me and another young chap, Cecil Rose, to take a mob of herd bulls to Gallipoli outstation some 80 miles (130 kilometres) away. The herd bulls were of the Munro breed, low-set shorthorn beauties well known throughout the North-West. We started off with a young Aboriginal stockman called Limerick, and made it to the Buchanan River by the first night. Next day we headed up the Buchanan and continued in easy stages to Gallipoli, taking about 10 days to reach the bore where we were to leave the bulls.

We planned to tail the mob for a few days to settle them down in their new run, so after pulling the packs off at the turkey nest we strolled over to the engine shed to say good day to the pumper. Rather than erect windmills, in those days many of the stations employed men who lived at the bores. They serviced the eight horsepower diesel engines that drove walking beams connected to pump rods and buckets that raised water from the bores. The diesel engines ran night and day and were housed in small galvanised sheds in which the men slept and ate. An eight horsepower diesel makes a hell of a racket and how any of them slept with one a few feet from the bed is beyond me. A ration truck from the station once a week was the limit of any human company. Some of them were avid readers and could discuss, with authority, topics like philosophy, the origins of man, astronomy and alternative religions.

However, our pumper was something else: he had trodden a path at least 6 inches (15 centimetres) deep round the top of the turkey nest, and had a wild look in his eyes. The loneliness had obviously got to him. We boiled the billy and gave him a pint of tea. He took a swig and, looking somewhere over my left shoulder, said, 'A min min took me dorg y'know'.

I looked at him stupidly and said, 'A min min did what?'

'A min min took me dorg,' he repeated without emotion.

Cecil Rose choked on his tea as I thought, 'Christ, we've struck a hard case here'.

The pumper went on: 'It would have took me too, y'know, only I talked it out of it.'

'You talked to it?' said Cecil in a strangled voice.

'Yair,' said the pumper, 'it's friendly like now; comes up and has a yarn to me every night.'

After the pumper had returned to his galvanised hell hole, Cec and I sat and looked at one another. 'The poor bastard has gone troppo,' I said. 'I've heard of min min lights, but never a talking one.'

Cec nodded. 'He's as silly as a cut snake. The sooner we're out of this the better.'

I nodded agreement. I was looking forward to off-siding for the horse breaker when we got back; but we both knew the bulls would have to be settled down first.

That night, after a frugal repast, we were lying on our swags enjoying a smoke when Cec shot upright. 'What the hell is that?' he said.

I looked where he pointed. A light was shining brightly by a point of gidgee and it moved in an undulating way at an angle towards us.

'Well, I'll be buggered,' I said, 'the old bloke was right about the light, anyway.'

I looked over to where Limerick sat crouched over his own fire. 'What name?' I asked him, indicating the light. He rolled his eyes but made no reply.

We watched the min min for half an hour, then it disappeared as suddenly as it had appeared.

After some discussion, Cec and I agreed we would tie up a horse the following night and investigate the mysterious light.

Gypsy was a good style of roan mare that had done some night work, but she seemed to resent the idea of being tied up the following night with no cattle on camp, and stood hip shot and bored as we waited for the light to make its appearance.

Eight o'clock came with no sign of the min min. Eight-thirty passed with still no sign of the mysterious phenomenon. The point of gidgee was south of our position, and as I watched the Cross swing slowly up the night sky, I felt a slight sense of relief that our idea of the previous night may not have to be put into practice. Then, there it was, just off the point of gidgee as before.

'There she is,' said Cec.

'That's it, all right,' I agreed.

Silence for a while. I looked at Cec. He was looking at me. Gypsy stamped a hoof and it sounded unnaturally loud. Limerick slid into the swag and stuck his head under the blankets.

'Well, best of luck,' said Cec. 'I'll keep the fire stoked up.'

I walked slowly over to the mare, untied the reins and swung into the saddle. Once mounted, I felt confidence return. Ringers spend most of their lives in the saddle, and with a good horse under him, a ringer will face almost anything. I urged Gypsy into a trot as we headed for the point of gidgee. The light did not appear to be moving, but was not getting any nearer, and finally we passed the timber with the light looking much the same as it had from the camp. I rode about a mile further, with the light still no closer, then it changed direction, bowling along in a wide arc around me, as though heading back to the point of gidgee. I found it impossible to judge how far away it was—it could have been anything between 50 yards (46 metres) and a mile (1.6 kilometres).

Gypsy took no notice of it, not even glancing at it as I turned her round and rode back towards the camp, with the min min slightly in front and to our right. Halfway back to the point of timber the light stopped, pulsated and went out. I rode on, thinking that was the end of the night's performance when suddenly the mare propped, threw her head up and snorted softly. With ears pricked, she was watching something between her and the camp, and it was obviously something she did not like.

There was still no sign of the light, but I felt the mare tremble slightly and I was aware of the hairs standing up on the back of my neck. At that moment the camp seemed a long way away. Gypsy snorted again and, wheeling away from the timber, took off at a gallop. After a struggle, I eased her back to a canter and we headed back to the camp, wide of the gidgee point.

As I had no intention of pounding into the camp as though the hounds of hell were after me, I reined Gypsy into a walk and glanced back. The min min light was back in position by the point of timber.

I dismounted and, squatting by the fire, told Cec the story, endeavouring to keep my hands steady as I rolled a smoke.

Cec looked at me incredulously: 'But you must have got to it. It never left the point of gidgee. You rode right to it.'

I shook my head. 'I never got close. Did you see it go out?'

Cec looked puzzled. 'The only time it went out was when you rode between it and the camp.'

'Well, mate,' I said, 'if you want to check yourself, the mare is there. If not, let her go. I'm hitting the swag.'

The light did not show again. Two days later we packed up and headed back to the head station.

I have seen three min min lights since then; however, none left the impression that first one did. The word 'min min' is possibly Aboriginal in origin. The light was often seen in the early days east of Boulia close to where the old Min Min pub once stood. The light remains a great mystery of the outback. It still has scientists baffled.

HORSE BREAKING

IN THE DAYS when cattle stations had hundreds of working horses on the books, the horse breaker played an important part in station life. In a good season a large cattle run could have 40 or 50 unbroken horses waiting for the travelling breaker. These unbroken horses, or colts, as they were generally called, would not have been handled as yearlings, and as some of them would be four and five years old, a breaker needed to be a top horseman.

The horse breaker was usually employed on station wages plus so much per head. As most of the stockmen were themselves fine horsemen those days, a couple of rides out of the yard was usually enough to have the colts accepted by the stockcamp. As most stations required the breaker to shoe the colts as well, a lot of horse breakers employed an offsider. Four to six colts a week was good going for most breakers.

'Simmo', the character in the next verse, was my younger brother, Alan Simpson, who was reared west of Mackay. On leaving school he worked on stations in the Eungella and Clermont districts, but soon turned to horse breaking. Over the next 38 years, he broke in horses in Queensland, the Territory, and in the Kimberley area, drifting further out as station methods changed.

A fine horseman, Alan was breaking in up to the time of his accidental death in 1988 at the age of fifty-eight.

Alan Simpson breaking in a horse in the Clermont district in 1950.

Taking the sting out of a fresh horse.

SIMMO THE BREAKER

'Simmo the Breaker is dead, you say!
You must be joking, and anyway,
I've heard of rumours in the past
That Simmo the Breaker had breathed his last.
No, he'll turn up, I have no fear,
In his run-down truck and his breaking gear.'

On a station far in the Kimberleys,
To break in colts with the practised ease
Of a man who has mastered the breaking game,
From Nebo to Derby they know his name.
The best of the breakers without a doubt
To service the stations of further out.

Almost a legend among his peers,
Born out of his time by forty years,
The staunchest mate that a man could find,
They broke the mould when they made his kind.
Reared in the bush when the world was wide,
the horse was king when he teamed to ride.

But times are changing and methods too—
Mobs for the breaker of late are few,
Besieged by progress I've heard him swear,
'The Kimberleys are the Last Frontier!
The last retreat of the old bush ways,
There a breaker like me could end his days'.

'But Simmo dead? No, it couldn't be,
The man was as tough as a gidgee tree,
As hard as nails, and it's truth to tell
You couldn't kill Simmo with shot and shell.
Yet you say he's dead, and you swear it's true—
Simmo gone, and I never knew!'

Yes, we scattered his ashes on the breeze
O'er the distant runs of the Kimberleys.
There where the plains and the rough hill meet,
The breaker is home in his last retreat.
When the trade winds sweep o'er the sunlit plains—
When the trees bend low to the monsoon rains—
When the Southern Cross hangs bright and clear
He will be as one with his last frontier.

PROTOCOL AND HABITS
OF THE CAMPS

THE RELATIONSHIP BETWEEN bosses and ringers in the cattle country was a lot less formal than on the sheep stations, where a fairly rigid class system was maintained. On a sheep property there was a clearly defined line of demarcation between inside, or homestead staff, and the workers. Fraternisation was not encouraged. Cattle stations certainly had a separate kitchen and dining room apart from the 'big house' for the ringers, but there the similarity ended. Ringers were always on first name terms with boss drovers and head stockmen, and in many cases, on first name terms with the manager. Unlike stockmen on sheep stations, who were home each night, ringers spent most of the year living in stockcamps or on the road droving.

Some managers of cattle stations spent time in the camps and many liked to keep their hands in on a favourite camphorse. Protocol demanded, however, that all instructions to the ringers were given through the head stockmen. Most boss drovers and head stockmen led from the front and the ringers were in no doubt as to who was in charge. Camp cooks, however, were given a fair bit of leeway; keeping the dough roaster happy was in the interest of all. Cooks needed room around the fire to tend to their billies and camp ovens, so even in the coldest weather ringers did not encroach on the cook's domain. If one did, a shovel full of hot coals and a quick flick of the cook's wrist sent the intruder back-pedalling.

There were other unwritten laws in camp life and usually the cook became the self-appointed guardian of these. For instance, no one ever sat on, or close to, the tucker table, and woe betide anyone who sat on a bag of flour or sugar. There were no chairs; ringers sat on their heels or with crossed legs on the ground. Camps were full of tough characters those days, but few challenged the cook. The sight of an irate babbler with right on his side and a fire shovel in his hand tended to discourage any argument.

There is a popular myth that bushmen are careless about personal hygiene; nothing could be further from the truth. It is true ringers often slept in their clothes those days, but they bathed whenever possible and were fanatical about washing before a meal. The reason for this was

Setting up camp.

simple: everyone handled the tucker. A lot of meals consisted of a loaf of bread or damper and a slab of corned meat placed on the table for the ringers to help themselves. Anyone who failed to wash was likely to find himself thrown fully clothed into the nearest waterhole or cattle trough.

In my time in the outback, stockcamps moved regularly and drovers, of course, were on a new camp every night; as a result, toilet facilities were non-existent. When a ringer wished to do what has been euphemistically called a 'No. 2', he merely went a respectable distance from the camp and squatted down. He went down wind, of course. No one who went up wind ever made the same mistake twice.

Toilet paper was also unheard of. In fact paper of any kind was scarce in stockcamps, and limited to the droving contract and waybills when on the road with cattle. But bushmen are masters of innovation: in timber country, straight, even dry, sticks took the place of paper—one reason why experienced bushmen never pick up a stick off the ground to stir their quart pots. In open country, another solution had to be found. Fortunately the downs are strewn with small stones called gidgee stones. They are roughly round in shape and up to a cricket ball in size, and they did the job admirably.

New chums, who had to put up with a fair bit of chiacking, often had ribald comments shouted after them as they trudged away to relieve themselves. Helpful pieces of advice such as: 'Look out you don't wipe your arse with a death adder', or 'Put your belt round the right turd when you're finished' were common. However, new chums survived, and most of them ended up as smart men.

Few ringers felt comfortable with a woman in the camp. Northern Territory ringers had little contact with white women and they tended to regard them with awe and respect—exotic creatures to be worshipped from afar. They were unanimous in their opinion that the camp, with its primitive conditions, was no place for such delicate individuals. There were women, of course, who held their own with men on the stockroutes. The Zigenbine girls, daughters of Harry Zigenbine, were probably the best known of these outstanding women.

Bill Yeomans, on horseback, chats to legendary Rocklands drover Walter Cowan, who is standing by his wagonette.

BUSH COOKS

BUSH COOKS ARE, to paraphrase Rolf Harris, 'a dangerous breed, mate!' There were, and probably still are, some remarkably good cooks in the outback; and there were also some bloody awful ones. I've known cooks who could bake bread in camp ovens better than any city baker, and I've also known some who couldn't boil water. The one thing they all seemed to have in common was their nature—they all seemed to be crooked on the world. They were, almost without exception, 'death adders'—snaky as hell and just waiting for someone to put a foot wrong. Despite this, if a camp was blessed with a good cook, it was a happy camp.

Camp cooks, whether good or bad, were always, as a rule, clean; however, there is always the exception to any rule. Many years ago I was ringing in a stockcamp where a remittance man who went by the name of Piebald Jack was employed as the dough roaster. One morning when mustering, the head stockman doubled back to the camp to get a pair of spurs he'd forgotten. At the camp he found Piebald Jack with his trousers down, steaming his piles over the tea billy. He claimed the treatment gave him relief; it did not, however, do a lot for the flavour of the tea. The head stockman advised Piebald Jack to move on and steam his piles elsewhere.

The best packhorse cook I ever struck was Jack Brumby, a part-Aboriginal ex-ringer who cooked for Looking Glass Joe Dowling on the road with Nutwood bullocks. Jack was something of a rarity; as well as being a top cook, he was a happy, good-natured individual.

Before going droving with Dowling on one occasion, I had been working on Nutwood, a station north-east of Daly Waters and south-east of the Elsey, and it was one of the roughest runs in the Top End, with large areas of thick lancewood scrub and cattle as wild as hawks. The cook in the stockcamp was even rougher than the terrain and a bludger to boot. After a long day of track mustering and scrubber running, we often got back to camp at nine or ten o'clock to find the cook in his swag and a meal of cold corned beef and damper awaiting us. One night when we got to camp we found him awake and complaining bitterly about something or other. The head stockman's reply spoke louder than words; he stood up and knocked the cook clean over the fire. The cook's demeanour improved markedly after that, but unfortunately his cooking did not.

Looking Glass was waiting to take delivery of the store mob we had mustered. I had planned to go in with the mob, so I joined his camp when he took over the bullocks, pleased to leave behind me the cook at the Nutwood stockcamp. With Jack Brumby in charge of the camp ovens, every day seemed like Christmas Day to me. The bread he baked was the lightest and finest-textured bread I had ever eaten. He swore he had no secret recipe, yet I never knew him to have a failure.

I watched him when I had a chance and his routine never varied. He would mix up the dough at night in a bread bucket, using flour, salt, yeast and warm water, then he made a thick batter that was left to stand overnight in the bucket. Jack took great care with this part of the operation, covering the bread bucket with a blanket and standing it close enough to the fire to obtain the correct amount of warmth.

First thing next morning Jack tipped the dough out on to a bit of tarpaulin. The mixture had risen during the night and Jack would knock it back by vigorous kneading, at the same time adding more flour. The dough was then put back in the bucket to rise again, and to be carried to the next camp strapped on top of the tucker pack.

As soon as Jack had unpacked, he attacked the dough once more. This time, after knocking it back, he formed the dough into loaves and placed them in the Bedourie ovens to rise for the last time. By the time the bread had risen for the third time, Jack had two shallow holes ready for the camp ovens and had an ample supply of hot coals on hand. After he had shovelled the required measure of coals into the bottom of the holes, in went the ovens, and more coals were placed on the lids. That was all there was to it, but the result was food for the gods.

Most bush cooks could hold their own when it came to repartee. There is an old story about a bush cook who gave up tending camp ovens to start a small pig farm on the outskirts of a western town. A chap who used to employ the ex-cook met him in the main street one day.

'G'day, mate,' he said, 'they tell me you're cooking for pigs now.'

'No,' replied the erstwhile babbler, 'these days I'm cooking for gentlemen.'

The wide range of expertise among bush cooks led to the establishment of a scale to assess their worth. This scale classified cooks much as the Richter scale classifies earthquakes, and considering the gastronomical eruptions caused by some babblers, the comparison is not without merit.

The scale went like this:
Cooks
Cookoos
Baitlayers
Tucker F . . . ers
Wilful Bloody Murderers

A packhorse drover's dinner table.

Looking Glass Joe

Now the road mobs from Nutwood would gallop all night,
They were big piker bullocks inclined to take fright;
Bred away in the cane-grass and scrub-covered hills,
They were mustered with coachers and plenty of spills.
There was not a boss drover that I can recall
Who had taken them on and delivered them all.

With a rattle and crash through the timber they'd go,
And the first man to tame them was Looking Glass Joe.
Now old Joe with wild cattle was known to be good,
He could lift cleanskins faster than anyone could,
He could front leg a piker with consummate ease
And would wheel a wild scrubber as quick as you please.

He had heard of the Nutwoods and reckoned he'd show
That wild cattle were child's play to Looking Glass Joe.
So he mustered his horses and headed out West,
And the team that he gathered was one of the best;
Jacky Britt and Jack Brumby, and Joe's brother Jack
Were as good as you'd find on the Murranji track.

Billy Thompson went too, so I said, 'What the hell!'
I was ripe for a change so I signed on as well.
Well we picked up the mob, and their rep' was no lie
For a lot of the bastards were older than I.
They were scrub-bred and wary, long-legged and lean,
And the horns that they tossed were the biggest I'd seen.

With a man in the lead so they'd draw nice and slow
We got started for Queensland with Looking Glass Joe.
There were nights when they galloped from darkness to dawn,
There were nights when I wished that I'd never been born,
For they rushed and they rattled through scrubs deep and black
But we wheeled them and rung them, and herded them back.

On the nights when they camped Joe would say to me, 'Son,
You can saddle a nighthorse, there's work to be done'.
Then we mustered the scrubs and the flats for the strays
That had led the wild rushes of earlier days.
There we galloped and drafted bush cattle all night,
To return with our catch in the first of the light.

But I said, 'Joe, you're mad, putting rogue bullocks in
This galloping mob that is hock deep in sin,'
He pushed back his hat, 'Yeah, perhaps that is so—
But I must have me numbers,' said Looking Glass Joe.
What with rushes and musters and long days as well,
I wished Looking Glass Joe and his bullocks in hell.

Well we drove them for four months and one bloody day
We delivered at Morstone, and picked up our pay.
We were proud in the end, I suppose rightly so,
For we'd mastered the Nutwoods with Looking Glass Joe.
Thirteen fifty we took at the start of the drive,
And at Morstone the count, fourteen hundred and five.

Now the store mobs from Nutwood would gallop all night,
They were big piker bullocks inclined to take fright.
Up till then not a drover that I can recall
Had completed a trip and delivered them all.
With a rattle and crash through the timber they'd go,
And the first man to tame them was Looking Glass Joe.

ABORIGINAL STOCKMEN

AUSTRALIA, OR MORE correctly the pastoral industry, owes a considerable debt to the Aborigines, both male and female. Big companies employed large numbers of them at very low wages, and the resulting profits must have been substantial. Drovers also employed them at the same low wages; however, at the contract price offered by the same big companies, there seemed little option. Many unsuccessful attempts were made to have the droving price increased, including the 1956 drovers' strike in which I was appointed spokesman.

Despite the exploitation of Aborigines through low wages, the system was not totally without merit. Firstly, they received some reward for effort rather than a government handout. Secondly, they usually worked and lived, albeit as hired hands, in what they still regarded as their tribal area. It is difficult for whites to understand the relationship that exists between Aborigines and the land. If one combines religion and patriotism, I doubt if the combination would come within a bull's bellow of that relationship.

Aborigines made good stockmen, and the older, more experienced ones were highly respected and acted as excellent role models for the young. On every Northern Territory station there were Aborigines who were excellent buckjump riders. Despite the fact that many of them could ride anything wrapped in hide, few could be called all-round horsemen, however. Their seat and hands left a lot to be desired and they seldom demonstrated any affinity with the horses they rode.

They all enjoyed fast exciting work, but tended to regard the more humdrum tasks with little interest. A problem for the head stockman was that the majority could not be relied upon when not being supervised, perhaps understandable under the circumstances. Most of the older Aborigines showed an outstanding loyalty to their white bosses, however.

The smartest Aborigines with wild cattle that I worked with were from the Roper River and Hodgson River areas. Their tribal lands teemed with game, wild fowl and fish. As with all coastal people, their physique was far superior to the inland Aborigines, who lived in one of the harshest environments on this planet. That they survived at all says a lot for the resourcefulness and bushcraft of Australia's indigenous people.

The Aboriginal stockmen from the Roper and Hodgson were good trackers and could throw any beast, regardless of age and size. Although

THE NORTHERN TERRITORY OF AUSTRALIA

ABORIGINALS ORDINANCE: 1918-1947

RECOGNIZANCE

Be it remembered that on **5th** day of **August** 19**55**

Bruce Simpson of **Camooweal**

personally came before the undersigned Protector of Aborigines in and for the

District of **Elliott** and acknowledged to owe to our

Sovereign Lord the King the sum of **£100** pounds, sterling, to be made

and levied on his goods and chattels, lands, and tenements respectively to the use of

our Lord the King, his heirs and successors, if he the said

shall fail in the conditions as hereunder set out.

E. Y. Seaton

The conditions of the above-written recognizance are that the said

B. Simpson shall return the aborigine **Rusty Walker**

to **Gordon Downs** within **Three months** from the

date of these presents :

AND that the said **Bruce Simpson** shall pay to the

said aborigine **Rusty Walker** wages at the rate of **£7-10-0 with cattle** per week

whilst employed by the said **Bruce Simpson** **£5-15-0 with empty plant** in the

Northern Territory of Australia and wages at the rate of **Award** per week

whilst employed out of the Northern Territory of Australia in the State of Queens-

land/Western Australia, then the said recognizance to be void or else to stand in full

force and virtue.

Taken and acknowledged the **8th** day of **August** 19**55**

Commenced employment with B. Simpson with cattle on 31st, May, 1955.

[signature]
(Protector of Aborigines)

OFFICE ONLY.

Date returned to District:

Advised by: File No:

In the 1950s, anyone wishing to employ Aboriginal stockmen had to obtain a licence and a recognizance like the one above. The system was designed to protect Northern Territory Aborigines from unscrupulous employers. However well meaning, it demonstrated the patriarchal attitude of the times.

the work they did was at times dangerous, it was also exciting and challenging. They were constantly trying to outdo each other and tended to regard the whole business as a game rather than as work.

When throwing a beast after jumping off your horse, as you have to in scrub, timing is vital. The beast has to be caught when it starts to roll in its stride but before it breaks into a trot; by that stage in the chase, the tail is often wet and slippery with hot dung.

Norman was an older man whose experience and presence of mind saved his life one day when he jumped off to throw a full-grown scrub bull. The monster, with horns that could rip a man or horse up in a flash, had broken out of a mob we were running. Just as Norman grabbed its tail, he stumbled and lost his grip on the slippery tail, falling on his back with his shoulders up against a tree. In a split second the bull was at him, shaking its head and blowing snot all over the prostrate ringer. If he had as much as moved a finger, the bull would have disembowelled him, but Norman lay there with the bull only inches away and never blinked an eye until we got the beast away from him.

As Norman calmly remounted his horse Nipper, a young Aborigine with me grinned. 'Close up finish that time, ol'man.'

Norman gave him a withering look. 'No more,' he said. 'Mebe bull altogether finish you.'

Splinter, one of the ringers in the Nutwood camp who was with me on that occasion, worked for me years later on the road droving. He was getting on in years then, but just as good a man as ever.

Aborigines are by nature a happy and musical people. In the stock-camps I worked in, I do not remember many nights when the sound of singing and laughter did not re-echo through the bush.

Changes to government policy and higher wages have put an end to all that, and most of the Aborigines once employed on the stations have drifted to our towns and cities.

Tommy Dodd

Tommy Dodd, Tommy Dodd, is your spirit still free
As it was when I met you out on the Barkly?
Riding tall in the saddle, packhorse by your side,
With the confident air of a man who could ride.
I remember the words that the boss had to say
At the Buchanan camp when you reined in that day:
'I've seen some good riders, but honest to God,
The horse isn't foaled that can throw Tommy Dodd.'

    I've seen some rough horses, seen many good rides,
    I knew Nathan and Cleary, and others besides,
    But the horseman I put at the top of the tree
    Was long Tommy Dodd of our own Territory,
    As good as the best in Australia.

Tommy Dodd, although coloured, a man can go far,
If he only has faith and he follows his star,
With your own culture shattered, when boyhood had flown
The skills of the stockcamp you took as your own.
And they knew, Tommy Dodd, you had mastered those skills
When the wild pikers broke in the scrub-covered hills,
You were there, Tommy Dodd, and your place was the lead
For you rode like a Centaur as one with your steed.

    I've seen some rough horses, seen many good rides,
    I knew Lewis and Vitnall, and others besides,
    But up with the guns at the top of the tree
    Was long Tommy Dodd of our own Territory,
    As good as the best in Australia.

You have ridden buckjumpers that jarred every bone,
But it seems, Tommy Dodd, that you couldn't be thrown,
From the banks of the Daly right down to the Todd
You were known and respected by all, Tommy Dodd.
Tommy Dodd, Tommy Dodd, is your spirit still free
As it was when I met you out on the Barkly?
Riding tall in the saddle, packhorse by your knee,
A man in control of his own destiny.

I've seen some rough horses, seen many good rides,
I worked for Sam Fuller and others besides,
But up with the guns at the top of the tree
Was long Tommy Dodd of our own Territory,
As good as the best in Australia.

WHISPERING GUMS

Sentinel gums by the river,
Twisted and gnarled and grey,
Saplings back in the Dreamtime,
Patriarch gums today.
Unmoved by the long years drifting,
Sturdy and gnarled and old,
Unbowed by a thousand tempests,
Unconquered by droughts untold.
Whispering gums by the river,
Close wrapp'd in your own mystique,
You whisper the age-old stories—
If only you could but speak.
The scars on your trunk slow healing,
Scored deep by a Stone Age blade,
Show clearly the desert nomads
Camped long in your spreading shade.
Oft' then when the twilight deepened
On the wind came a rhythmic beat,
The lilting chant of the women,
The shuffle and stamp of feet.
Whispering gums by the river,
Twisted and gnarled and old,
The stories you softly whisper
They never shall be retold.
Ne'er a corroboree fire
Gleams now through the silent land,
From the whispering gums they vanished,
Those who could understand.

ASSIMILATION

A *fighting son of a warlike race,*
Woodinga strode with a hunter's grace
To the very brink of the cliff's rough face,
   Blue shadowed by afternoon.
He snarled at the white men camped below
Where a precious spring seeped sweet and slow,
Then his challenge rang like a hammer blow,
   For he was a Kalkadoon.

Jimmy Quartpot sweats on the smoko bell
As he cleans the yard at the bush hotel,
Though no one expects him to do it well
   As he's only a flamin' coon.
He'll spend his pay on the cheapest booze,
And the lockup floor is the bed he'll use,
For his wits are all he has left to lose
   And he is a Kalkadoon.

Skull Hole

A grisly name for such a place,
Where big gums shade the water
Deep and cool and clear below,
The cliff face looming over.
A rugged rockhole hidden far
From noise and smog and traffic,
Where pythons slumber coil on coil
Within each secret crevice.
A Bora ground lies scattered there,
Its builders long forgotten,
The big roos pass its ravaged rings
To water at the shallows.
A mystic place it seems at night
When moon-cast shadows shiver,
When Boobook owls along the creek
Call back to one another.
A Goa sub-tribe camped one night,
Not knowing they were followed,
The rock face caught their savage song
And sent the echoes ringing.
At last the dancers sank in sleep,
As night winds fanned the embers
The Black Police threw their cordon round,
Grim-featured, quiet avengers.
The sickly daylight broke at last,
It broke in death and terror,
Behind the Goas loomed the cliffs,
Before them blazed the rifles.
And there upon the crimson sand
Amid their stolen plunder
The Goas learned the White Man's Law,
A brief and bloody lesson.
Now Boobooks call along the creek
When darkness cloaks the ridges,
No campfires glow beside Skull Hole
And there is no more singing.

THE MORSTONE TEAM

AFTER ACCOMPANYING LOOKING GLASS JOE, who was delivering a mob of Nutwood bullocks at Morstone, I took a job in the stockcamp there. The station, situated between Camooweal and Burketown, was a bullock depot owned by Vestey's. Many of the big store-conditioned mobs from the Territory and Kimberley region walked in and spelled at Morstone for 12 months before being trucked east from Mt Isa. Morstone was not in the true sense of the word a fattening depot, but the spell did wonders for the road-weary bullocks. Morstone is aptly named; the story goes that the original selector, after travelling across the adjoining property called Rocklands, decided that his run had more stones, hence the name.

I found the work on a bullock depot a lot easier than on the breeding places on which I had spent the last three years and I thoroughly enjoyed the change. The stockcamp was a small one by most standards, however all the ringers were experienced men and good blokes to get along with, and as a result the camp was a happy one. The O'Shanassy River ran through the property, heading north-east to join the Gregory. On the open downs country north of the river were large limestone outcrops; these large flagstones were a very real danger when mustering or when draughting cattle on an open camp. Bad accidents did occur and some eight years after I worked on the place, Tommy Burrows was involved in a fall that almost ended his life. It is due solely to Tom's indomitable spirit that he not only survived but came to terms with his resulting disability to become one of the Territory's real characters.

When I was on Morstone, the homestead was situated on the O'Shanassy River. It was a beautiful spot and why the complex was later moved out on to the blazing downs at A bore is beyond me. In one of the vehicle sheds near the yards was an old tabletop wagon, and running in one of the paddocks were a dozen Clydesdale draughthorses. They were fine, big upstanding horses branded FV, the horse brand symbol of Fitzroy Vale, a Vestey station near Rockhampton. No one seemed to know anything about them or how long they had been on Morstone.

They were of particular interest to Ted Keilor and me, for as lads we had both gained experience with draughthorses. However, the station work went on and the Clydesdales continued to live the life of Riley in their paddock. The stockcamp was only a small one, and some cattle work had to be done over the summer months, most of the ringers were kept on the books during the slack. There was not a lot to do, and no doubt the manager was thinking of a way to keep us occupied when one morning at smoko he said, 'The area around the cattle troughs needs stoning up badly. We may get stuck into it shortly.'

It was not the type of work that ringers were asked to do those days and the manager's words were greeted with stony silence from everyone except Ted. After we finished smoko, I had a go at him.

'I didn't think you were the type of bloke to have ambitions about becoming a truck-driving navvy?'

'I'm not. Come and have a look at this.'

I followed Ted over to the shed that housed the old wagon. He patted the splinter bar.

'She's as sound as a bell, only needs a bit of axle grease.'

I looked at him in amazement. 'You're thinking about the Clydesdales?'

'Bloody oath. Will you be in it?'

Ted's eyes were shining. I grinned.

'All right, but let's check the wagon over properly.'

We went over the old tabletop thoroughly; the paint was peeling but the woodwork was sound and the two sets of shafts seemed solid enough. The iron fittings were certainly rusty, but, as Ted said, a liberal application of grease would work wonders. The heavy iron tyres were loose on the wooden felloes, but both Ted and I knew that a good soaking would remedy that. When we had finished the inspection, I stood back.

'Well, Ted, we should be able to get her rolling again, but what about the harness?'

'Come on, then, let's go and have a gander.'

We both knew that there was an old team harness stacked at the back of the saddle room.

For the next hour we wrestled with dusty winkers, collars and hames tangled up with backbands and chains. We ended up with seven sets of harness arrayed on the stockyard rails; we also had breechings and saddles for the shafters.

We were admiring our handiwork and grinning at one another like schoolboys when the manager strolled up. He stopped short, looked at the harness, then at us.

'What the blazes are you doing?'

Ted pushed his hat back.

'We're getting ready to stone up those troughs. We'll muster the horses tomorrow.'

The manager's jaw dropped. 'You're both as mad as cut snakes.'

He turned and walked away, shaking his head.

'Right,' said Ted. 'This gear is as dry as a wooden god. You go up and get some fat from the babbler while I look for axle grease.'

I strolled into the kitchen. The word had obviously got around for the cook greeted me with: 'Well, if it's not Ben Hur's offsider. To what do I owe this honour?'

'You can help by donating any old cooking fat you haven't already used to clog up our arteries.'

The cook wasn't a bad bloke; I left his domain with half a bucket of rendered fat, to which I added some stock tar and a dash of kerosene. I returned to the yards, where Ted had armed a few of the more curious ringers with rags, and the big grease-up began. After the harness had been thoroughly treated, we borrowed a lancewood rail from the yards; we then cut a heavy short fork. Using rail and fork as a lever and fulcrum, we removed each wheel in turn in order to grease the axles. After a liberal application of lubricant on the turntable and kingpin, we turned our attention to the ironwork on the two shafts. Finally, we doused the wheels with water and hung wet bags over them.

At the meal table that night we both came in for a fair bit of good-natured ribbing. Ted took it for a while, then addressed the cook.

'You know, I feel sorry for these blokes.'

'Yeah. Why?'

'Well. I know who'll be handling the horses and who will be loading and unloading those bloody big stones.'

The next morning Ted and I mustered the Clydesdales and ran them into the station yards. After smoko we returned to see if the horses had been handled before, and if so, how much they remembered. Draught-horses are cool-blooded types, usually fairly docile—our potential team was no different. We had little difficulty in catching them and found they would lead quite well after a bit of coaching—they had obviously been handled before leaving Fitzroy Vale. Ted and I were delighted, for our plans of becoming teamsters looked like being realised.

'So far, so good,' said Ted. 'Let's get stuck into their manes and tails.'

It took us a while to get rid of the knots and thin out the tangled manes and tails, but when the cook rang the gong for lunch, we had the Clydes-dales looking like brewery horses. That afternoon we harnessed each in turn, then using a lead, we got them to snig a heavy log around the big holding yard.

Within two days we had them snigging the log around the station outbuilding and standing quietly when brought to a halt. The manager, who still regarded our activities with amused tolerance, let us have a free rein, and we made the most of the opportunity. It is impossible to spend your life with horses and not feel a great attachment to them. In the fast busy atmosphere of a stockcamp, however, a quick pat and a rub around a mount's ears is about all that is possible; with the Clydesdales it was different. We had time to indulge our great love of horses, and the boyhood memories of horse teams we both shared came flooding back.

A horse team is not guided by reins but answers to the voice of the teamster, who walks beside the horses. There was always some variation in teamsters' commands, but most used 'Gee up' and 'Whoa' to start and stop; 'Gee back' or 'Whoa back' to the team, and in particular the shafters, to back the wagon; and to the leader or leaders, 'Gee off' and 'Gee over' to turn right and left. The leaders are the key element in any team, for they guide the rest of the horses and the wagon. In a small team, one leader is sufficient—Ted and I picked out an active, intelligent bay mare and started training her with light reins. In a couple of days she was answering to our calls without the reins, and Ted and I decided she would do the job nicely.

We were just about to take her back to the yards when Ted had an idea.

'Let's harness them as a team. I reckon they are ready. We'll hook them up to a couple of big logs and see if Princess here can really do the job.'

In half an hour we had them out on the flat working as a team. The bay mare, christened Princess by Ted, needed a little guidance at first, but she soon settled down. She had just swung the team around when the manager appeared. I called whoa to the horses and they stopped obediently.

'Well, I've got to hand it to you two,' said the boss. 'I think the idea of the wagon will work.'

'Of course it will work,' said Ted. 'We're almost ready to give them a trial in the wagon.'

'Yes, well don't worry about that yet. Just keep them going as you are.' He paused. 'I'm getting the agent to send out a teamster on the next mail.'

We looked at him in disbelief—Ted recovered first.

'What the bloody hell do you want a teamster for? We've done all the work. We can handle it.'

'Driving a team is a specialist's job. You can both give him a hand, of course, and keep the horses going until he arrives.'

We both liked and respected the manager, but we knew he was wrong about the team. After he had gone, Ted and I looked at one another in dismay.

'Where in the name of Christ is he going to get a teamster from?' Ted fumed.

'I'm stuffed if I know—it's a bloody stupid idea, but he's the boss.'

We unharnessed the horses and let them go in the house paddock just as the dinner bell went. We both had a wash, and as Ted grabbed a towel he snarled, 'If any bastard has a go at me over this, I'll drive his bloody jaw through the back of his neck.'

I laughed. 'Come on, mate, it's not the end of the world. He's got to find someone who can handle the horses better than we can.'

When we sat down at the table, we found that everyone was on our side over the teamster business. It was some consolation, but did little to dispel our disappointment.

During the three days before the mail truck arrived we drove the team around the homestead paddock and between the station outbuildings. We made the best of the situation, but our hearts were not in it. It was only the rapport that we had established with the horses that prevented us from giving the whole idea away.

In due course the teamster arrived. Ted and I looked him over. When he left us to throw his gear in the quarters, I turned to Ted. 'He's a bit young to be a teamster.'

'Teamster, my arse,' snorted Ted. 'If he's a teamster, I'll carry a boar pig to Bourke.'

The next morning we ran the Clydesdales into the yards, to find all hands and the cook perched on the rails. We shut the gate and joined them as the teamster crawled through the rails. It was at once apparent that he was intimidated by the big draughthorses.

The manager looked at us. 'You'd better give him a hand to catch them.'

'I suppose you'll want me to wipe his backside for him, too.'

Ted had slipped into the yard before the manager could reply. We caught the horses, but the teamster was clearly out of his depth. I calculated that his experience with teams had probably been restricted to a one horse baker's cart. Later that night, the boss sacked him.

Our joy, however, was short lived. Next day the manager informed us that a far more experienced man was coming out on the next mail. It was evident that he was not going to be beaten.

The next teamster certainly showed more promise than the first one. He had obviously handled draughthorses before and seemed comfortable with them. As the days went by, Ted and I wondered when he was going to hook them up to the wagon. He kept putting it off, until finally, at the manager's insistence, we gave him a hand to harness the team to the old tabletop wagon. We had thrown a number of heavy posts on to steady the horses, and to let them know what a load felt like. To my surprise, the new teamster screwed the brake on as well.

'I wouldn't do that,' said Ted. 'Let them get started first. You can always put it on later if it's needed.'

The brake on a wagon is placed just in front and above the front near wheel; it is applied by winding it on with a handle. The teamster reluctantly wound it off, and we called to the horses. They started forward, only to hit the collars and come back. Ted urged them on again and this time they got the wagon moving at a lively pace. The horses would have steadied up themselves, but the teamster panicked; he raced for the brake, and the wagon ran over his foot.

Ted pulled the team up and in a clearly audible stage whisper said, 'The boss isn't having a lot of luck with his bloody teamsters.'

The manager, who had been an interested spectator to the whole show, ignored the jibe. He told us to unharness the team and prepared to take the bitterly complaining teamster into Mt Isa.

We messed about with the horses until he departed, then grinning at one another, we got the team going. To do otherwise could have made jibs of them. The horses started without trouble and took little notice of the wagon rumbling along behind them. We drove them up past the station, along the road to Camooweal, then turned them in a wide circle back to the yards. We both knew that the team had passed its first test with flying colours.

We had them out again the next day when the manager returned. We swung the team off the road and pulled them up as he braked beside the wagon.

'I know when I'm beaten,' he grinned. 'You can take the team out to A bore tomorrow with the ringers and start on the troughs.'

A MYSTERIOUS FIRE

GLENORMISTON STATION IS one of those cattle properties that is as far west in Queensland as it is possible to go. The run's western boundary is the Territory border; the south-western boundary roughly follows the Toko Range. Although situated in low rainfall, semi-desert country, Glenormiston has an abundance of natural surface water, with the Georgina River running through the eastern part of the station. Quite often the old river would flood out into the channels when there had been no local rain at all.

Further west the run is watered by Pituri Creek. This creek got its name from the pituri plant, a narcotic shrub that grows in the area. Pituri was not only used by the local tribes but was also traded along well-established trade routes to the north. I have picked up many green diorite axe heads on Glenormiston that must have been carried hundreds of miles along these trade routes.

In Pituri Creek there are two fine lakes, Lake Wondita and Lake Idamea, beside which the Glenormiston homestead is built. Both lakes teem with waterfowl, fish and molluscs; before the coming of white men the area must have carried a large Aboriginal population. There is no doubt the tribe would have jealously guarded their fine hunting grounds and the locations where the prized pituri grew.

I found on Glenormiston considerable evidence of tribal activity, including rock paintings, bora grounds and middens. Unfortunately, in 1947, when I worked on the station, there was little else to remind one of the proud Pitta-Pitta tribe that less than 80 years before had hunted and fished along Pituri Creek, as their ancestors had done since before the dawn of history. In a few short years a people and their unique culture had vanished.

When out mustering one morning, three companions and I discovered what I can only describe as the remains of a very old and puzzling fire. With me were Charlie Trottman, a veteran Aboriginal stockman who had been in the district all his life, and two young ringers, Bruce Hanson and Ross Ratcliffe. We were riding along a ridge about half a mile (800 metres) from water. It was a very dry season with little grass about and a dust storm a few days earlier had further denuded the ridge, blowing away loose topsoil.

Charlie suddenly reined in his horse and said, 'Fire here one time ago.'

We dismounted and, sure enough, our horses' hooves had turned up burnt ground and scraps of charred material. We could also see bits of old iron lying half buried in the soil over a fairly large area. In 10 minutes we had gathered the iron mounts from packsaddles, as well as steel plates from riding saddles. Other relics included a number of steel clothing buttons.

It was strange that Charlie Trottman could recall no event during his lifetime that would explain the fire, for this was obviously the scene of a major disaster. Someone had lost the equipment of a full camp.

Ross Ratcliffe suddenly spoke: 'I'll tell you what we've found here—it's Leichhardt's last camp. The blacks speared them all and burned their gear.'

Bruce Hanson grinned. 'Perhaps it's the last resting place of Noah's Ark.'

'Laugh if you like,' replied Ross. 'I'll bet I'm right.'

'What about the iron?' said Hanson. 'The blacks would have taken that for spearheads.'

'Perhaps not,' I said. 'The Aborigines soon learnt to use iron, but not before they had been in contact with whites for some time. If the local blacks did wipe out the explorers here, they would have taken the axes and knives, but the shaping of iron would have been beyond them at that stage.

'Anyway,' I added, 'we had better get moving. We're supposed to be mustering.'

'Right,' said Ross. 'But we'll come back as soon as possible with shovels and a sieve. If we can find coins here, that will settle the matter.'

We all agreed to the plan, and as I rode away I saw an odd-looking stirrup iron half out of the ground. Jumping off my horse, I pulled it free, to find its mate lying just below it. The irons were of a design I had never seen before. The bottom bars looked like this:

I cleaned them up at the station and later in Brisbane had them chromed. These strange stirrup irons created quite a bit of interest over the years, but when I sold the droving plant, they went with it.

Unfortunately, we never did get back to the site of the fire. The three of us left Glenormiston after I had a disagreement with the manager. I do not know to this day what event caused the mysterious fire on Glenormiston. I do know, however, that iron and steel will survive for very many years in the almost moisture-free air of the semi-desert. It could be that Ross Ratcliffe was right after all.

WHERE LEICHHARDT LIES

Is this the land where Leichhardt lies,
Unfound though the years have fled?
Stark red desert 'neath blazing skies,
Where the ghostly pools of mirages rise,
From the claypan's barren bed.
Where is the spot that he lies at rest,
By channel or gibber-plain?
Did he grimly hold to the journey west
Or, disillusioned and sorely pressed,
Did he turn to the north again?
Did he turn to the north as the Israelites
Once turned to the promised land?
Through days of torture and nightmare nights
To a fate unknown went the ill-starred whites
To death in the black men's sand.

This is the land where the whirlwind goes
In the path of the men who fell;
Where the stars are pale and the min min glows,
And the sandhills shift when the storm wind blows
From the south like a blast from Hell.
Sweeping north go the dull red waves,
Storm-crests of a long-stilled sea—
Deep down under in smothered caves
Do they shield forever the long-lost graves,
And the key to the mystery?
Did he die a hero or die accursed
By the comrades he had led?
Did he fall to fever or blinding thirst?
Was he trapped by floor when the channels burst,
And the north-spawned waters spread?

This is the land where the desert blacks
Still wander, a scattered band.
Do they mutter low of the 'debil tracks'
In the long-ago, and of fierce attacks
In the heart of their sacred land?—
Where the fine red dust of the Centre cloaks
In a close embrace and strong,
The spinifex hills by the rock-bound soaks
Where the twisted limbs of the desert oaks,
Are crooning a deathless song.
Is this the land where Leichhardt lies?—
Land of the 'great unknown'.
Grim red desert and blazing skies,
Guard well your secret from questing eyes
For this is his land alone.

STOCK DISASTERS

THE PASTORAL INDUSTRY in Australia has experienced many serious disasters, or smashes, as they are called. These smashes have involved the tragic and often substantial loss of all types of stock from both natural causes and human error.

When one considers the perils faced by drovers from rushes, dry stages, poison plants, sandstorms and scrub, such smashes are under-standable. The Murranji Track was probably responsible for the loss of more road cattle than any other comparable stretch of stockroute. The Birdsville Track, with its dry stages and blinding sandstorms, also took heavy toll of travelling stock.

Also understandable are station stock losses from natural causes such as bushfires, floods and drought. There has always been a belief, however, that smashes on stations as a result of human error should never be allowed to happen. In truth, smashes could quite easily occur, and at times they did, for wherever man-made watering facilities were in use, the potential for a smash was present. In my day station waters were inspected no more than once a week, so if a watering facility failed in summer time, two or at most three days were all that were needed for the station to experience a major smash.

A smash involving a large number of stock could be a traumatic experience for those considered responsible. Years ago a mob of station cattle perished on Barkly Downs, and the manager, an efficient and conscientious man, could not live with the consequences and committed suicide.

During the years that I worked on stations I witnessed three smashes on three different cattle properties, and curiously enough, they all involved station horses. Two were the result of problems with man-made watering facilities, while the other was due to a natural disaster no one could have anticipated.

Alexandria had four thoroughbred station sires. The longest standing and the best was a stallion called Spaza, who sired fine stockhorses—true waler types with big tops and clean legs. He ran with his brood mares up the Playford River from the homestead, in a paddock that was watered by a windmill that pumped into an earth tank. A pipe from the tank led to the trough and, like most waters, the mill and tank were securely fenced off; only the trough could be reached by the horses.

Up the top end of Alexandria was some very rough country, and beyond that was a sort of no-man's-land, inhabited by a few reckless characters who were reputed to be a bit careless with their brands. Towards the end of one Wet, the manager asked Cecil Rose and me to take a small pack plant and have a look around up there, a sort of show-the-flag exercise. I've no idea what we were supposed to do if we ran into the hard cases, but neither of us planned to act the hero.

After an uneventful sojourn in the hills, we headed back down the Playford to the station. We called in at the stallion paddock—and rode into the middle of a smash. The stallion was dead, as were most of the mares and foals, and the remainder were on their last legs. The disaster had Cec and I puzzled for a while, for the mill was still pumping, then we saw that a dead foal in the trough had turned the water green and putrid. We saved one foal out of the whole paddock and took turns at carrying the feeble little bundle of skin and bone back to the station. The foal, christened Spondulicks, survived and was reared at the homestead.

Plant horses like this one were often drowned while swimming in hobbles in water holes. If the horse's hind legs got caught over the hobble, the animal had little chance.

Due to the heat, it is impossible to work cattle during the worst of the summer, and stockcamps usually finish mustering well before Christmas, starting up again some time in March. After working in the Glenormiston stockcamp in the latter part of 1947, 1 stayed on at the station over the slack period, doing leather work and saddle repairs. It was rather monotonous work for someone used to stockcamp life, so when one morning George Bannah invited me to go for a run out to the spell-horse paddock with him, I agreed with alacrity.

The 20-odd mile (30 kilometre) drive over the bush road to the paddock passed pleasantly enough, for George was an affable sort of chap who did not mind a yarn. As the spell-horse paddock was in fairly open country, we could see it long before we reached it. As with the paddock at Alexandria, it was watered by a mill and tank, with the standard fence around them; the only difference was that due to bad ground, the tank was a steel one. As we got a bit closer, I could see what appeared to be horses around the trough, and I had a sudden feeling of déjà vu, for horses, unlike cattle, never hang around water after drinking.

I was about to say something to George, when he said in a puzzled voice, 'The place looks different somehow.'

Then: 'It's the tank; the bloody tank's gone!'

And gone it had; one side of it had burst, spilling the entire contents on to the fenced-in area and turning it into a morass. The mill was still pumping into the ruins, but none of the water had run through the fence into the paddock, where stockhorses lay dead about the trough. The few that were still standing stumbled about with hollow flanks and sunken, glazed eyes.

George and I stood and looked at the mess in dismay, then he turned and ran to the truck.

'I've got to go back and get gear and pipe to run the water out to the trough.'

'It'll be too bloody late; they won't last that long.'

There were two 5 gallon (22 litre) buckets on the back of the truck. As though reading my mind, he threw them to me.

'Do what you can till I get back.' Then he was gone in a cloud of dust.

I pulled off my boots and rolled up my trousers, then filled the two buckets at the outlet pipe. The mud was almost up to my knees, but I struggled over the fence and poured the water into the trough. It barely covered the bottom.

Some of the horses were too far gone to respond, but a few others sucked at the small amount of water, and I knew I could save them with a bit of luck. For the next hour I battled back and forth doling out the water to them, for a quick bellyful would have killed the few survivors faster than no water at all.

George duly returned with all hands and I was given a spell with the buckets. As I rolled a smoke, I looked at the pitifully small number we had managed to save, but I felt satisfied that I'd done all that was possible.

The third incident occurred on Lorraine Station in the Gulf, when the splendid station sire Blue Horizon perished in a flood with all his mares and all but one of his foals. Blue Horizon was a New Zealand-bred grey stallion, a stayer of the famous Nazami blood line. He was brought over to run in the Melbourne Cup, but he sustained an injury when being taken off the boat and that put paid to his racing career.

Purchased by Lorraine as a station sire, his first crop of foals were kicking up their heels in the paddock when the Leichhardt River, rising 50 feet (15 metres) in one night, sent down a wall of water that swept them to their death. The paddock was not low lying; in fact, water had never been over it before. A few years later the surviving foal, the last link with the great Blue Horizon, was broken in by my brother Alan.

The Call of the Road

The stockhorses come with the rising sun,
   From the silver-leaf racing hard,
And we watch for the last time as they wheel
   By the gates of the station yard.

For the wind that whispers the white gums through
   Bears a message we must obey.
We will shake the dust of another run
   From our restless heels today,
Then it's off again on the paths of chance,
   In the West that is wide and green,
The channels are draining a record flood,
   Girth high is the grass between.
So we'll say goodbye to the Lorraine run,
   No more on her camps we'll ride.
We will brand no more on the Landsborough end,
   Nor muster Myally side.
Time's tireless fingers have turned a page,
   And a chapter is writ and shut,
As we bid adieu to the IZB
   And the mates of the camp and hut.

With his kind eyes searching, a puzzled colt
   May question perhaps the change,
While our favoured pets of the camp must learn,
   The touch of a hand that's strange;
For we leave behind us the good bay mare,
   And the filly by Bengal too,
May they never bend to an unkind will,
   Nor the hands of a jackaroo.

There's a touch of remorse in a horseman's heart,
    Few others could understand,
When it's au revoir to the stockcamp string,
    Farewell to the station brand.
Unfettered and careless, our swags are home,
    For horizons are wide and yet,
There was never a parting since time began
    That did not hold some regret.

But the wind that whispers the white gums through
    Bears a message we must obey.
We will raise the dust on another run,
    Ere the close of another day.
Then it's off again on the open road,
    In a West that is green and wide,
And our destination—it matters not,
    Let chance and the West decide.

R & R IN NORMANTON

NORMANTON HAS ALWAYS played an important role in supplying the needs of those hardy souls who spend their lives working and living on the Gulf Country cattle stations. Situated on the Norman River, the town is roughly 20 miles (30 kilometres) from the coast and has a colourful history dating back to the early days of settlement.

In 1949 a group of six of us from a Gulf station journeyed to Normanton for the annual rodeo and races. We were all ringers, with the exception of Maloney, who was the station's cowboy (an odd job man employed to milk cows and cut wood). Maloney was an ex-jockey who still involved himself at times in the race game and told endless tales of past glories on southern tracks. He was also a victim of the grog, and a typical two-pot screamer at best. We accepted without question that Maloney would need looking after.

The best pub in Normanton for ringers was the Albion, run by members of a well-known Gulf family. We hit town just before closing time and, running the utility in behind the Albion, we trooped into the bar and ordered rums all round. After a couple of drinks we buttonholed the publican, who readily agreed to let us roll our swags out in the backyard and use the hotel facilities. Taking a bottle of OP rum with us in case the mosquitoes were bad, we retired to our swags to gather strength for the days ahead. Work habits are hard to break and next morning I was awake as daylight broke over the Gulf town. I was not, however, the first to surface. Maloney was sitting up in his swag having a boozer's breakfast: a packet of Bex in one hand and a pannikin of rum in the other.

The head stockman reared up out of his swag: 'For Christ's sake, someone take the rum away from that drunken ratbag or we'll have to wet nurse him all day.'

Wardie, who was the closest, reached over and retrieved the half-empty bottle from the protesting culprit. We lay in our swags for a while, yarning and waiting for the town to come to life. Finally Wardie stood up and stretched.

'What about breakfast? Will we try the pub dining room?'

'I don't think so,' said the head stockman, 'not with Maloney. There could be women present.'

'Will we give the Dogger's cafe a whirl?' I said.

Everyone agreed, so the matter of breakfast was settled. The Dogger had been a dingo poisoner in earlier times and the name had stuck. He was, however, a good cook and presided over a clean and well-run cafe; moreover, his servings were reputed to be generous.

After a quick shower and a change of clothes, we rolled up our swags and headed up the street to Dogger's for breakfast. Maloney, lurching along between Don and Arthur, had managed to tuck only part of his shirt-tails into his trousers, and the way his hair was falling over one eye added to his rakish appearance. Suddenly he stopped.

'I think I'll tip the circus,' he announced.

The head stockman propped. 'Listen, you bloody reprobate, you tip anything at Dogger's and I'll have your guts for garters.'

Maloney looked at him owlishly for a second or two then walked on. 'Tipping the circus', as Maloney called it, had become something of an obsession with him. At some time in his chequered past he had seen an entertainer strip a tablecloth from a fully laden table without disturbing anything. Maloney's great ambition was to perform this feat one day.

We forgot about Maloney and his drunken ravings as we strolled to the cafe. The Dogger greeted us warily, but the traditional breakfast of steak and eggs that he placed before us was welcome enough. Steaming in the centre of the table was the grandfather of all china teapots. After washing down the steak and eggs with tea we leaned back in our chairs and had a smoke. It seemed that our stay in Normanton was off to a great start. Finally, we stood up and walked to the counter to pay the bill.

Just as we reached the counter, Maloney lurched to his feet, snatching the tablecloth as he did so. He gave it a mighty heave and fell flat on his back. An avalanche of plates, cups and saucers, cutlery, cruets and the giant teapot followed him to the concrete floor.

For a second or so we stood transfixed, then the kitchen door flew open and out stormed the Dogger, murder in his eyes and a butcher's knife in his hand. The head stockman reacted at the same time. In two strides he had Maloney by the scruff of the neck, lifted him to his feet and propelled him to the door. Before heaving Maloney into the street, he slipped his hand into the cowboy's hip pocket and deftly removed a roll of notes.

The sight of the money did a lot to mollify our host. All in all, Maloney's unsuccessful attempt to 'tip the circus' cost him dearly, but it did little to dampen our high spirits. The rest of the day passed quietly enough, with the only incident being a quickly organised whip-around for funds to bail out a mate who had shown a certain lack of judgment in punching the local sergeant of police on the nose.

The next day was rodeo day. The morning broke clear and bright and full of promise. We had breakfast in the hotel dining room, leaving Maloney drinking with the dawn patrol.

The rodeo grounds were crowded when we arrived at ten o'clock, and the bar area was particularly congested. We finally managed to get a position at the bar, where we ordered drinks and decided that as we were only interested in the buckjump event on later in the afternoon, our best plan was to stay where we were. We had been at the bar for perhaps an hour when the head stockman looked at me.

'Do you know that bloke behind you?' he asked.

'What bloke?'

'Turn around and have a gander,' said Wardie, 'but do it slowly.'

I turned round, stepping to one side as I did so. A character was shadow boxing—punching holes in the air a foot (30 centimetres) or so from where the back of my head had been.

I looked hard at him. 'What's the trouble?' I asked. He said nothing, but continued to dance and belabour empty space.

'It's right,' I said without turning. 'I think he's harmless.'

'You had better make sure,' advised the head stockman, 'before he king-hits you into the middle of next week.'

I stepped forward and clipped the shadow boxer lightly on the chin. He dropped his raised hands and backed away with a hurt expression in his eyes, then was lost in the crowd. I turned back to the bar and picked up my drink, relieved that the situation had been resolved so easily.

'Who the hell was that?' asked the head stockman.

'I don't know. I've never seen him before. He's obviously short of the full quid.'

'Yair,' drawled Wardie, 'but if I were you, I'd keep my eyes peeled for a while.'

The incident was soon forgotten and the time passed pleasantly enough at the bar. I noticed that Wardie was drinking double rums and was well on the way to being drunk.

'Wardie,' I said, 'if you're riding later, you'd better ease up a bit.'

He looked at me and grinned. 'I'm here to enjoy myself. She'll be right.'

Wardie was one of the toughest characters in the Gulf. He hated police and was at times a difficult chap to handle in drink. He had stayed out of trouble this trip, but his past battles with the law were something of a legend. Biting off part of an arresting officer's ear was one of his more celebrated feats in this field of endeavour. Nevertheless, Wardie was a staunch mate liked by all.

By the time the buckjumping event was due to start, our mate was in no condition to ride. However, nothing we could say would change his mind. He had the bad luck to draw a big black horse aptly named Black Angel. It was a horse Wardie may have ridden sober, but drunk he didn't have a bolter's chance.

The black horse threw him face down into the dirt, then bucked over the top of him. Wardie struggled to his feet and somehow climbed the high fence, but he overbalanced at the top, catching one spur to end up hanging head down, dazed and bleeding, like a side of beef in a butcher's shop. We got him down and carried him clear of the fence, when he suddenly came to and shrugged us off.

'Where,' he roared, 'are the bloody coppers who did this to me?'

It was an explosive situation, for the rodeo grounds were crawling with police. Somehow we got Wardie out of the grounds, into the ute, and back to the hotel. There we agreed the best plan was to pour rum into Wardie until he choked down and slept it off. Wardie finally quietened down and our plan was progressing smoothly when a policeman walked down the pub verandah and past the open bar door.

'There goes a walloper now,' said Maloney.

In a flash Wardie was off the barstool and out the door. We tackled him and fell in a tangled heap on the verandah. The policeman spun around.

'What's going on?' he demanded.

We explained to him that our mate had been hurt at the rodeo and was still concussed. He thought for a moment then said, 'I would put him to bed if I were you.'

He was just turning away when Maloney put his bib in again. 'Just as well you didn't try to arrest him. It took six of you coppers to take him in Cloncurry.'

Instantly the demeanour of the policeman changed.

'Who the hell are you?' he snapped.

'He's a mate of ours too,' I told him. 'He's a bit of a comedian, but a bit too drunk to be funny.'

I wheeled Maloney back to the bar without waiting for a reply and was still abusing him when the rest of the group returned to the bar with the still protesting Wardie.

Arthur looked at me. 'Why didn't you tell that copper Maloney was a dangerous escaped lunatic? It might have got him off our backs for a while.'

The head stockman looked at us and shook his head. 'I think the lot of you are lunatics. How the hell I got mixed up with you blokes is beyond me.'

Arthur grinned. 'Fate,' he said. 'Just unkind fate. By the way, hit your kick—it's your shout.'

We finally tucked Wardie up in his swag and left him snoring in concert with Maloney, who had thankfully choked down earlier. I had just walked back into the bar when a chap I had worked with at one time called me out to the verandah.

'Are you going to the ball?' he asked.

'Does it bloody well look like it?'

'Well, you should, mate. This girl, a governess where I work, she wants to meet you. You could do all right for yourself.'

'Pull the other leg,' I said.

'No it's true. She wants to meet the bloke who writes that verse for the *North Queensland Register*. I told her I knew you and she's been on my back ever since for an introduction.'

'Are you fair dinkum?'

'Bloody oath. She's a real good sort, too. I'd do a line for her myself but I couldn't write a poem to save my life. It's up to you. But she hates drink. You'll have to lay off the grog and get cleaned up.'

I looked down at my shirt, torn and bloody from struggling with Wardie.

'Have you got a coat and tie? You'll need them.'

'Where the blazes would I get a coat and tie?'

'Tell you what,' he said. 'There's a hawker in town. I saw his van in that empty allotment up the street. I'm off now. See you tonight.'

I walked thoughtfully back into the bar. There was little money to be made writing verse, but perhaps the fringe benefits would help to make up for that. One thing was for certain—I did not intend to spend a month's wages in finding out. If the governess wanted to meet me, she would have to take me as she found me.

The head stockman eyed me as I walked in. 'More trouble?'

'No,' I said casually. 'I'm going to get cleaned up later and go to the ball.'

Arthur grinned at me. 'I'll bet a bull's pizzle to a Vestey reference that you're on to a sheila.'

The head stockman nodded. 'I think we'd better keep an eye on you tonight.'

'Go and get stuffed,' I told them without rancour. 'But if you do go up to the hall, for God's sake leave Maloney behind.'

I knew the ball would be well attended, for unlike the majority of Territory runs, Gulf stations were home to many of the fairer sex. The floor was crowded when I arrived at the hall, where the dance band were playing toe-tapping music for a gypsy tap. In due course I met the governess, and true enough, she was a bit of a stunner and seemed like a nice girl. She had in tow a jackaroo from the same station who had a long nose and a supercilious look about him, but after a quick appraisal, I dismissed him as serious opposition and asked the governess to dance.

She was light on her feet and danced well. I soon discovered, however, that she was one of those young women who consider it noble and romantic to rescue those misguided individuals who have set out on the pleasant journey down that steep gradient known as the road to ruin.

'Why do you stockmen drink so much?' she asked. 'It's such a waste.'

'Well,' I replied, 'we're a thirsty bunch and after all there is little else to do.'

'Oh, but there is. There are so many worthwhile things to do.'

I grinned at her. 'You could be right. Let's talk about one or two.'

She coloured slightly and said rather stiffly, 'You know what I mean. Why waste your life in the rough environment of a stockcamp?'

I thought it was time to cool my companion's missionary zeal.

'Look,' I explained, 'I'm good at what I do and I enjoy it. Let's talk about you.'

Just then the music stopped. As we went back to her seat, I heard a commotion at the front of the hall and looked up to see that Maloney had arrived. He was waving a bottle of rum and looked as if he had been dragged by the feet through a patch of thick scrub. His entry into the hall was being barred by a large man in a suit. I excused myself and, cursing inwardly, went to his rescue.

The large character glanced at me as I walked up. 'If you know this chap get him out of here,' he said in a stage whisper the whole world could hear.

I got Maloney outside and asked him where the others were.

'I can't find them and I couldn't wake Wardie up.'

'All right, come around to the back of the hall; there's bound to be someone there.'

A group of ringers were drinking by a tank behind the hall. I took Maloney over to them.

'Do you blokes mind if my mate joins you? He's too drunk to get into the hall.'

'No sweat,' one of the drinkers said. 'Here, have a rum yourself.'

It would have been churlish to refuse, so I sat down and took them up on the offer. I yarned for awhile, then, promising to see them later, I returned to the dance. The governess and the long-nosed jackaroo were in earnest conversation when I joined them.

'Sorry about that,' I said as I sat down.

'It's quite all right,' she smiled. Then reproachfully added, 'You haven't been drinking, have you?'

Before I could answer, the jackaroo piped up. 'We both detest strong drink,' then he added for good measure, 'I personally despise men who drink.'

I was considering what to do about the jackaroo when a ringer stuck his head in the back door and bellowed, 'Simpson, you'd better get out here. Your mate is starting a blue.'

'Perhaps,' said the governess, 'you should go and look after your friend.'

'Yes,' echoed the jackaroo, 'go back to your boozy mates.'

I stood up. The overwhelming urge I had to rearrange his nose would have to wait. It would be a good idea, I thought, as I left the hall, to strangle Maloney first.

At the back of the hall I met Arthur, who had just arrived. We walked over to where Maloney was sitting with a group around a fire. A chap everyone called 'the professor' was on his feet waving his arms and talking loudly. Maloney looked up as we arrived.

'This clown,' he said, jerking his thumb in the direction of the professor, 'this clown reckons there is gas coming out of that bore. Any silly bastard can see it's water.'

'Is this fellow a mate of yours?' asked the professor.

'Yes, he's under our protection. If anyone kills him, it will be one of us.'

The professor sat down, so I did likewise. I poured myself a nip from Maloney's bottle, then passed it to Arthur. The town's artesian bore was close to the back of the hall and steam from the heated water rose into the cool night air.

'Geologists claim,' said the professor, 'that gas comes out of that bore pipe.'

'Gas, my backside. You're an idiot,' said Maloney.

'Shut up, Maloney,' said Arthur.

'It's true,' went on the expert. 'I've seen the report. It's natural gas, that will light if ignited.'

'You're as silly as a cut snake,' said Maloney. 'If I was 20 years younger, I'd knock the gas out of you.'

I told Maloney to belt up and poured myself another rum. The argument continued until finally Arthur stood up and said, 'Come on, let's go and have a closer look.'

We all trooped over and inspected the bore. The outlet pipe went up for about 8 feet (2.5 metres), then out at a right angle, and the hot artesian water flowed out into a large pond at the base of the bore, then ran out along a bore drain. Someone had placed stepping stones out to the concrete base at the bottom of the pipe.

'We could hoist someone up there and they could try to light it,' suggested Arthur.

'Good idea,' I said. 'Let's hoist Maloney up with a rope around his neck.'

He looked at me and laughed. 'No, I was thinking of you; you're a lightweight and pretty active.'

After a lot of urging, I agreed, as it seemed the only way to resolve the argument. After pulling my boots off, I put a box of matches between my teeth and climbed up on the shoulders of Arthur and another ringer. After a great deal of trouble I got into a position to attempt the great experiment. It was not easy; I had to maintain my balance, take care not to do myself a mischief on the hot pipe and at the same time strike matches.

Whatever was coming out of the pipe was blowing the matches out as soon as I struck them. I was leaning forward to try again when the matchbox slipped out of my hand. I made a futile grab at it, lost my balance, and fell with a loud splash into the water below. It was hot all right. I shot out fast, like a half-drowned, half-scalded rat. As soon as I hit dry land, I made for the fire, dripping water and mud as I went. I was almost there when I looked up and saw the long-nosed jackaroo approaching. He stopped short when he saw me, then, with a horrified expression on his face, he turned and fled back to the hall.

Weeks later I found out that the governess had sent him to tell me she was keeping me the last dance.

On Monday morning we poured Maloney into the back of the utility and climbed aboard ourselves. We were a sick and sorry lot, but we were firmly convinced we had had a great time, although it was doubtful the head stockman shared our opinion.

WHERE THE GIRLS AND THE CITY LIGHTS ARE

All's astir in the dawn of this long waited morn,
    All the ringers are busy and gay;
And we pack up in haste, we have no time to waste,
    For we go to the station today.
Our hearts they are light, as we girth the packs tight,
    And our thoughts they are straying afar,
Where the surf meets the sand, where the corner pubs stand,
    And the girls and the city lights are.

We have mustered the run, all the branding is done,
    The stockcamp is finishing here.
We have sweated and toiled, but our swag straps are oiled,
    For a spell at the end of the year.
The wagonette's packed, with the gear neatly stacked,
    Then we're off with a ringing 'Hurrah',
And a crack of the whip on that oft thought of trip,
    Where the girls and the city lights are.

The horses we ride take a long swinging stride,
    For they know that the station's ahead,
They have done the work well, and each one's earned the spell,
    In the creek paddock where they were bred.
The boys sing a song and the plant jogs along,
    As we farewell the faint morning star,
And a picture comes clear, of the music and beer,
    Where the girls and the city lights are.

Though it's thirty miles straight to the home paddock gate,
    We'll be there tonight, without fail,
For we're chequed up and set, with a good thirst to wet,
    And tomorrow we catch the down mail.
We'll leave all the packs on the saddle room racks,
    Well greased with fat and stock tar,
Then we'll swing the door to, like the bellhops will do,
    Where the girls and the city lights are.

The old station cook may remark with a look,
    That 'the blasted stockcamp should stay out',
But we'll hand him back cheek, for in less than a week,
    We'll be dining on oysters and stout.
For we're going straight through, like a bolt from the blue,
    Though we've visions of Tim Howard's bar,
But we won't touch a drop till we finally stop.
    Where the girls and the city lights are.

MULGA CORNER

There's a spot in busy Brisbane mid the clamour of the town,
Where the bushmen from the outback always gather when they're
down;
The buildings loom above it and its traffic signals glow,
And it hardly seems a possie that a Mulga man would know.
Above the roar of motors comes the newsboy's raucous shout,
And it seems a strange location for a man from further out;
The city crowd unheeding hurries by the corner pub,
But they love old 'Mulga Corner' do the pilgrims from the scrub.

When the droving is all over and the branding has been done,
And the mustering camps have finished on each godforsaken run,
When the storms have brought their blessings to the North and to the
West,
And the yard builders and fencers and their kind have 'give it best',
When the tired old year is dying and the talk is Xmas Cheer,
Then the townfolk turn to surfing and the bushmen turn to beer,
Then you'll find them flush and happy mid the noises of the street,
Home and hosed at 'Mulga Corner' where the bushmen always meet.

There'll be men from Cunnamulla and Thargomindah too,
With the stockmen off the Cooper and the men from the Barcoo,
There'll be ringers from the Gulf runs where the cleanskin mobs they
steal,
There'll be drovers in from Quilpie and the drovers from the 'Weal,
There'll be fencers from Cloncurry who would sink a hole in Hell,
With the Diamantina ringers and Georgina men as well,
From the Isaacs to the Herbert they'll be there to drink their fill,
With the drifters off the Barkly and the lads from Charleville.

There they'll skite and curse and argue and blow down each other's
ears,
Till a man would need a shovel to get in to order beers,
And they'll show you how to spur 'em when the outlaws twist and
chop,
For the riders at the 'Corner' never fail to say on top.
There the drovers tell of rushes in the gidgee and belar,
Till the mobs get boxed in dozens round the old 'Australian' bar.
There they'll sway upon the bar stools as they draft the wily steer,
And lug a snorting brumby with a beer glass for an ear.

And although the city's murmur and the traffic's clang and roar,
Drift across the bar room from the street outside the door,
You can hear the sound of cattle as they bellow in the yard,
And the storm wind in the mulga if you care to listen hard.
You can hear the stockwhips cracking down the stockroutes brown and
bare,
For the spirit of the outback somehow seems to linger there,
It's a little bit of bushland mid the clamour of the street,
And they call it 'Mulga Corner' where the bushmen always meet.

SKILLS OF THE RINGER

THE TERM 'RINGER' is derived from the practice of wheeling or ringing a galloping mob of cattle back upon itself. Ringers were employed by stations and drovers as horsemen. They were never employed as general station hands in the Territory or in outback Queensland. Those days no boss out there would ask a ringer to pick up a crowbar or shovel. Most of the work they did was on horseback and all were competent horsemen and cattlemen. In the bronco yard most could take a turn on the bronco horse and all could brand, castrate, earmark and dehorn speedily and efficiently. Some of the more experienced could geld colts and spay cattle, and most were expert in throwing cattle, either from a horse or on the ground. There were some ringers who worked only on stations and some who stuck exclusively to droving, but the majority did both jobs and welcomed the change.

The Australian stockman's seat on a horse leans more towards comfort than style. It is not a seat that a dressage instructor would approve of, but then dressage instructors do not spend up to 15 hours a day in the saddle. The Australian stock saddle enabled stockmen to adopt the forward seat—both body and legs inclined forward. It was important for a ringer to have good hands on a horse; hands held low are essential in pulling a young horse about and teaching the mount stock skills. Freshly broken horses were usually given to ringers after two rides out of the yard, and the young horse's education was then gained in the camp. Bridle reins are an easily read two-way communication channel for a good horseman.

Greenhide or untanned hide played an important part in outback life. Particular ringers won reputations as makers of fine greenhide ropes, and although some were of plaited greenhide, most were made by twisting three strands of hide about 1 inch (2.5 centimetres) wide together. Excellent ropes resulted that were strong and durable and that held a loop well, making them ideal for roping in the bronco yard. Greenhide leg ropes and hobble straps were other items ringers were skilled in making, when time permitted.

Australian tanned kangaroo hide is without doubt the strongest and most versatile leather in the world for its weight. Many ringers became expert at plaiting, and made 'roo hide belts, hatbands and whips in their spare time. The bulk of their work was far superior to that available in shops.

Peter Treloar

Open broncoing on Rockhampton Downs in 1949.

Despite the narrow base of their employment, ringers have proved many times that should the occasion arise, they can turn their hands successfully to just about anything.

THE MUSE AROUSED

THE POETRY OF Paterson, Lawson, Ogilvie and Morant was very popular with ringers in the cattle camps of the North-West. The reason for this was simple; nothing much had changed. The lifestyle they wrote about was almost identical with our own. We had to amuse ourselves those days, and around the fire at night we often recited our favourite bush verses. I preferred the work of Henry Lawson and Harry Morant, who both portrayed the bush in a realistic way; Ogilvie and, to some extent, Paterson tended to be romanticists. However, there were many in the stockcamps who disagreed.

As our lifestyle was so similar to the lifestyle described by the great bush poets, it was a natural and logical thing for many bushmen, including myself, to try their hand at writing verses. The Sydney *Bulletin* was regarded as the bushman's bible those days, and with the optimism of youth, it was to the '*Bully*' that I sent my first literary effort. The paper was renowned for the encouragement it had given over many years to Australian writers. However, the character who put together the answer to the correspondence page pulled no punches; he was frugal with his praise and devastating with his criticism. The page was titled 'The Muse Aroused' and appeared on the inside of the *Bulletin's* famous red cover. This gave rise to it becoming known as the red page, and owing to its pithy comments, it was regarded by readers as a feature page. In fact, so widely read was the red page that getting a mention there came to be regarded as a kind of literary recognition.

I waited impatiently, then at long last there it was—not my verse in the body of the *Bully*, but my name in the Red Page, with the comment 'pardonable if very young'. I gave up writing verse for a while after that, then I started contributing verses to the *North Queensland Register*, above the nom de plume of Lancewood. A couple of years later the *Bulletin* printed 'Where Leichhardt Lies'; it gave me a lot of pleasure to have the verse accepted, and I hoped that the Red Page critic read it. I received a cheque from the Sydney *Bulletin*, one of their special ones with a parrot in one corner saying, 'Thank God that's paid'. I should have kept it, but in the great tradition established by Henry Lawson, I cashed it immediately.

In 1972 a group of dedicated volunteers under the banner of the Winton Tourist Promotion Association launched the Bronze Swagman

Award for Bush Verse, an annual Australia-wide competition. I was lucky enough to win the first swaggy with 'Gold Star'. In 1975 1 got the judge's nod with 'Vale Rusty Reagan'.

The Bronze Swagman Award is still going strong, and the Winton Tourist Promotion Association is doing a great job in preserving and encouraging a style of literary expression that is as Australian as gum trees.

BOSS DROVER

AT THE END of 1951 I went to Brisbane for a holiday. It gave me a chance to get away from the bush while I considered my future. I had spent a number of years working on stations both in Queensland and the Northern Territory, including three years with the same company. I knew in time, had I stayed with them, I would have been offered a management, but the personal restrictions entailed in becoming a company man held little appeal for me.

Droving had always interested me. While working on Alexandria, I had seen the big mobs of aged store-conditioned bullocks walking through from the East Kimberley runs. I had heard yarns around countless campfires of rushes, dry stages and epic trips with cattle to New South Wales and beyond. I knew I needed a new challenge, and becoming a boss drover seemed a logical step. I had worked for some colourful drovers such as Looking Glass Joe, Sam Fuller and Arthur (Spider) Hollins; I had also worked scrub cattle, so I was confident that I could do the job. Becoming a boss drover was not, however, all that easy; it took both money and opportunity, and at that moment, I had neither.

Like most ringers, I never put too high a priority on building a nest egg. I also found that to maintain a reasonable sense of values it was essential to have a holiday in the south occasionally. Now at age 28 I found myself short of a quid, stuck in the city and going nowhere. Dame Fortune, however, is full of surprises, and in the next few days she dealt me a hand that would change my life.

I was having a drink in the Australian Hotel the day after my bout of soul searching when in walked Eric Beaumont. I knew Eric well; at one time he had been the common ranger at Boulia and I had worked his racehorses for him after leaving Glenormiston. We yarned over a round or two of drinks for a while, then pushing back his hat, he addressed me out of the corner of his mouth.

'You goin' out to the races tomorrer?'

'I'm not sure. Do you know something?' Then to the barman, 'Yes, same again.'

Eric waited until the drinks were served, then in a hoarse whisper, he gave me the drum.

'It's the good oil. Great Guru in the fourth—can't be beat.' I thanked Eric and the conversation turned to topics of a less highly classified nature until we parted.

The next day was Saturday and at ten o'clock Bruce Hanson arrived at the boarding house where I was staying. I had known Bruce since our time on Glenormiston, and as the pubs were open, we headed down to 'Mulga Corner' for a noggin. During the session, I told Bruce of Eric's tip and at lunch we grabbed a cab and went out to Doomben. Just before the fourth race, I saw Eric talking to a bookie; he saw me and came over.

'Get on to 'im quick. He's at tens still, but it won't be for long.'

I put a quid each way on Great Guru and joined Hanson at the fence just as the horses left the barrier. Unfortunately for me, the jockey on Great Guru spent most of the race in what can best be described as transcendental meditation and the pair lumbered past the post dead last. I decided that the money I had left would be better spent at the bar, where I proceeded to drown my sorrows.

As Bruce Hanson and I were leaving the course, we ran into Looking Glass Joe Dowling and his wife. They asked us both back to their hotel for a drink. When we joined them in the hotel lounge, I could see that Joe had something on his mind. After he ordered drinks, he came to the point.

'The road's no place for a gel. I want you to take over me plant.' I sat stunned as Joe continued.

'You can run it on half shares. You shouldn't have any trouble getting cattle. If we're going to make any money, though, you'll have to employ at least three blacks, so you'll need a couple of reliable white ringers.'

'What about me?' said Hanson.

Looking Glass Joe gave Bruce the once over, then looked at me. 'Is he any good?'

I smiled at Hanson's discomfort. 'He'll do me. Where's the plant now?'

'At Thorntonia.'

Joe's brother, 'Armchair' Tom Dowling, was manager on Thorntonia and I knew that Jack Britt was running the camp. I looked at Joe.

'It's a deal. Let's hope the season breaks early.'

'Well, if you're a bit short, I can organise a job for you both on Thorntonia. I'll ring Tom up and let him know you're on the way. You can keep an eye on the plant horses if you're on the place.'

Looking Glass Joe was no fool, and where his horses were concerned, he trusted no one.

Three days later Bruce Hanson and I threw our swags on a mail train and headed for Mt Isa. I was on my way to become a boss drover. Within 12 months of going on the road, I would have a droving plant of my own.

BACK TO CAMOOWEAL

BRUCE HANSON WAS a happy-go-lucky kind of chap who was always good company. He had been working in Brisbane for some years and was delighted at the chance of returning to the outback, to work for me with Looking Glass Joe's plant. As a result of his high spirits, the long trip to Mt Isa was seldom boring. As we approached the mining town I told him of my first experience in the place.

He grinned at me. 'Did the manpower blokes ever catch up with you?'

'No, they never did. Perhaps they believe I am still working at the lead smelters.'

'You'd be nicely leaded up by now if you were. I can think of better ways to put lead in my pencil.'

When the train stopped at the Mt Isa station, we shouldered our swags and retraced my steps on that first visit. The town now was a great deal larger than it had been then, and had an atmosphere of growth and affluence. I noticed with interest that the building once occupied by my friends of the manpower department now housed the AWU. The Argent Hotel, however, seemed unchanged. Its long cool bar still offered relief from the heat, and from dehydration, and there was, of course, plenty of beer on tap. Young Hanson and I had a couple of drinks, then went up to see Peak about a lift to Camooweal.

Since my first visit I had got to know Clayton Ewert, the driver, quite well. He greeted me with a grin.

'If you're going to the Territory, I hope you've got a permit.'

I laughed and introduced Bruce Hanson, adding, 'No, you'll only have the pleasure of our company as far as Camooweal this trip.'

'Well, I'll be leaving early tomorrow morning. Go and say good day to Les—he's always pleased to see someone with a quid.'

We paid our respects and the fare to Les, then returned to the coolness of the Argent bar. We were having a quiet beer when a shift finished at the mine. Hanson looked in disbelief as the crowd rushed the bar. We grabbed our beers and got out, leaving them to it.

We stayed at the pub overnight, and were up at daylight. As we carried our swags out the front of the hotel, Hanson declared he had heard movement in the kitchen. Never one to miss out, he walked in and organised tea and toast for us both. Now well fortified, we tossed our swags on the back as Clayton pulled up. The first rays of the rising sun were striking the top of the tall smoke stack at the mines as we left the town.

The country out along the Camooweal road looked very dry. I had told Clayton of my plan to take Looking Glass Joe's plant on the road and asked him what he thought of the chances of the season breaking. He told me that the signs didn't look good, and they had missed out on early storms.

Clayton passed me his tin of tobacco. As I rolled a smoke for him, I asked, 'What is the old town like?'

'It's bloody lively, just about everyone is in town and will be until the season breaks and the work starts.'

'Oh well, we'll only be there until the Burketown mail goes. You can drop us off at the bottom pub. We should get a camp there, if only on the verandah.'

We arrived in Camooweal to discover that the Burketown mail was undergoing service difficulties. Yamagouchi, who ran the service, had blown up the engine in his truck. Although the mail would of course still get through, passengers, on the other hand, would have to wait for the truck to be fixed.

It's an ill wind that blows nobody any good, and two attractive—and unattached—girls who were working at the hotel at which we stayed did much to occupy our time and ease our woes as we cooled our heels in Camooweal. The days passed pleasantly and when eventually I learnt that the Burketown mail would soon be back in action, it was with real regret that I prepared my departure for the following day. I was just crossing the street from Freckleton's store when Looking Glass Joe and his wife pulled up en route to Darwin. I told him of the hold up.

'Throw your swags in the back and I'll run you out as soon as we've had some lunch.'

When I told Hanson the news, he was less than excited by our turn in fortune.

'What! Go out today! We can't.'

'Why not?'

'I'm on a promise, that's why. I've finally cracked it, and you want me to leave town.'

'I'm sorry, mate, but we've got to go.'

With studied reluctance Hanson rolled his swag and carried it out to the front verandah. I felt sorry for him, for I knew the amount of spade work he had done in wooing the cook at the hotel.

We were soon saying our farewells to the girls, however, and I knew by the look on her face that the waitress with whom I had passed such an enjoyable week was aware of my mate's plight. Then Looking Glass Joe blew the horn and we were away.

Hanson and I put in nearly two months on Thorntonia. I had always got on well with Jack Britt, the head stockman, with whom I had worked on Alexandria and on the road droving. Thorntonia had some rough country on it and it was good to be back in the saddle and handling touchy cattle again. The girls wrote to us both, I think Hanson wrote back, but my mind was more on getting started on the road and I never got around to answering the letters I received from the waitress. There had been some scattered rain about and although the season had not broken properly, I decided to take a chance and start out.

Hanson and I mustered the plant horses, bludged a bit of tucker from Britty and threw on the packs. I planned to go into Camooweal and pick up rations and horseshoes for the trip out west. Hopefully, in the meantime we would get decent rain. Hanson was delighted with the plan, for it would give him a chance to further pursue his courtship of the cook.

On our arrival at Camooweal we found good horse feed on the common close to the Rocklands boundary and set up camp by a large coolibah tree. It did not take long for us to strike up a reacquaintance with the waitress and the cook, although I was taken to task for not answering any of the waitress's letters. They invited us to dine with them that evening, much to Hanson's delight, for when we rode back to the camp together in the small hours, there was a look of satisfied bliss on his face.

As the days passed we were enjoying ourselves too much to hurry with the shoeing of the plant horses. As a result, it took us about two weeks to complete the job. If we were not up at the pub, the girls were down at the camp. I dare say Mrs Toohey, the licensee, was sick of the sight of us. The time finally arrived, however, when we had to get going. We said our farewells to the girls and I promised the waitress that I would let her know where to get in touch with me. I also said I would try and get back for the Camooweal races. In the end, I did neither; although not an easy decision to make, I knew that droving was seldom conducive to romances of a permanent nature. The waitress left Camooweal shortly afterwards.

When Hanson and I left Camooweal we were still hoping that the season would break. However, as the days passed with no sign of rain, we realised we were heading into one of the worst droughts since the turn of the century. The further we travelled, the worse the stockroute became, and obtaining good horse feed was a constant challenge.

Crossing the Rankine Plain early one morning, we witnessed a strange phenomenon. Hanson noticed it first—a bank of low cloud in the south-east that rolled towards us at great speed; it boiled like a giant breaker and swept past not more than 50 feet (15 metres) above our heads. Behind it was a clear blue sky and a brisk, cool sou'easter. I watched it disappear without even laying the dust and looked at Hanson.

'Well, I think, mate, we have just seen the Wet for this year.'

At the Buchanan, we met Boy Beaumont bringing in a mob of Brunette bullocks. He informed me there was no chance of the stockroute remaining open without rain. I had been promised a mob off Eva Downs but began to doubt that the Chambers Brothers would start bullocks on the road under the prevailing conditions.

I arrived at Eva half blind with sandy blight to find my worst fears realised. There would be no droving off Eva Downs. Hanson went back to Brisbane and joined the army, and I took a job on Eva to get feed for the plant. When the rains finally came, I accepted an offer from Vestey's and headed further west.

DROUGHT

Old Camooweal is gripped by drought, the plain is brown and bare,
Relentlessly the dusty streets, reflect the blinding glare;
The burnished sky that's overhead shows little sign of rain,
To us that wait it seems that it may never storm again.
The temperature has passed for days, one hundred in the shade,
While drovers watch with anxious eyes, the clouds that rise and fade;
Their horses still are far from strong, there's nothing on the route,
Impatiently they wait for rain, to head for further out.

The old Georgina's bed is dry, and parched beside the town,
Twelve months have passed since last we saw the grey floods rolling
down.
Each evening brings the dry storms up, to split as dry storms do,
While oldsters quote with knowing looks, the drought of 'Ninety two'.
There's little work upon the runs, where cattle losses rise,
And waterholes have given out, beneath the blazing skies,
Now at the bores through night's release, through noon day's blinding
heat,
The pump head dips and rises to the engine's steady beat.

Inside, they've had some decent falls and how the herbage grew,
The ringer lads are heading in, in search of pastures new;
We envy them for we must stay, to kick our heels about
The bottom pub with naught to do, but drink and curse the drought.
But all ill winds must bring some good, and eyes of sparkling grey
And loving arms we've found that help to while the nights away.
In time perhaps the rains will come, to flush the dry creeks down,
But Old Man Drought rides high today, above the drovers' town.

FOOTLOOSE AND FREE

Old memories gather like moss on the years,
Of triumphs and hardships, of laughter and tears;
But one lingers yet like a snatch of a song
Of an old western river slow drifting along,
A friendly old river that glided and ran
From its hill shrouded source ere the dreaming began.
We were camped on that river, young Hanson and I,
Our swags were our homes, and our roof was the sky.

As footloose and free as the river that flowed
With a plant of fresh horses to take on the road;
On the river the eddies and wind ripples played
And we shod up the plant in the coolibah's shade.
The horse feed was good, life was easy and free
For time mattered little to Hanson and me.
We'd hobble the plant in the last of the light
Then welcome our girls from the township each night.

There we planned and we dreamed, young Hanson and I,
With our girls 'neath the dome of a star studded sky,
Those stars ages old that blazed constantly down
Seemed almost as close as the lights of the town.
The scent of wild clover came fresh on the breeze
That whispered it way through the coolibah trees,
The river and stars cast the oldest of spells
As the bush night re-echoed our Condamine bells.

But the last horse was shod 'neath the coolibah tree
'And dreams are for dreamers,' said Hanson to me,
The road further west held a challenge ahead
'And roads are for riding,' to Hanson I said.
Yet we both were aware of an unspoken doubt
That some day would haunt us on roads further out,
But we threw on the packs as the dawn fires burned,
We kissed both the girls, and we never returned.

NORTH-WEST MONSOON

We have struggled on with the starving stock,
    When the routes were brown and bare,
When the stench of death was in every breath
    Of the drought-dry dusty air.
We have battled on through the long dry years,
    When the South wind called the tune,
But our hopes revive as the clouds arrive
    With the old north-west monsoon.

We knew someday that the Wet must come
    As the big Wets did of yore,
When the grey floods spread from the riverbed
    To the steps of the homestead door.
A blood-red sunset flamed last night
    And a halo blessed the moon,
Now the dark clouds fly down a windswept sky
    In the van of the big monsoon.

Spawned on a far off Asian coast,
    And nursed o'er the Timor Sea,
The scuds sweep down over bush and town
    And the big drops dance with glee.
The outside channels are running now,
    There's a fresh in the long lagoon,
While the old frogs croak, from their sleep awoke
    By the call of the big monsoon.

The rain on the roof beats a gay tattoo,
    Since we heard it last how long?
The chimneys leak and the old trees creak,
    And our hearts are filled with song.
We can turn our backs on the bad times now,
    And our overdrafts we'll forget,
For the flying scuds and the first small floods
    All heralds an Old Man Wet.

There'll be losses yet to the floods and bog,
*   'Ere the rains of the monsoon pass,*
'Ere the floods recede and the cattle feed
*   Knee deep in the native grass,*
But drought's grey spectre has gone at last,
*   Though he left us none too soon,*
Our hearts are light and we'll sleep tonight
*   To the song of the old monsoon.*

PACKHORSE DROVING

PACKHORSE DROVERS HAD the reputation of being rather hungry or mean. However, this was more a case of necessity than desire. As everything had to be transported on eight packhorses—rations for up to eight weeks as well as water, beef and horseshoes—it is also not surprising that the tucker in a packhorse camp was a little short of gourmet standard.

Each packsaddle carried on each side a large leather packbag, or in the case of a water pack, a 5 gallon (22 litre) canteen on each side. The total load was distributed thus: two packs carrying water canteens, one shoeing pack, one corned beef pack, one flour pack, one cooked tucker pack, and two dry ration packs. These dry ration packs carried sugar, rice, coarse salt for salting beef, coffee, tea, potatoes, curry powder, tobacco, and cream of tartar and soda.

When packing a horse, the packbags had to be weighed by hand, as an unbalanced load would roll on the horse. As loading like this creates a dead weight, about 50 kilos plus a swag is a fair load for a packhorse.

The cooked tucker pack carried the cook's swag, plus an axe and a small tarpaulin, and a nest of billy cans strapped on top. The rest of the swags went on other packhorses, plus two or three Bedourie camp ovens, a rifle, and a nighthorse peg for open camps to complete the load. When crossing open country, like the Rankine Plain, a small amount of wood was also carried. This was augmented by using dried cow dung.

A packhorse plant gave a drover two advantages. Firstly, the plant gave him total mobility—he could go wherever he wished in order to find grass. Secondly, it made his job a lot easier, if he was shorthanded—the horse plant, usually taken to the next camp by the cook and the horsetailer, could be driven along with the bullocks.

LIFE ON THE STOCKROUTES

WHEN I WAS involved in the droving industry, cattle were still being walked from the West as they had been in the days of Nat Buchanan. Drovers still used packhorses or wagonettes to move their camp gear in the time-honoured manner of the early overlanders.

The store mobs were still big touchy aged bullocks from the vast unfenced runs of the Territory and the East Kimberleys. It was possible to walk a mob 500 miles (800 kilometres) without seeing a fence, in those days. The size of the mobs varied between 1350 and 1500. Trips were often of over 1000 miles (1600 kilometres) and four months on the road with a mob was common.

Store bullock drovers usually took 40-odd horses on the road with them, made up of eight pack or wagonette horses, eight nighthorses, and four or five day horses per man. The droving team consisted of three ringers and the boss with the cattle, a cook and a horsetailer. It was unusual for a full team to go right through a long trip. Very often the boss drover ended up being short-handed.

Mob watering at a stockroute bore.

Things were usually lively for a couple of weeks after taking delivery of a mob of store bullocks from the West; this was when most of the trouble with the mob occurred. Things went along a lot more smoothly after the mob were broken in to the road, but it was never boring, as every day brought another stage of the stockroute, and often new problems.

Because of the distance between waters, dry-daying bullocks—that is, watering every second day—was a common practice. If after a dry day there was no water ahead as expected, you had a dry stage on your hands.

Drovers were given a number of beasts as killers at the start of the trip. These bullocks were to be killed for beef as the drover went along. However, in a bad year these beasts soon became too tough to eat, and the drover would succumb to the temptation of filling the beef bags with one of the fat station cattle that grazed by the stockroute.

Getting grass for his mob was the first responsibility of the boss drover. This was never a problem in the Territory, as fenced stockroutes were unheard of out there and no one bothered them but when a drover got well down into Queensland the situation was quite different—fences on both sides of the stockroute lane, and a station hand to 'see the mob through'. Drovers, however, are an enterprising lot, and were usually equal to the challenge. Many a mob 'rushed' at night and ended up knee-deep in Mitchell grass in a grazier's paddock.

Droving was a hard life, but it was a free and easy one that had its rewards.

Song of the Wave Hill Track

Our bullocks are fresh and the season is good,
*   For we follow the yearly Wet.*
The first mob back on the Wave Hill track,
*   And the rain clouds gather yet.*
We took our mob from the mustering camp,
*   Just on a month ago,*
Twelve hundred head and all scrub bred,
*   They carry the 050.*

Our horses are fat and the creeks are full,
*   The feed is the very best;*
We'll poke them along with a cheery song,
*   And say goodbye to the West.*
We camped last night past the timber's edge,
*   Where the grasses grow like grain,*
Behind our back is the timbered track,
*   Before us—the blacksoil plain.*

The blacksoil plain where mirages dance,
*   And shimmer and then are gone,*
Past Brady's grave where the grasses wave,
*   The stockroute wanders on,*
O'er the rolling downs that rise and fade,
*   Past many a river bend,*
O'er the tableland where the lone mills stand,
*   And on to the journey's end.*

But we are young and our hearts are light,
*   And the life that we live is free,*
With a cheque to spend at the journey's end,
*   Not a care in the world have we,*
For time and distance are nought to us,
*   And the bullocks are feeding slow,*
The first mob back on the Wave Hill track,
*   Five hundred miles to go.*

Downs the River

The season was late when we left with the stores,
Feed scarce as we travelled the Barkly.
Round the permanent holes and the government bores
The tableland stretched away starkly.
We struck early storms as we farewelled the downs,
And the northerlies warned of their coming,
Away in the Gulf from the cumulus crowns
The sound of the thunder came drumming.

How we cursed at the rain when it pelted that night
And added confusion to worry;
How we cursed at the bullocks that bellowed in fright
And flung up the mud in their hurry.
But the morning star shone with a crystal clear light
Through a rift in the clouds ere dawning,
And the butcherbirds welcomed the sun with delight
And carolled their joy to the morning.

We are staging along down the Georgina now
And we water the mob while it's feeding,
By the banks of the holes it is grand to see how
The button grass clusters are seeding.
The scent of the herbage comes sweetly and strong
From the channels all matted with clover,
And water birds circle from each billabong
In the lead of the travelling drover.

The mob rests at noon with the water hard by
The trees where the quartpots are steaming.
Through sunlight and shade 'neath a water-washed sky
The river goes drifting and dreaming.
She winds on her way through the heart of the west
Turning and spreading and slowing,
This river the furthest out bushmen love best
Where the southerly busters are blowing.

Those who drink her pale water as pure as snow,
Be they bushmen or townsmen or rover,
Will some day return where the coolibah's grow
By the tracks of the travelling drover.
For she fashions a spell like a gossamer thread
Yet it holds a man fast and forever
To the creeks that run back through her vast watershed
And the length of the old winding river.

A TALLY OF BULLOCKS

SOME OF THE 121 000 head of cattle that walked down the Georgina River route in 1950 are listed below.

DROVER	MOB	FROM	TO
Boy Beaumont	1200 bullocks	Rocklands	Tanbar*
Peter Pedwell	1280 bullocks	Brunette	Dajarra
Barlow Jackson	1242 bullocks	Avon	South Galway*
Fred Barlow	1500 bullocks	Soudan	Monkira*
Ben Benson	1250 bullocks	Alroy	Dajarra
Larry Darcy	1300 bullocks	Helen Springs	Vergmont*
Walter Green	1360 bullocks	Rockhampton Downs	South Galway*
Jack Laffin	1500 bullocks	Soudan	Coorabulka*
Sid Howard	1350 bullocks	Creswell	Dajarra
Arthur Hollins	1500 bullocks	Helen Springs	Winton
Don Booth	1500 bullocks	Alexandria	Coorabulka*
Jack Britt	1400 mixed	Thorntonia	Brighton*
Chas Wolfgang	1200 bullocks	Barclay	Roxborough*
Norm Stacey	1266 bullocks	Victoria River	Walgra*
C. Papworth	1370 bullocks	Wave Hill	Dajarra
Tom Lewis	1626 bullocks	Wave Hill	Winton
Keith O'Keefe	1500 bullocks	Anthony Lagoon	Davenport*
Steve Donovan	1500 bullocks	Wave Hill	Dajarra
Roy McMullen	1250 bullocks	Alroy	Dajarra
Hurtle Lewis	1240 bullocks	Newcastle Waters	Kynuna
Jack Vitnall	1280 mixed	Alice Springs	Davenport*
Doug Scobie	1297 bullocks	Victoria River	Walgra*
Jack Charlton	1600 bullocks	Helen Springs	Dajarra
Reg Tighe	1350 bullocks	Wave Hill	Dajarra
W. Little	1280 bullocks	Elsey	not known
John Darcy	1207 bullocks	Victoria River	Walgra*
Bert Crouch	1250 bullocks	Alroy	Wyandra
Boy Elliot	1200 bullocks	Inverway	not known
Bill Ardill	1365 bullocks	Wave Hill	Dajarra

DROVER	MOB	FROM	TO
Splinter Pendergast	1355 bullocks	Victoria River	Walgra*
Edna Zigenbine	1417 bullocks	Bedford Downs	Dajarra

Fattening properties

EARLY OVERLANDERS

DROVING IN AUSTRALIA is almost as old as settlement itself. The discovery of a way over the Blue Mountains in 1813 started the movement of stock on the hoof in earnest, and in the next few years thousands of cattle and sheep walked over the mountains to the rich pastures beyond.

Late in 1836 Joseph Hawdon overlanded 300 head of cattle, through Aboriginal tribal country from the Murrumbidgee to the new settlement at Port Phillip. Within 18 months 5000 head of cattle and 150 000 head of sheep were to follow in his tracks.

From that time on, as explorers opened up the interior, overlanders, with their herds and flocks, followed hard on their heels. The Overland Telegraph (OT) played an important part in opening up the Northern Territory. It was the OT, or rather the need to supply meat to the workers, that motivated the droving of the first stock to the Top End.

The Milner Brothers left Cooper Creek in 1870 with some 4700 sheep, with Roper River as their goal. The trip took nearly two years and covered almost 3000 miles (4800 kilometres), taking them through the centre of Australia. The journey was not without tragedy as John Milner was clubbed to death by Aborigines at Attack Creek. His brother Ralph battled on, and finally arrived at the Roper in early 1872 with 3000 sheep for the fresh-meat hungry workers.

The government had promised a £10 000 reward for the first party to get meat to the OT workers. However, during the trip there had been an election, and as a result Ralph Milner missed out. It would appear that politicians' promises haven't changed over the years.

The first cattle to reach the Territory was a mob of 400 head owned by Dillon Cox. The mob was headed for the Roper to provide meat for the OT workers. In charge was D'Arcy Uhr, one of the best bushmen in Queensland. He followed the route that Leichhardt took on his first trip, around the Gulf coast. Uhr arrived at the Roper in 1872, only to find the work on the line completed. Cox wanted him to continue to Darwin, but Uhr contended that his job was finished when he reached the Roper. This first ever dispute over a droving contract in the Territory was settled in court with the government resident, Captain Douglas, presiding. D'Arcy Uhr complied with the court ruling and took the mob to Darwin—an epic trip over virtually unknown country. The route he took became the recognised route from Queensland, until the Murranji opened up.

The OT line, completed in 1872, left a number of isolated telegraph stations strung from south to north across the inhospitable centre of Australia. Many of these stations were later to become important towns. The immediate problem they created for the South Australian government in the administration of its Territory was one of supply.

The most practical method, it was decided, was to provide each station with its own flock of sheep for use as a meat supply. Alfred Giles, a noted bushman, won the contract to supply the lonely outposts with mutton on the hoof. He left Beltana in South Australia with 5000 head and started north along Milner's tracks.

At Barrow Creek, Giles met Tim Nelson, who was droving 100 head of cattle to Darwin for killers. Nelson had come from Undoolya Station, a newly established run in the MacDonnell Ranges east of the Alice Springs telegraph station. It had been taken up by Bagot and Smith and was the first pastoral lease in the area.

In 1879 Giles again headed north, supervising the droving of 2000 head of cattle and 12 000 sheep to stock Springvale and Delamere, taken up by Dr W Brown, in the Katherine area. However, the race to establish properties in the Top End had already been won; Travers and Gibson had already taken up Glencoe on the Adelaide River the year before. The man who stocked it for them was the legendary Nat Buchanan.

In 1878 Buchanan left Aramac with 1200 head bound for Glencoe. Roughly following D'Arcy Uhr's track around the Gulf coast, he travelled up the Roper to Elsey Creek then north to the Adelaide River as Uhr had done. The unfortunate Travers who went with Buchanan did not make it. While alone in the camp near the Limmen River he was killed by Aborigines.

In 1880 Buchanan was again headed for the Territory with 20 000 head, in 10 mobs, to stock newly taken up stations. Buchanan was the first man to take cattle to the East Kimberley region, droving 4000 head to stock Ord River run.

The overlanders who followed in the tracks of Uhr and Buchanan overcame flooded rivers and fever and encountered the wrath of Aborigines whose tribal lands they were crossing. The length of those epic trips, and the problems encountered en route, were enough to crush the spirit of most mortals. The men who travelled the coast road in the 1880s were not supermen, but their indomitable spirit and their vision of the future overcame all adversity.

The building of the Overland Telegraph line, and the men who followed after, played a part in opening up the Territory; it was the coast road, however, that proved to be the vital link.

Many overlanders did a sterling job in those stirring days, but two men stood head and shoulders above the rest.

Nat Buchanan was an Irish Scot, born in Dublin, who came to Australia in 1837. Strong in Buchanan's make-up was the restless spirit of adventure and resourcefulness typical of the Celtic race. He seemed to be as much at home in the trackless back country of Australia as his forebears had been in the wild braes and bens of Caledonia. He had the reputation of dealing fairly with Aborigines, yet like all his peers he saw himself as a flag carrier in the great nineteenth century expansion of the British Empire. Buchanan was in some ways an enigma—a man who overcame the harshest conditions, mixed with and employed hard tough men, yet never lost an innate gentleness—and he always carried a green sunshade.

There was nothing complex about D'Arcy Uhr—a tough, hard-bitten Australian bushman, he would just as soon have a fight as a feed; he was a man who tended to shoot first and ask questions later when dealing with Aborigines. Uhr's trip from Charters Towers to Darwin in 1872 was a feat of bushmanship seldom equalled, and it ushered in a new era. Buchanan's epic droving trip, from Aramac to the Adelaide River six years later, saw that era firmly established.

In the 1880s stations were being established at a rapid rate in those districts west of the tangled scrubs that appeared to be an impenetrable barrier. Running in a northerly direction to the west of Newcastle Waters, the scrub had beaten the explorer McDougall Stuart, and had forced the early overlanders to travel the long and tortuous coastal route. As there was good cattle country on both sides of the scrub, it was only a matter of time before some adventurous character triumphed over the natural barrier.

In 1886 that character arrived in the person of G.R. Hedley. Leaving Newcastle Waters he struck out into the unknown. He came close to losing his life on an 80 mile (130 kilometre) dry stage, but he won through to Top Springs—the first white man to travel the notorious Murranji Track.

Later that same year, after good rain, Nat Buchanan and 'Greenhide' Sam Croker decided to try the short cut. In hand they had 100 horses and a number of cattle that had strayed hundreds of miles from Wave Hill.

Sam Croker had tracked these cattle south of the Murranji waterhole, finding surface water after the rain. Enlisting the aid of local Aborigines, who guided Buchanan and Croker to Murranji and Yellow Holes, they made it to Top Springs. The trip from east to west through the scrub proved that stock could travel the Murranji, as long as the waterholes were full.

Although the new track cut hundreds of miles off the coastal route, it proved to be just as hazardous. Neither waterhole lasted long; when full they were fever ridden, and when dry they often proved to be the points of no return for the unwary traveller.

Travellers to the Western Australian goldfields used the tracks extensively, but no cattle were brought back through the Murranji until 1904. It was a good season that year, so Sidney Kidman decided to send two mobs from Victoria River Downs through the Murranji to Austral Downs in Queensland. Both mobs were cows, and Blake Miller went first with 1100 head. Flavelle Smith took the second mob through the Murranji scrubs to Queensland.

Four months later two mobs of bullocks and a mob of cows from Wave Hill started through the Murranji. Jack-Dick Skuthorpe and Steve Lewis were in charge of the bullocks, and Charlie Phillott took the cows. All three mobs were from Wave Hill. Skuthorpe and Phillott drove their mobs to Killarney Station near Narrabri, while Lewis walked his mob to Hergott Springs, going south through Alice Springs. These last three mobs got little water through the scrub.

The following year Walter Rose left Lissadel with bullocks for Queensland. The season was bad and Rose found the Murranji Track closed. Walter Rose was not going to be beaten, however. He turned the mob north to the old coast route and, after many holdups, finally reached his destination two-and-a-half years after leaving Lissadel.

1909 was another bad year, with the Murranji closed to cattle. This did not deter the Farquharson brothers of Inverway Station, out toward the Western Australian border, They drove their bullocks to Top Springs on the west side of the Murranji and spelled them for a few days. Then, after the mob was given a good drink, they headed for the Bucket Hole 120 miles (175 kilometres) away. Thirsty bullocks will march like soldiers as long as you steer them straight. The Farquharsons nursed them by day, and by night they kept the bullocks going with a hurricane light in the lead. It was a great example of guts and cattle work, and they came to the Bucket Hole with only minor loss.

In later life, Walter Rose ran a hotel in Cloncurry. Jack-Dick Skuthorpe died of Gulf Fever on his run on the Nicholson River. Blake Miller, a Kidman man and a fine bushman, later managed Austral Downs. Later still he owned Undilla, a small station between Camooweal and Burketown. There he raised stalwart sons and fine stockhorses. Some of the best horses I've ridden carried the Undilla brand. Charlie Phillott retired to Charleville, and his family became well known in the Winton district.

As a lad I knew Frank Uhr, D'Arcy Uhr's brother. Frank, whose correct name was Herbert George Uhr, was in the Territory in the 1880s and helped stock Brunette Downs. One year he and D'Arcy left Goulburn in New South Wales with 500 head for Cape York, and after five months on the road they delivered the mob without losing a single beast.

Galloping Bullocks and Dry Stages

Reckless rides through the Murranji
When little mattered save do or die—
With rushing bullocks the stakes were high
Where the tangled scrub loomed over—
Nursing mobs where the dead men lie—
With grass and water in short supply
For a thousand miles as the crow might fly
To the channels green with clover—
Perishing cattle on stages dry
Where sandstorms rage 'neath a barren sky—
These and more in the days gone by
Were the lot of the old-time driver.

THE ELSEY CROSSROADS

THE COASTAL ROUTE travelled by D'Arcy Uhr, and Milner's track up the Overland Telegraph line met near Elsey Creek, a tributary of the Roper, on what would soon become Elsey Station. From that important junction one route went north to the Adelaide River and on to Darwin. Another would later turn south-west, around the Murranji scrub to the Victoria River, then on to Wave Hill and the East Kimberley region. During the 1880s and 1890s the race to acquire Top End land was on with a vengeance. It was a period of explosive development in which the Elsey crossroads became a major focal point.

The first white man to visit the area was the explorer Ludwig Leichhardt, who crossed and named the Roper late in 1845 on his trip to Port Essington. He named the river after John Roper, a member of the expedition who had been speared by Aborigines some months previously. Although grievously wounded, Roper battled on and survived the journey to the sea.

In June 1856 a party led by Augustus Gregory left the Victoria River to explore inland across to the Queensland Gulf Country. The exploration was backed by the British government and the Royal Geographical Society. John Ravenscroft Elsey, a young English surgeon and naturalist selected by the society, had been sent out to join Gregory the year before.

Gregory gave the name Elsey Creek to one of the tributaries of the Roper after the young surgeon and the name was destined to become a household word in Australia long after Elsey himself was forgotten. The young explorer boarded the Alnwick Castle to return to England on 15 March 1857, but on 31 December he died at St Kitts in the West Indies. He was just 24 years of age.

In 1862 the indomitable Scot John McDouall Stuart arrived at the Roper on his epic journey to Chambers Bay east of Darwin. The Murranji had thrice defeated him in his efforts to reach the Victoria River, but on this historic trip he finally cut through the scrub north of the site of Newcastle Waters and crossed Gregory's tracks east of Elsey Creek.

The routes of the three explorers came together at the Roper: Leichhardt from the east, Gregory from the west, and Stuart from the south. The focal point at the crossroads was established. The surveyors of the OT line followed closely the route taken by McDouall Stuart, and

Ian Tinney

The gate to Elsey Cemetery and Nature Reserve.

within two years of the placement of the first survey peg, stock were moving up the two great stockroutes to the Elsey crossroads.

Workers on the OT line named a number of waters on Elsey country: All Saints Well, sunk in Elsey Creek and completed on All Saints Day 1872; Warloch Ponds (named after a horse); Bitter Springs, at the junction of Elsey Creek and the Roper (later renamed Mataranka Springs); and the Red Lily Lagoons.

In 1878 Abraham Wallace was granted the Elsey leases and the following year he was given an extension of time to stock and establish the run. After mustering 2500 head of cattle from Bowen Downs, Mt Cornish and Nive Downs, Wallace started north with his nephew J.H. Palmer and four others in 1880. Following the coastal route opened up by D'Arcy Uhr, Wallace arrived at his run in April 1881. He camped at Warloch Ponds and built the first homestead close to the stockroute on Elsey Creek. It was the third station to be established in the Top End.

Until the opening of the Murranji Track, the Elsey crossroads saw the greatest movement of stock in the history of pastoral development.

THE STOCKROUTES

A GREAT TRUNK route from east to west facilitated the droving of cattle from stations in the East Kimberleys and the Territory to the Queensland railheads and fattening properties, and to Alice Springs in the south. Three feeder stockroutes crossed the Western Australian–Territory border at Gordon Downs, Ord River, and at Aubergne in the north. The first two met to pass through Wave Hill, where the joined route became the main artery. The northern branch ran through Victoria River Downs to meet the main route at Top Springs. Also joining at the point was the Dry River route, which brought cattle down from the Katherine area.

The combined stockroute then became the Murranji Track. After emerging from the scrub lands, this main route was met on Newcastle Waters by a stockroute that ran from east of Katherine through Daly Waters. The main route then ran south-east over the Barkly Tableland and down the Georgina River to cross the Queensland border at Lake Nash.

Before crossing the border the main route was joined by two other feeder routes; the first, from the Western Gulf, came in at Anthony Lagoon; the second, from Rockhampton Downs and Alroy, joined at the Rankine. Cattle also left the main route at Helen Springs bound for the Alice, and at the Rankine, to cross the Queensland border at, or rather near, Camooweal.

Now if the above makes very dry reading, it also describes what were, for a long time, very dry stockroutes. As drovers were dependent on surface water to water their mobs, droving was restricted to those few months after the Wet. In 1920 the authorities decided to undertake a program to create stockroute watering facilities. Sub-artesian bores were the answer, and over the next few years bores were sunk on most of the recognised routes.

A chap by the name of Peacock, with his son and daughter, put down many of these bores. The plant used was the old percussion type. It was hard work with the drill needing constant attention, and the heavy bits had to be sharpened often, using a forge and anvil. Charcoal for the forge had to be made on the job by burning timber in a covered pit in the ground. The Peacocks were connected with the Jones of Jones' jam fame. Living conditions were rough, but I dare say they were never short of jam for the damper.

Once the bores were down, windmills were erected over the holes. A Japanese national with the unlikely name of Ivan Steel did a lot of this work. Later, during the war, he was interned as a suspected spy.

Earth water tanks were built on the downs, but as the soil in the Murranji was unsuitable, steel tanks were erected there. The contract for putting up the earth tanks or turkey's-nests was given to one of the Territory's genuine characters—Davey Cahill of Shannon Downs. Davey used a monkey-tail scoop and a horse team to do the job. Now Davey never liked to wear trousers when he was working and, although traffic was light in those days, a number of travellers were met by the sight of Davey, swinging on the lever of the monkey-tail scoop, with his bare buttocks flashing beneath the flying tails of his flannel shirt.

With the improvement to the stockroutes the number of mobs walking to Queensland from the West increased steadily. During the early days of the Pacific war, when the Japanese threat was very real, the government introduced a plan to move as many head of cattle as possible out of the threatened areas. This again led to increased activity on the stockroutes.

Many unsuccessful attempts were made over the years to clear a track through the Murranji scrubs. Faced with the Japanese threat, the authorities brought in bulldozers to clear a corridor. This was a short-term benefit only, as the regrowth soon became a problem. Additional bores were also sunk during the war years. Bill Chambers put down Windy Bore and a new bore at Anthony's Lagoon. Bill's father, Sid, had taken up the vacant Eva Downs block in 1936, and Bill and the rest of the family overlanded there in 1938.

The cessation of hostilities did nothing to halt the movement of western cattle to Queensland; indeed, the demand for beef, due to immigration and a higher standard of living, was responsible for one of the biggest booms in overlanding in our history.

Despite the improvements on the Murranji Track, it remained a headache to drovers right to the end of its use. The scrub in places was impenetrable; night camps were bad; windmills sometimes broke down; and ironwood poisoning added to the other problems. There were good drovers and bad stockroutes in other parts of Australia, but nowhere did the drover feel as alone as in the dark, brooding, and uninhabited scrubs of the Murranji. In the early days men perished from thirst on the Murranji during the dry season and fell victim to fever during the Wet. Murranji waterhole is more of a swamp than a hole, and there are reputed to be at least 20 men buried there. It is not a pretty spot.

THE MURRANJI

It lies a silent, stagnant swamp o'erhung with brooding trees,
Beside the lonely road that winds out to the Kimberleys.
The wild dogs chorus there each night from scrub on every side,
And there in torment and alone some twenty men have died.
The wild blacks called it Murranji before the white men came
To blaze the road and stockroute west that bears its sinister name.
A pest plagued swampland in the Wet—a mud hole in the Dry,
Both thirst and fever, deadly foes, then stalked the Murranji.

They stocked their stations further out, and brought their bullocks back,
With water fifty miles apart across the dreaded track.
Through endless scrub with packhorse plants they travelled day and
night;
When fever struck no mortal man could help them in their plight,
With brains awhirl they lent upon their mates who rode beside,
Who nursed them and who buried them in rough graves where they
died.

The Halls Creek diggings boomed out west and further every week,
The rumour of the riches spread—good gold up at 'the creek'.
A few made fortunes overnight, with gold the stakes are high,
Both others staked a final claim beside the Murranji.
And often troopers on patrol or drovers passing through,
Would curse the spot and start upon the task they had to do;
The scattered bones were gathered then, the sun-bleached skull was
found,
Another coolibah was marked beside another mound.

They came from many climes and lands, they steered by many stars,
Their paths converged to meet and end beneath these coolibahs.
One was a Swede who'd travelled far, he was of Viking blood,
He'd won his spurs in other lands in blizzard and in flood.
The craze for gold was in his veins, he swore he'd beat the track;
He reached the Murranji at last with aching legs and back.
He stayed a while to drink and rest and wash away the sweat,
And by that twisted coolibah the Swede is resting yet.

Two were but lads from New South Wales who rode to meet a mob,
The 'Never' held no fears for them, 'twas just another job.
Ah! reckless youth that reckons not what carelessness can cost,
They heard the Murranji was low—they gambled and they lost.
One found his final resting place by way of English pride,
For England shipped her wayward sons then when the world was wide.
A lone, aloof remittance man, none dared to ask him why,
Ere fever stilled those guarded lips beside Murranji.

They all left family ties somewhere, knew hopes and dreams and fears;
How many mothers' heads have bowed through waiting down the years?
No crosses stand, no railings guard each long neglected plot,
The names unknown, they slumber in one acre God forgot.

This message written on one of the tanks at Government Bore
Number 11 on the Murranji stockroute reads:
'C. Prendergast past here with 1082 head of galloping Newrys.'

TAKING DELIVERY

BEFORE A DROVER took delivery of a mob in those days, each bullock had to be inoculated against contagious bovine pleuropneumonia, commonly known as 'pleuro'. This was done by inserting a 'seaton', or short length of woollen yarn soaked in serum, in the soft tissue at the end of the beast's tail. The instrument used in this very minor operation was a large bladed needle with an open eye at the point of the blade.

As a result of this compulsory requirement, every station, no matter how under-improved, had at least one set of yards with a crush or race. As well as being inoculated, each beast was bang-tailed (the tassel on the end of the tail was cut short) to denote that it was a road bullock.

After the mob was put through the yards, it was ready to be handed over to the drover. The bullocks were counted by stringing them out between the manager and the drover, and when the number was agreed on, the droving contract was signed. The contract set out the price per head per hundred mile (160 kilometres) the drover was to receive, as well as the distance per week (water permitting) the drover was to travel. Most contracts also specified payment for holding time when drovers could not travel due to a direction from a stock inspector or other authority. This was usually commensurate with the contract rate for mileage lost. Waybills showing brands and earmarks of the mob together with a permit to travel were also handed to the drover.

Once the contract was signed and the drover had taken delivery, he was on his own—completely responsible for the well-being of the bullocks and the delivery of the full mob at the destination. As a drover was not paid for droving those bullocks lost during the trip, delivering anything less than the full mob would result in financial loss to the drover as well as possible damage to his reputation. A drover who made a very bad delivery by finishing the trip hundreds short, or by arriving with the bullocks in very poor condition, would be unlikely to be employed by that pastoral firm again. He may, in fact, find it hard to continue as a contract drover.

Contract drovers, knowing that future work depended on their reputation, set their priorities accordingly—the bullocks came first every time. Experienced ringers used to droving knew and appreciated this, and if anyone did grumble, the boss drover was quick to remind the culprit of the facts of life on the stockroutes.

Song of the Droving Season

On the runs of wide horizons, where mirages haunt the sky,
They are mustering the road mobs and the busy days slip by,
Reckless musters through the ranges o'er the plains that stretch before,
And the dust clouds slowly spiral from the drafting camps once more.

In the dawn light from the stockyard comes the sound of action too,
And the bang-tail knives are flashing as the bullocks rattle through,
Then the drovers take delivery where they count them on the plain,
And the restless mobs go stringing down the stockroutes once again.

Down the Wave Hill track they're coming twelve and fifteen hundred strong,
And the lonely nights are gladdened by the watch's lilting song.
Dusty pads are wearing deeper—wearing deeper as they wind,
For the Vestey mobs are walking with the 'Bull Heads' close behind.

Baldys, Shorthorns, wild-eyed pikers—mobs of every breed and brand,
From the wilds of West Australia to the Barkly Tableland.
While the bullocks of the Gulf runs are awalking with the rest,
Oh! the blackened quarts are boiling on the stockroutes north and west.

Down the rivers too they're stringing to the flats of channel grass,
And the brumbies wheel and whistle as the bullocks slowly pass.
Stringing down the lonely stages as the dust wrack swings aloft,
From the rolling downs of Avon, and the hills of Yelvertoft.

Dusty mobs from Alexandria, from Brunette and Creswell, too,
Placid top fats for the rail heads, rangy store mobs walking through.
Mobs for sale and mobs to fatten on the river flats inside,
Oh! the good old days still linger where the outback drovers ride.

Slowly mobs are feeding camp-wards as the evening shadows fall,
And the horse bells' mellow music drifts with twilight overall.
By the plains and scrubs and rivers where the western stars burn bright,
The friendly fires are glowing in the drovers' camps tonight.

NIGHTHORSES AND NIGHT WATCHING

THE PICK OF a store-cattle drover's plant was his nighthorses. These were fast, sure-footed horses with good eyesight, and the temperament for the important and often dangerous job of controlling touchy mobs at night. Good nighthorses were invaluable to a drover, as he depended on his reputation for future work. In a bad rush the quality of the nighthorse was often the deciding factor between holding the mob and disaster. Experienced nighthorses knew exactly what was expected of them. On a pitch-black night a drover had to depend to a large extent on the nighthorse to get to the lead of a rushing mob. Good nighthorses seldom put a foot wrong.

As there were no yards or fences on the outback stockroutes, watching the mob at night was an essential part of droving store bullocks. The mob was fed to the camp towards dusk and gradually pushed together until they formed a compact mass in front of the fire. Some drovers camped the mob up to 100 yards (90 metres) from the fire; others liked to have the bullocks close, leaving just enough room to ride between them and the fire.

The hours of darkness were split into watches, with the length of each watch depending on the number of men available. Two-and-a-half hours was normal with a full team. Drover's time was always set on six o'clock sundown, as this did away with having to adjust the watches due to the shortening or lengthening of the days. The boss drover always did the last or daylight watch—the horsetailer, the first.

The man on watch rode round the mob singing, reciting or whistling. This had a calming effect on the bullocks and prevented them from taking fright as the rider loomed up out of the darkness. A well-known drover once took delivery of bullocks from Brunette Downs, and in his employ he had a young chap who had never been on the road. Before the lad went on watch, the boss explained to him that he had to sing to the mob. On being informed that the lad knew no songs or poems, and could not whistle because he had lost his two front teeth, the boss scratched his head and said: 'Well, lad, these are Brunette bullocks and the Brunette brand is 505, so go out and tell 'em that'.

Throughout the trip the young chap chanted: '505 is the Brunette brand, the Brunette brand is 505'.

I don't suppose the bullocks minded: after all, he was singing their song.

GOODBYE OLD CHAP

You may rub your head on my coat, old chap,
  As you stand by the gate in pain,
While I loose the knot in the greenhide strap
  That you never shall wear again.
You may nudge my hand as you've done so oft,
  In the days that have gone for aye,
For you'll carry me never again on watch,
  Round the mob at the break of day.

You will draft no more as the grey dust swings,
  From the camp on the blacksoil plains;
You will prop no more by the stockyard wings,
  When we yard for the cattle trains.
No more you'll wait for the mob to splash,
  By the light of a storm lit sky;
Mid the thunder's roar and the timber's crash,
  Round the camp in the Murranji.

Ne'er again by the nighthorse break you'll doze,
  In the chill of a winter night,
When the south wind moans and the back log glows,
  And the stars wink cold and white.
We may find another with swinging gait,
  To hack through the trucking town,
And there'll be others to quietly wait
  By the break as the sun goes down.

We may find another to match your pace,
  Through the scrub when the fireworks start,
But never another to take the place
  That you hold in a horseman's heart.
Your mates have stood on the camp since dawn,
  You are watching alert and keen;
The packs are on and the girths are drawn,
  But the fence stands there between.

The plant is off on the road again,
    And here by the paddock gate,
In the days to follow, and all in vain,
    You'll whinny and watch and wait.
And often out on the Wave Hill track,
    When the evening shadows fall,
Our thoughts will turn to the gamest hack,
    And the best nighthorse of all.

Actor, farewell! Till your last long sleep,
    May never the creek run dry,
May the grass be whispering fetlock deep,
    Forever, Old Chap, Goodbye.

SELECTING AND SETTING UP THE CAMP

IT WAS VERY important, when droving touchy bullocks, to select the best possible camp site, but quite often drovers had to make the best of a bad situation. Camping a mob on drummy or hollow ground was something drovers avoided like the plague. If bullocks took fright on that sort of camp they would gallop all night. In scrub or timber country, drovers picked the most open spot clear of standing or fallen dead timber. The noise of a dry branch snapping would be enough to start a rush.

Wherever possible, drovers looked for a camp with reasonable feed close by so that the mob could be fed up to the selected spot. If bullocks had not had water during the day, it was important to camp them upwind of any half-dry, inadequate waterhole.

Drovers always put the fire between the camp and the bullocks. Behind the fire was the tucker pack and 'table'. In a packhorse plant the 'table' was a bag or small tarpaulin laid on the ground and the packs were set out in a line, side on to the bullocks and beyond the fire. If the drover had a wagonette, it was used in place of the packs. The men unrolled their swags behind the wagonette or packs, and close behind the camp the nighthorses would be tied up. Drovers relied on the fire to split the mob should the bullocks rush towards the camp.

Bullocks have been known to go over a camp. A mob of Territory bullocks once flattened a wagonette camp at a spot called The Dead Dog on Austral Downs. I've never seen a mob go over a camp, but I have seen both end packsaddles flattened as the bullocks split around the fire.

When a mob was playing up, the safest place to be was on a night-horse, but usually there were only two or three nighthorses tied up. If you missed out on getting a nighthorse, the next safest place was either by the fire or up a handy tree. If the bullocks were giving trouble, everyone slept with one eye open.

A character called 'Snuffler' was once on the road with a galloping mob. Snuffler, who was a smart, conscientious ringer, was always first out to help the man on watch wheel the mob. After 10 days or so of this, Snuffler had had enough. On this particular night away went the mob again, passing quite close to the camp. The boss and one ringer flew up a nearby tree, and when they had reached a safe height, they paused to listen.

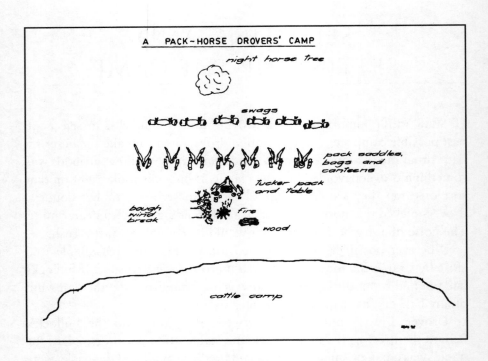

A PACK-HORSE DROVERS' CAMP

night horse tree

swags

pack saddles, bags and canteens

Tucker pack and table

bough wind break

fire

wood

cattle camp

Road bullocks being moved off camp as the sun comes up.

'Christ, boss,' said the ringer. 'Listen to 'em go. That's a bad rush.'
'She'll be right,' replied the boss. 'Old Snuffler will wheel them.'
'That's what you think,' said a voice from above. 'Old Snuffler is just one branch ahead of you bastards.'

RUSHES

RUSHES WERE A fairly common occurrence when droving the aged, touchy bullocks from north and west of the Murranji Track. A rush is the Australian term for what the Americans call a stampede. To the uninitiated a rush can be a terrifying experience. Most were at night and often in difficult or scrubby country. The causes were many and varied, and sometimes there seemed no apparent reason for the bullocks to take fright.

The sight of 1500 big bullocks exploding from a massed camp, with a noise like thunder, was not one that drovers relished. When a mob rushed there was only one thing to do, regardless of scrub or broken ground— that was to ride like blazes until the lead was reached. This could at times take 1 or 2 miles (2–3 kilometres), and once there, the idea was to ride in on the leading bullocks shouting or, if the country allowed, cracking a whip. This had the effect of turning the lead around, and back on the bullocks galloping behind.

Once the lead was wheeled like this, the mob began to ring and the rest of the bullocks caught up. If there were two men on watch, as there sometimes were with fresh mobs, it was important that both men rode up the same side of the rushing bullocks. A man on each side or wing could lead to disaster and was called 'Chinaman Laning' a mob.

There was always the chance of a 'Chinaman Lane' developing with inexperienced men, particularly if the mob was being double watched at the time of the rush. I never liked the idea of double watching, where two men rode towards one another, met, then turned around to ride back and meet on the opposite side of the mob. If the mob rushed, they either went in front of both men or behind them both. Either way, in the heat of the moment, both men were likely to try for the lead and a lane would result.

A far better way to double watch was to have both men riding in the same direction, but on opposite sides of the mob. This way, when bullocks rushed, they went in front of one man only, and that man took the lead. His mate did not change direction but rode round and backed the lead man up.

A lane could take rushing bullocks miles from the camp and could result in a slower rider having the leading bullocks wheel over the top of him. If a drover got caught with a lane, he really only had two courses of action open to him: firstly, he could pull out immediately, and leave the job to the other rider; secondly, he could cut through the galloping mob where it had thinned out, putting both men on the one side of the bullocks. The latter was a last resort and was fraught with danger, but at times it had to be done.

When bullocks were rushing, it was important to have someone keep the fire blazing brightly. This was to protect the camp and to let the men with the mob know exactly where they were in relation to the camp.

A mob would sometimes take fright without actually rushing. The bullocks would jump or splash then pull up of their own volition. Although it was important to get to the lead quickly, if a rush developed experienced drovers always waited until they were sure of just what was happening.

After a rush the boss drover always counted his bullocks the next day to make sure none had been lost. If the mob was still too stirred up to get a count, he track rode in a circle beyond the area the mob had covered the night before. Quite often after a bad rush, injured bullocks would have to be destroyed.

Rushes ending in human death were rare, and when one considers the risks, it is a wonder there were not more.

MY FIRST RUSH

I HAVE BEEN involved in dozens of rushes—some very bad ones—during my years on the road. The first one, though, I can recall very clearly. I suppose it has similar memory triggers to most first time happenings, like the first girl one kissed or the first time one got full—but also I was without doubt indirectly responsible for the rush.

I was on the road with a boss drover with 750 spayed cows. It was not a long trip—about a month. The camp was a packhorse one, with a cook and a horsetailer, and the boss and I were with the cattle. Travel was slow due to the very stony nature of the route, and to make matters worse, the boss would leave me early in the afternoon and ride on to get a drink of tea from the cook, meeting me again when I got the mob within feeding distance of the night camp.

I was flat out keeping the mob moving, up one wing and down the other and across the tail. One afternoon I lost the fall off my whip, and in frustration, I put a few small stones in my quart pot; I found that by rattling this, I could keep the cattle moving over the stones faster than was possible with a whip.

As the days went on, I found I had to put larger stones in the quart to get the same result. I also noticed that the spayed cows were becoming very nervous and jumpy because of the constant rattling, and I was careful never to use the goad in the presence of the boss.

When the crunch came, I was on watch riding a bay mare who, like me, had never been in a rush. I was looking at them at the time, but they went so fast, I do not remember seeing them get up. The mob passed quite close to the camp, and the bay mare and I were going after them at somewhat less than full pace when the horsetailer flew past us and shouted over his shoulder: 'Back me up'.

The mare, taking a lead from the horse ahead, stretched out at a gallop. It was timbered country, but not thick scrub; nevertheless, it took us over half a mile to wheel the mob. As soon as we turned the leaders around, a mob split off behind me, and it was on again. This time the mare and I took the lead, with the horsetailer backing me up. Spayed cows are noted for splitting like this and it took some time, with first one of us in the lead and then the other, before they steadied up.

For the rest of the night the horsetailer and I watched the mob where we stopped them. Near daylight the boss jogged up saying he had been checking to see if any cows had split off the tail—and I was young enough to believe him. The mob rushed every night until we trucked them a week later, and after that first night, I must admit I enjoyed the excitement immensely. I dare say, however, that the spayed cows were pleased to see the back of me.

After trucking the cows we retired to the pub, where I heard the boss skiting about the smart lad he had with him. He would not have been so generous with his praise if he'd known it was me who caused the problem in the first place.

GOLD STAR

The sun went down and the storm clouds rose,
  Dark browed with the threat of rain,
As they put the mob through the netting fence,
  To the camp on the blacksoil plain.
'Twas a short half mile 'cross the plain just there
  From the hills on the western side,
To the gloomy depths of the myall scrub,
  Where scarcely a man could ride;
Near a mile across and as bad a scrub
  As ever a stockman saw,
Then a bluegrass flat and a twelve foot drop,
  To the river that ran before.

As quiet as milkers the bullocks seemed,
  As they moved on, feeding slow,
With heads all turned to the cattle camp
  In the sunset's ruddy glow.
But a spark remains in the quietest mob,
  That can leap to a roaring flame,
In the maddened rush as the ringers know,
  Who have followed the droving game.
They had splashed a bit when we took them first,
  As the Gulf mobs often do,
But they settled down to the dull routine,
  Of the road in a week or two.

For they learnt the lesson the drovers teach,
  To the tune of the whip's barrage;
And seldom it was that a mob played up,
  When Mac was the man in charge.
For he'd served his time when the game was tough,
  In the days when the West was young;
When a man was judged by his bridle hand,
  And his skill when the scrubbers rung.

A sunburnt son of the far North-West,
　　Where the fenceless stockroutes are,
And the pride and joy of the drover's life,
　　Was his chestnut mare Gold Star.
I had heard tales told in a hundred camps,
　　Of Mac and his chestnut mare.
From the Gulf coast down to the New South side,
　　Ere I ever met the pair.
A thing of beauty she was to see,
　　And a tower of strength to ride,
With a lean game head and a lion's heart,
　　And a free and swinging stride.

There was never a nighthorse foaled, Mac swore,
　　That could stay with the chestnut mare,
Through scrub or holes in the mad pell-mell
　　Of a rush 'neath the lightning's flare,
For a dozen years she had served him well,
　　And always the mobs were held;
But he rode her only at odd times then,
　　When the fresh store mobs rebelled.
A favoured pet with the plant she ran,
　　From the bridle and hobbles freed,
But she watched the mob with her soft ears pricked,
　　As it spread on the plain to feed.

Mac came to me as I hobbled up,
　　By the camp in the failing light;
And I heard him say as I caught the bay,
　　'Better tie up the mare tonight'.
'Better tie up the mare' was all he said,
　　But he spoke with a troubled frown,
And I saw him glance at the thunderheads,
　　That had grown since the sun went down.
I went on first round the sleeping mob,
　　While the quarter moon on high
Was blotted out by the leaden clouds,
　　As the watch dragged slowly by.

It was Jim's watch next, and stepping down,
    By the fire I called his name,
Then the heavens split in a blinding flash,
    And the whole camp seemed aflame;
I stood transfixed by the startled bay,
    Then cursing I swung around,
For merging low with the thunder crash,
    Was another grimmer sound.
I offered a silent prayer of thanks,
    For a nighthorse that knew the job,
As the bay horse reefed at the bit and raced
    Round the wing of the rushing mob.

But the lead was off to a flying start—
    A start that was far too great,
And even then as I urged the bay,
    I knew we would be too late.
They hit the scrub with a splintering crash,
    And strong on the storm wind borne,
Came the pungent breath of the fear crazed mob—
    The tang of the hoof and horn.
I had eased the bay to a saner pace,
    And pulled out a little wide,
When I heard Mac's shout, then his chestnut mare
    Was galloping by my side.

'Ride as you never have ridden, lad,
    No matter what risk or cost,
We must beat them out on the further side,
    Or half the mob is lost.'
Mac was never a man to flinch at night
    In scrub, or to ease the pace,
And I'd never relive for a thousand mobs,
    The span of that nightmare race.
A gully loomed in a lightning flash,
    It was strewn with stumps and wide,
But the old mare rose in the lead of me
    With never a change of stride.

As game as ever she took the jump,
    We were but a length between,
But the power and strength of her quarters then
    Was not what it once had been.
She landed badly and blundered on,
    Striving to rise in vain—
She turned clean over while time stood still,
    Then the darkness closed again.
The bay horse lit and his shod fore feet
    Struck fire from the jutting stone,
With a backward glance and a bitter oath,
    I rode on through the scrub alone.

Rode on alone through the windswept scrub,
    Though that dark clad rider 'Death'
Rode stirrup to stirrup with every stride,
    And I cursed him with every breath.
The roar of the storm and the timber's crash,
    Was a Hell's own mad refrain;
And I threw the reins at the bay horse then,
    And rode like a man insane.
The bay was bred where they know a horse,
    And value the old game breed,
But we burst at last from the myall scrub,
    Too far from the flying lead.

Then high and shrill rose a horse's wail,
    That died in a kind of sob,
And Gold Star passed like a bird in flight,
    Down the lead of the rushing mob.
The Poley saddle was empty then,
    And the loose irons swung beside,
No brown hands gathered the flying reins,
    To steady and urge and guide;
Her mane and tail were as burnished brass,
    In the lightning's vivid flood,
And the foam that she flung from the bit-rings back
    I saw then was red with blood.

With a wicked light in her kindly eyes,
  Ears back and her teeth laid bare,
She wheeled them back from the river's edge
  With nothing but yards to spare.
She wheeled them back from the yawning brink
  Till they rung on the narrow plain,
And I rode and sang till they settled down,
  With their backs to the slanting rain.
I was looking round for the chestnut mare,
  But never a shadow stirred;
When I heard Jim's voice and the song he sang
  Was the finest I'd ever heard.

We watched them there through the lonely hours,
  Till the dawn broke chill and grey,
And showed the spot by the timber's edge,
  Where the chestnut night-mare lay.
Jim called to me and I rode across
  As he knelt by the dead mare's side,
She had wheeled the lead as her life blood flowed,
  The faster with every stride.

We buried Mac as he would have wished,
  For he does not sleep alone,
By the posts and railings that guard his bed,
  Stands a rough built mound of stone.
They rest together the man and mare
  Where the shy scrub cattle feed,
On the narrow flat by the river's bank
  Where Gold Star wheeled the lead.

BOOMERANG BRADY

BOOMERANG BRADY, SO called because of a bowed leg as a result of a horse falling on him in his youth, was renowned as a horseman in both Queensland and the Northern Territory. When Boomerang set out on his last ride in December 1923 he had not long recovered from an accident that had almost cost him his life. Lying in the bush for over two days, as a result of a fall from a horse, Boomerang was almost finished when found by stockmen from Newcastle Waters. One of his rescuers, Wally Langdon, was to later win fame as a member of the proud Northern Territory Mounted Police when he and an Aboriginal tracker captured Tiger, an Aborigine who had gained notoriety as a troublemaker.

When Boomerang Brady left Newcastle Waters later in December 1923, he was heading for Queensland with a racehorse in his plant that he swore would beat the best gallopers at Mackay, his destination. Unfortunately Boomerang never made it. Crossing Eva Downs he became sick and finally fell from his horse and died on the road on Christmas Day 1923.

Boomerang's only companion was an old Aborigine who must have been shattered by the tragedy. However, he took his boss's watch and 26 gold sovereigns from the body and covered it with a small tarpaulin, then rode on to report the death. It meant a ride of over 60 miles (100 kilometres) to Anthony's Lagoon, as Eva Downs had been abandoned two years earlier. At Anthony's Lagoon the Aborigine reported Boomerang's death to Constable Bill McCann, the policeman stationed there, and handed him the valuables taken from his boss's body.

The Wet had just begun in the Top End and it was a week before McCann could get back to bury the body. There, without ceremony, he dug a grave in the middle of the road and Boomerang went to his last rest with a few short words. The grave remained unmarked for some time, with the road making a detour around it. The Territory was a hard, rough place in those days, and I've heard jokes told of the grader driver who, in attempting to straighten the road, brought about the resurrection of Boomerang Brady. However, the detour remained, and later a sister of Brady, Mrs Whittaker, had a headstone and fence erected to mark the final resting place of one of Australia's best horsemen.

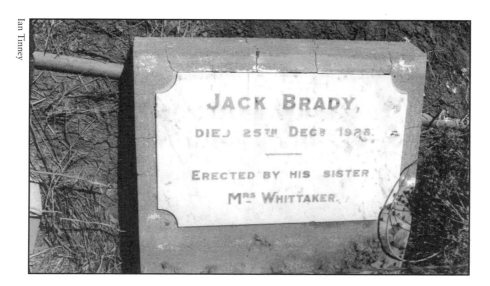

The headstone of Jack 'Boomerang' Brady's grave.

Boomerang's grave is on the stockroute and, at the end of a day's stage, drovers always camped there and tied their nighthorses up to the grave's fence. I'm sure Boomerang would have welcomed them.

Brady's Grave, now protected by a picket and wire
fence, is beside the road on Eva Downs.

The Drover's Yarn (or Brady's Ghost)

A drover it was that told this tale,
  In the bar of the top hotel;
He hooked a boot in the brass footrail
  And his gaze through the doorway fell.
'Back in the thirties it was,' said he,
  'In the days when me beard was black.
I was coming in from the VRD
  With a mob on the Wave Hill track.

'Fifteen hundred all built for speed,
  Lean gutted and wild as Hell,
They sulked by day and refused to feed,
  They were demons when darkness fell,
For they galloped as only a scrub mob can,
  And most of you fellers know
A man needs horses like Peter Pan
  When the Bull's head bullocks go.

'I've seen some stags that could carve it out,
  But that mob just seemed to fly.
We lost two hundred, or there about,
  As we came through the Murranji.
And the camp I had, if you'd call it that,
  Would have driven a saint to booze,
A one-eyed cook and a myall black
  And a couple of jackaroos.

'But we battled out on the downs at last
  And I knew that the rest we'd save,
For they settled down and the worst was past,
  When we camped by Brady's grave.
My two gun horses were on that night,
  They could gallop both fast and true,
My favourite bay, whose name was Flight,
  And a big black horse called Blue.

'The mob fed up like a milking herd,
    Contented as stags could be,
They camped at once and they hadn't stirred,
    When I went on watch at three,
But a deadly stillness a man could feel
    Was over the camp that night—
Not a bullock moved, they seemed scarcely real
    In the pale moon's eerie light.

'I often had seen those signs before
    And I knew that the harm was done.
Then the bay horse leapt to the muffled roar
    As the whole mob went as one.
I swung Flight into a racing stride,
    To wheel 'em before they spread,
When the old horse swerved in his tracks and shied,
    And I gasped as I turned my head.

'For passing close in the dim half-light
    And riding a coal black steed,
A phantom rider, all glowing white,
    Was racing to swing the lead.
It was Brady's spirit, I knew full well,
    As the ghostly pair sped on,
And the black horse flew like a bat from Hell,
    The way that the lead had gone.

'Well, I followed up in a kind of daze
    As the spectre wheeled the lead,
And we flogged them back through the dusty haze,
    To the camp with surprising speed.
They steadied down when we got them back,
    But I knew by the eerie glow,
That Brady's ghost, on his nighthorse black,
    Was still riding to and fro.

'I'll admit I never was scared so bad,
    And I've seen some queer things too,
But that mob of bullocks was all I had,
    So what was a bloke to do?
The sky in the east was growing pale,
    And the phantom had gone from sight,
When there came from behind me an anguished wail
    "It's perishing cold, all right".

'I jumped as shot, then I wheeled about,
    For the voice was one I knew,
And the sight I saw was without a doubt
    All the stranger for being true,
For strike me dead as a gidgee post
    The "steed" was poor old Blue
And the spectre I thought was Brady's ghost,
    Was a naked jackaroo.'

TRACKING LOST
ROAD BULLOCKS

COMING IN ONE year with bullocks from the West, I camped 3 miles (5 kilometres) back from a bore on Anthony's Lagoon. I was short-handed; my younger brother Jeff was doing both the cooking and horsetailing, while John Schondrock and David, an Aboriginal ringer, gave me a hand with the cattle. The mob was a bit stirred up, having been put through the government cattle dip on Anthony's the day before, and walked off camp a lot that night, keeping us busy until about midnight. I stayed out with David for a little while, then, as the mob seemed to have settled down, left him to it and rode into the camp to catch what sleep I could before doing the last watch.

I'm not sure what woke me, but when I looked out, I could see bullocks all over the place. Jumping on a nighthorse, I started putting the mob together. There was no sign of David, but I had no time then to worry about him. I caught up with the lead half a mile on towards the bore, on the edge of the timber. As I pushed the bullocks back on camp, I almost rode over David asleep under a tree. His horse had pulled away as the mob moved off camp and was found back with the horse plant.

Next morning I looked over the bullocks; the lead was there all right, but the mob did not look right; then I saw that bullocks from the front of the right wing were missing. Groups of bullocks tend to take up the same position in the mob during the trip. On counting the mob, I found I was 87 head short. I sent John Schondrock off to see if he could pick up the missing bullocks quickly, while I settled the mob down again on what feed there was.

John rode back about ten o'clock and said that the bore was lousy with bush cattle, and that he had seen nothing of the missing 87 head. Realising that tracking the missing mob would probably be an all-day job, I caught a big brown horse with an easy gait and the guts to go until he dropped. I instructed Jeff and John to wait until mid-afternoon to water the mob, when the bush cattle would be easy to shift, then to feed the bullocks back to the same night camp if I had not returned. Stowing a bit of damper and beef in my saddlebag, I mounted the brown gelding and trotted off.

When tracking missing road bullocks there are three factors that, if known, can be of great help. Firstly, the tracks of cattle that have been on the road for a while are easily identified, as their toes are worn down from constant walking. Secondly, road bullocks will stay together for some time; it may be weeks before a group of road bullocks will split up among bush cattle. Thirdly, road cattle, if they escape from a drover, once they are out of country they know will almost always travel into the prevailing wind.

I gave my horse a drink at the bore, where at least a thousand head of station cattle waited for the day to cool off before going back out to feed. I knew they would have obliterated any tracks left by my bullocks, so I rode out in a wide arc about 3 miles (5 kilometres) from the bore. Tracks of the station cattle heading into the water still covered the pads and I failed to pick up any tracks of road bullocks. Sure that the missing 87 head would have to be further out, I doubled back in a wider arc about 5 miles (8 kilometres) from the bore, and picked up the telltale tracks of my missing bullocks about two o'clock. It was easy tracking for a while, enabling me to follow them at a trot. Later, in more difficult country, tracking became slower, but late in the afternoon I rode up on the missing bullocks camped in a patch of scrub. They were lying down, contentedly chewing their cuds, and rose to their feet with marked reluctance when I started them up for the drive back to camp.

After watering the 'absent without leave' mob at the bore, I got back to the camp with them about ten o'clock. Everything was under control; the main mob was on camp and there was a rough meal cooked.

One of the first things I did on my return was to pay off David. I gave him his cheque and some tucker and told him to carry his swag out to the road and wait for a lift. It meant from then on there would only be three of us with 1350 bullocks and 40 head of horses. However, both Jeff and John were top men, and, like most drovers, I preferred to work short-handed rather than depend on men who could not be relied upon.

HORSETAILING

THE HORSETAILER WAS an important member of the droving team, as he was responsible for the well-being of the 40 or 50 horses in the drover's plant. Without fit horses, a drover would soon be out of business, and as a result, good horsetailers were always in demand.

In a bad season, a horsetailer would have to take the horses out a few miles from the camp to get good horse feed, and often he would take a blanket with him and camp with the horses. Before daylight the horsetailer would unhobble the horses and drive them to the camp, where he would catch the horses needed for the day's work. After breakfast, when the cattle had left the camp, he and the cook would pack up and start off, providing, of course, no horses had cleared out during the night.

A boss drover would often leave it to an experienced horsetailer to pick the camp for the coming night. On reaching the selected spot, the cook and the horsetailer would unpack, and he would then gather wood for the cook and cut boughs for a windbreak for the fire. After selecting a nighthorse tree close behind the camp, if the weather was cold he would build a bough windbreak to protect the nighthorses from the cold wind.

After taking the horses to water, the horsetailer turned them out to feed, and if no shoeing had to be done, he could relax for an hour or two. As the bullocks neared the camp, the horsetailer hobbled the horses out for the night and caught the nighthorses. After watering and hobbling the horses that had been ridden that day, the horsetailer did the first watch, providing, of course, he did not have to camp out with the horses. Hobbles were carried by each horse on a thin strap placed around the mount's neck.

To locate the horses before daylight, each plant of horses carried five or six bells. An experienced horsetailer could go straight to his own horses even when other horse plants carrying bells were hobbled close by. Although bells may be identical to the eye, each bell had a minute difference in tone that an experienced man could identify.

CAUGHT IN THE WET

WHEN I WENT out to the West in 1955, the mob I was to take was not yet ready, so I was enlisted to run a scratch camp with my own men and station Aboriginal stockmen. By the time the mob was ready for delivery, I was almost out of tucker—you cannot carry a hell of a lot on eight packs. Unfortunately it had been a late Wet and the station loading had not arrived; rations on most of the western runs were in short supply. I scrounged what I could, including a bag of last season's flour, and started the long trip to Queensland on 31 May. It would be 13 October before we delivered the mob.

I was lucky in having a good team of ringers that year: Kevin Ryan and Ron Condon were cooking and horsetailing; Luke McCall and two Gordon Downs Aborigines, Rusty and Tommy, and I were with the mob. The first damper made with the scrounged flour was a disaster. When cut, the middle was a glutinous mess that stuck to the knife. The cook explained that the flour was full of weevils, and on inspection this proved to be no exaggeration. The weevils had obviously devoured all the nutriment in the flour. My suggestion to the cook to throw the flour out and cook the weevils did not, I'm afraid, meet with any enthusiasm, but there was little anyone could do.

As we were short of everything, including tobacco, I decided to take a short cut between Inverway and the police station at Old Wave Hill; it would knock at least two days off the normal trip down the stockroute. Mick Cousens, a top bushman, had told me of the short cut earlier in the year. It meant heading straight bush in a rough easterly direction for about a week, then turning north and following the Victoria River to Old Wave Hill.

The weather had looked threatening for almost a week, and a few days into the short cut, down came the rain in torrents. The whole of the Top End was inundated, with over 10 inches (250 millimetres) falling in a couple of days. We had to hold up for three days, as travel was impossible due to bog and flooded creeks. To make matters worse, the last of the tucker was gone and we were without tea and coffee. The only tobacco we had was the chewing tobacco favoured by the Aborigines. We did, however, have meat, but only fresh meat, as we had run out of coarse salt to make corned beef. As a result, we had to kill a young beast every couple of days, then work the two Bedourie ovens overtime to cook as much as possible before it became flyblown. Fresh meat can be very welcome in a drover's camp, but a diet of nothing but fresh meat *sans* table salt soon palls.

Finally, we were able to move the mob on—albeit slowly. It was a very frustrating time for the men, who were sick of the sight of fresh meat and were itching to get to Wave Hill and once more resume a normal diet. We had been travelling two days when, on the second night, I lay back on my swag and was promptly bitten between the shoulder blades by a redback spider that came from God knows where. After dispatching the spider, I called for a volunteer to perform the old cut-and-suck routine. At first no one seemed all that interested, then Rusty Walter stepped forward with a gleam in his eyes that made me wonder if the fresh meat diet had, in some way, affected his mind. His intentions, however, were good and he attacked my back with gusto, and a half-sharp razor blade. He soon had the blood flowing like Irish whiskey at a wake, and as a finale to the operation, he whipped a wad of chewing tobacco from behind his lower lip and applied it with a flourish to the wound. Next morning, apart from a sore back, I was as fit as a fiddle.

For the next few days we were in conkerberry country and the bushes were laden with the small blackberry-like fruit. To say that the men made the most of the opportunity to vary their diet would be an understatement; every time I looked over at a rider, he would be off his horse with his head stuck in a conkerberry bush. I can't say I blamed them.

The day before we crossed the Victoria River, we were feeding the mob over a well-grassed flat that had steep breakaway gullies running through it. I had blocked up the lead, and glancing back, noticed one of the Gordon Downs ringers was missing. When I saw the back of his horse visible in one of the breakaways, I assumed he was answering a call of nature and went on steadying the lead. Next time I looked over, there were two horses in the breakaway and I saw Luke McCall riding over to investigate. As I watched, I saw Luke ride into the gully, dismount, and disappear as well. Intrigued now, I waited to see what would happen next. After five minutes nothing had happened at all—the backs of three horses were in sight, but no men. The mob was feeding quietly so, unable to restrain myself any longer, I rode over to the breakaway. There I found my team sitting in a patch of watermelons. Three or four ripe melons were broken open beside them, their hands and mouths were full, juice ran down their chins, and there was a look of absolute bliss in their eyes. I lost no time in joining them.

Before turning north we had to cross the Victoria River, now running in full flood due to the recent rain. I sent the horses and packs further up the river with Ron Condon to find a shallow crossing, and prepared to swim the mob across. When swimming cattle, it is vital to put them into the flood in a straight formation and to keep them swimming in a direct line for the further shore. The force of the water will bend them downstream, but on no account must they be allowed to ring, for if this happens, losses from drowning cannot be avoided. It is also important to be mounted on strong swimmers that will allow the rider to remain in the saddle, enabling him to see if the mob is swimming as desired. As a precaution, the stirrup irons are crossed over the pommel and bridle reins are checked to make sure the ends are untied. When swimming, a horse is steered by splashing water either side of his head.

We were all riding good swimmers, and after discussing tactics with the lads, we started the mob for the river. With myself out front to give the mob a lead, two men on the downstream wing, one upstream and a man on the tail to force the mob along, we put the cattle into the water. It is important to select a suitable spot on the opposite bank for easy access from the water for the cattle. This cannot be done before it is evident how far the current will sweep the mob downstream, but fortunately, at the spot we selected to cross, this did not pose a problem. Everything went to plan and the crossing was made without loss.

We finally reached Old Wave Hill—so called because of the wavelike formations on the hillsides. The cook and horsetailer had got some rations from the police station and met the cattle at dinner camp. There was a billy of tea by the fire, an opened tin of jam and freshly cooked johnny cakes. Hardly the stuff a gourmet's dreams are made of, but to us it was a banquet.

After numerous pints of tea and a couple of smokes, I rode over to the police station to give notice and to present my waybills for inspection. The young constable there seemed quite concerned for our welfare, saying we were a week overdue and had been posted as missing. As there had been no sign of us on the stockroute, he had been about to organise a search for us. I thanked him for his concern, but made no mention of the short cut. Then I rode back to the mob thankful in the knowledge that there was again tucker in the camp, and that I had a team of men who would stick to me through thick and thin.

AN UNEXPECTED DRY STAGE

DRY STAGES OF up to 60 miles (100 kilometres) are always a matter of concern to a drover. Nevertheless, they can be negotiated without too much trouble if the drover is aware of what is ahead and has prepared for it. An unexpected dry stage that occurs due to circumstances beyond the drover's control and leaves him short of preparation can at times be a serious problem.

I struck one of these unexpected stages coming in with western bullocks one year. A lot of cattle from the western runs are used to watering at springs and creeks and take some time to adapt to watering from troughs at stockroute bores. The mob I had was particularly stubborn; they would not drink at all at Red Rock Bore and at King Creek Bore drank very little. The next three waters were springs, then there was just one more bore, called Pussy Cat, before I entered the Murranji scrubs. The mob drank well at the first two springs; however, the night before Top Springs—the last of the natural waters—the bullocks rushed and were stirred up all night. As a result they were very toey at Top

Number 11 Stockroute Bore on the Murranji.

Springs and kept taking fright and galloping back out of the water. When I finally gave up, very few had had any sort of a drink and most had had no water at all. This situation did not concern me greatly, as I considered that the drier they were when I reached Pussy Cat Bore, the better chance I had of breaking them into trough watering before we reached the Murranji, a route watered solely by stockroute bores.

It was late in the afternoon when I took the mob off the water and went out a few miles and camped. I had checked at Top Springs on the water ahead at Pussy Cat and had been told it was low but that there was ample to give my bullocks a good drink. Next morning the mob fed a little, but, being thirsty, soon started walking, and this suited me. I steadied the lead to let the tail keep up and we made good progress. It had been threatening rain all morning and rain is the one thing that can cause a smash on a dry stage. Bullocks will try to turn into any wind coming off rain, making progress almost impossible; if rain falls, they will scatter after puddles—all in all, a hell of a mess.

We had covered about 5 miles (8 kilometres) when I was surprised to see my brother Jeff, who was horsetailing, lapping back to the mob. He reined in beside me and said 'There's no water for the mob at Pussy Cat. I was flat out getting horse water. You'll have to go on to No. 13 or turn back.'

After a few well-chosen words, I thought things over. The way the weather was, I could not afford another dry night, so it was either go back to Top Springs or try to make No. 13 bore in the Murranji scrub before dark. The bore was still about 20 miles (30 kilometres) away and I had to make a detour around Pussy Cat Bore, and then get the mob up the stony jump-up to the Murranji tableland as well. No drover likes to turn back. I looked at the sky. The rain was still holding off.

'Is the plant still at Pussy Cat?' I asked Jeff, and he nodded. 'Right,' I said, 'go on to 13 and set up camp at the bore; see if you can get a spot within two or three hundred yards; water the horses and hobble up early, then come back; we'll need a hand.'

He looked at me doubtfully. 'Do you think you can make it before dark?'

'I don't know,' I said, 'but we'll have a moon for an hour or two, and we'll probably need it.'

After Jeff had ridden off, I looked over the mob, Most of them had been without water for two days and had walked 25 miles (40 kilometres) since their last drink, but the die was cast. Thirsty bullocks will give you their best and it is important not to get impatient with the slower ones on the tail of the mob, even though it means holding the lead up at times to allow the tail to catch up—very frustrating at a time like this when you can see the time ticking away.

We finally got back on the stockroute pads after passing wide of Pussy Cat Bore and headed for the jump-up, still some miles away, but standing out plainly with its dark, tangled crown of scrub. It was late afternoon when we got the last of the bullocks up the steep ascent and faced the last 7 miles (11 kilometres) through the Murranji scrub. The bullocks were distressed now and at times a low moaning sound ran through the mob, but despite this, they still walked well. Their instinct told them there would be water somewhere ahead.

Jeff met me about 4 miles (7 kilometres) out from the bore and, as I had arranged with the rest of the team, he and I cut off 200 of the leaders and took them on ahead to the water. The sun had gone when we got there, but I allowed myself the luxury of a smoke as I watched the bullocks as they were drinking greedily at the long trough.

Jeff grinned at me. 'At least the bastards have learnt to drink at a bore.'

I nodded. 'I'll go back and get another couple of hundred. When these have finished, feed them out towards the camp. I'll turn the next lot out to you.'

I trotted back and met the mob about a mile out and cut another 200 off the lead, instructing the three men with the rest to block them up about a quarter of a mile (400 metres) from the bore. It was almost dark when I returned to the trough, but a weak quarter moon cast some light through the overcast sky. A fire was blazing in the camp and as soon as the small mob had watered, I pushed them out to where I could just see Jeff tailing the lead bullocks.

The watering went on without mishap, but as we turned the last of the tail bullocks towards the camp, a few spots of rain fell, and the watery moon was slipping down behind the dark scrub line. We slowly pushed the bullocks together in front of the camp. The lead had had a bit of a pick on the rough feed, but the tail would have to wait for the morrow. Jeff had already tied up four nighthorses, and as I changed to one, I thanked God for having such a reliable mate with me.

I decided to double watch the mob, for although the bullocks were full of water, they were still hungry and jumpy from the long drive. The rain steadily got heavier and by ten o'clock it was coming down in sheets. We had our hands full with the mob and when the rain eased off a little around midnight, the fun really started. The bullocks crashed into the scrub, first in one direction, then in another. There were three of us out with them at that time and when we finally got them settled down, I asked Jeff to go into the camp and stoke up the fire, as it was almost out.

He tied up his nighthorse and was almost at the fire when the mob rushed straight at the camp, and I did not have a hope of wheeling them in time. It was a horrible moment for me, as I knew the four men in the camp, including my brother, did not stand a chance.

It was my brother who saved the situation: with no time to stir up the fire, he snatched up a torch the cook used, and by flashing it at the bullocks, split the mob round the camp. It is one night I would rather forget but when daylight finally came we still had the mob. A drover two days ahead of me was not so lucky: he lost over 200 head that same night.

DROVERS' TOWNS

BEFORE ROAD TRAINS took over, droving made a significant contribution to the economy of a number of outback towns. Trucking centres, in particular, received a large injection of funds during the droving season. Mobs of sheep, fat cattle and store bullocks from the Gulf Country and the Territory converged on these railhead towns to fill the seemingly endless rakes of rail trucks.

Towns that had dozed peacefully through the slack months re-echoed to the sound of shunting engines, shouting men, bellowing cattle and the crack of stockwhips. Businessmen in the town smiled in anticipation, for the jingle of their tills would soon mingle with the sounds from the trucking yards. The streets filled with train crews and bearded, travel-stained drovers and their men, who, unlike the drivers of road trains, would stay a while in town and spend their money with the reckless abandon of sailors in port. Many of the drovers used the trucking towns as a base for their operations, but there were other towns not on a railhead that became well-known drover's towns; of these Camooweal was the most celebrated.

The explorer William Landsborough passed by the present site of Camooweal in his search for Burke and Wills. He named the Barkly Tableland and, in his report, commented on the suitability of the country for grazing. Landsborough also named the Herbert River (later renamed the Georgina) and two fine waterholes in this river, Lake Mary and Lake Frances, he named after two of his nieces.

The first settler in the Camooweal district was John Sutherland, who arrived at Lake Mary in 1865 after an epic trip, with 8000 sheep, from near Rockhampton. The local Aborigines received a rude introduction to jumbucks when Sutherland's perishing sheep rushed through their camp in the middle of the night to drink at Lake Mary. Sutherland called his new run Rocklands, and for a few years he prospered. However, isolation, low prices, sickness, and resentful Aborigines proved too much. By 1868 early pioneers like Sutherland, Nash, Ranken (or Rankine) and Lorne had all abandoned their runs and retreated east with what stock they had left. Some of them were to leave their names for all time on the map of the Northern Territory.

Despite the problems of isolation, the Tableland country was too good to remain neglected for long; within 10 years Nat Buchanan had restocked Rocklands for Tetley and Crosswaite with cattle from Mt Cornish. Other settlers soon followed.

The town of Camooweal had its beginning in 1882 when J. (Mick) Cronin arrived at Lake Frances, 4 miles (7 kilometres) south of Lake Mary, with a horse team and a wagonload of supplies. Cronin was aware that the area was in need of a store, so unloading his wagon, he set up a business on the present site of the town. A hotel followed in 1883, opened by a man named Kennedy. Mick Cronin and his family were to play an important part in the future of the frontier town.

Drovers selected Camooweal as a base for two very good reasons: firstly, it was within a few miles of the Territory border, so it was an excellent jumping-off point for the Territory drovers; secondly, the town was surrounded by a common that could carry up to 1200 drovers' horses over the slack months.

The annual horse muster was a spectacular event, full of colour and hard riding. On the first day the downs country west of the town was mustered, then the timbered half on the east was cleaned up on the second day. Each day, the horses were drafted through the yards, with the common ranger presiding. Arguments over horses were usually settled in the time-honoured manner, without resorting to legal debate. Drovers used the yards to break in colts and to take the sting out of fresh horses, and nods of approval or shouts of derision registered the results of each contest.

When the drovers had sorted out their plants and shod all the horses, they headed out to pick up the mobs they had been offered. The trip out to take delivery could take over six weeks, and very often the Camooweal storekeepers—Tom Cronin, son of Camooweal's founder, and Joe Freckelton—would stand the drovers the cost of tucker and horseshoes until they returned.

Camooweal, as with most frontier towns, was in its heyday a fairly wild place. The police, most of whom understood the hardships of bush life, tolerated the high-spirited antics of ringers, which would probably not have been accepted elsewhere.

A large number of drovers lived in Camooweal and many owned homes with nicknames as colourful as the owners. 'Rum Jungle' was one, for obvious reasons; another, for equally obvious reasons, was christened 'The Sanatorium'; another situated in Beaumont Street was known as 'The Ringer's Roost'. I was the owner, or more correctly the co-owner, of the Roost. When I first bought the place for a modest sum, I thought I was getting vacant possession, as stated in the contract of sale. I soon found, however, that a few million white ants were already firmly entrenched in the residence. It took them some years, but with a single-mindedness that had to be admired, they finally ate the bloody place to the ground. Before that happened, however, the Roost saw many good times; it was an open house to anyone who cared to throw their swag over the threshold.

The long defunct Barkly Tableland Shire Council had its headquarters in Camooweal those days and its night cart serviced the town. One slack day, when the Ringer's Roost had its usual quota of non-paying guests, the driver of the night cart put in a complaint regarding the termite-ravaged condition of my outside dunny. Archie McInnes was the Shire Clerk. Archie was a bit of a character whom I often had a drink with at the top pub. He sent me a show cause letter, stating that a threat of this nature to the life and limb of the night cart man was of vital concern to the council. I replied promptly, advising him that all correspondence should be addressed to the real owners of the Roost: the termites. Honour was satisfied all round and the termites proceeded to devour the show cause letter.

Many old drovers and ringers retired in Camooweal to live out the remainder of their lives in familiar surroundings. There, as elder states-men of the droving fraternity, they held court in the pubs (Camooweal boasted two, those days), drinking rum and recounting epic battles with buckjumping horses, rushing bullocks and dry stages.

Wirrawarra Mick was one old boss drover who spent his last years in the 'Weal. Mick had been a top horseman and a fine cattleman, but what set him apart from his peers was his ever-ready wit. Advancing years and copious draughts of rum often left Wirrawarra Mick legless and, for his own protection as much as anything else, he often spent the night as a guest of Her Majesty. Next morning the sergeant's wife would stoke a meal into Wirrawarra and he would be released from *durance vile* just before the pubs opened.

I had not seen Mick for some time when I met him one morning making a beeline from the cop shop to the bottom pub for his first phlegm cutter of the day.

I greeted him with: 'Good day, Mick. What are you doing with yourself these days?'

Wirrawarra propped and fixed me with bright, but somewhat blood-shot, eyes.

'Doing with myself?' he quipped. 'I'll tell you what I'm doing. I'm serving a life sentence in nightly bloody instalments!'

A Tale of Termites

Stranger, please pause by this old bungalow,
For it hides a grim battle that ebbs to and fro,
A primitive struggle devoid of romance,
'Twixt the Camooweal drunks and the giant white ants.
No quarter is given, no mercy displayed
In this fight to the death with the termite brigade,
But if their rampaging is not soon reduced,
You can all say goodbye to the old Ringer's Roost.

There are termites to left and termites to right,
And their molars are grinding by day and by night;
They raid and they ravage and plunder unchecked,
And they're larger, much larger, than one would expect.
By wall plate and rafter they stealthily creep,
And God help our hides if they catch us asleep,
And if we can't turn their attack mighty soon,
We'll be under the stars by the change of the moon.

There are white ants below and white ants above,
In the floorboards and battens and rafters they love;
They deploy to the left and attack from the right,
And their molars are grinding by day and by night.
They break up our parties and ruin our rest,
And they are, in a nutshell, a damnable pest,
And if we can't deal them a kick in the slats,
I fear it's the end of these bachelor flats.

We've tried every method to stop their advance;
We've fought them with poison and baton and lance,
But it does little good, for in thousands they breed,
And they sharpen their fangs as they look for a feed.
An expert once called in to give us a quote,
But as soon as he entered they sprang at his throat;
He fought himself free with the leg from a bed,
And one flick and 'I'm going,' he screamed as he fled.

They've ravaged our larder, our furniture too,
And one night they punctured a carton of brew,
Then the word got around to the whole of their tribe,
And they bunged on an orgy I couldn't describe.
They've cleaned up our woodheap, our outhouse as well,
The 'Man who comes round' said he'd see us in Hell;
They've eaten our moleskins and eaten our Bex—
Two novels by Thwaites and a pamphlet on sex,
And if very soon we don't stop their advance,
Then I'll transfer the deeds to the flamin' white ants.

THE DROVERS' STRIKE

BOSS DROVERS WERE independent contractors, in competition, to some extent, for the mobs that stations planned to put on the road during the droving season. Despite this, there was never, to my knowledge, any undercutting of the contract price. The competition was limited to the reputations of the drovers and to the suitability of their plants. Many stations seemed happy to stick to the same drovers for years, providing they did the job.

The company that moved the most cattle out of the Territory and East Kimberley region was of course Vestey's, and because of the scale of their operation, many drovers got a start in the industry with cattle from their stations. Vestey's were not, however, the best of payers; their contract price of four shillings and sixpence (45 cents) a head per 100 miles (160 kilometres) had, in 1956, remained the same for some years, while other stations were paying five shillings (50 cents). Because of the length of the trips a few of us did, we were happy enough, but not all Vestey drovers were in the same position.

Early in 1956 I was shoeing the plant at the Ringer's Roost in preparation for the trip out West when I looked up to see a group of Vestey drovers entering the yard. I straightened up and greeted them.

'Good day. I thought you blokes would be flat out like me.'

'We're not going out.'

'What do you mean?'

'We're digging in our toes. Vestey's can get stuffed. We won't work for four-and-six.'

'This isn't a joke?'

'No bloody fear. We're going on strike. Are you with us?'

I sat on my heels and rolled a smoke. 'I don't know. What are your plans?'

'Well, we're on strike, and we want you to act as spokesman. You've had a good education.'

I let that pass through to the keeper. Because I wrote a bit of verse, they obviously regarded me as something of a Rhodes Scholar.

'I'm with you on one condition: you've got to stick it out. You've left it a bit late; we're all short of a quid and it's not going to be easy.'

They assured me they were all solid in their determination to toss the biggest pastoral company in Australia. I told them to organise a meeting of Vestey drovers in the billiard room at the bottom pub for eight o'clock that night, then continued shoeing the horse I had been working on.

Every Vestey drover in town was at the meeting that night. It was agreed that minutes of the meeting be kept, and that I should be elected in the approved manner. After the preliminaries were out of the road, we got down to business. A motion was passed requesting me to send a letter to Vestey's head office setting out our claims, together with another to Gilbert Macintosh, Vestey's road boss in Mt Isa, requesting a meeting in Camooweal. Both these letters were to be signed by all present, with the signatures in a round robin.

I was further empowered to organise the Vestey drovers at Elliott and Newcastle Waters. After some discussion, the meeting agreed that as the strike was not of a general nature, drovers were free to accept cattle other than Vestey's if the price was similar to what we were fighting for. It was a decision that was to have serious ramifications.

Next morning I put into effect the decisions from the meeting and sat back to await results. I received confirmation from Newcastle Waters that everyone there was behind us; but if we expected panic at head office, we were bitterly disappointed. The powers that be at Vestey's Sydney office simply ignored us, well aware that time was on their side.

A deputation met with Gilbert Macintosh as planned. However, he could not see us gaining a price rise and warned us that the company would, as a last resort, bring in drovers from Queensland to lift the cattle. Mac was a top bloke who had come up the hard way, and he was sympathetic, but he had a job to do. Later that day I received a wire from Vestey's head office confirming that the price was to remain at four-and-six.

I called a meeting for that night and advised the drovers of our lack of progress. They were just as adamant as ever that they would not work for four-and-six, and swore if the company engaged scab drovers, they would belt piss and pick handles out of them and bush their horses. I advised them against violence, while at the same time, I felt greatly heartened by the spirit they showed.

The weeks dragged by with the stand-off continuing. The company showed no sign of weakening, so the Camooweal storekeepers were approached for help and, to their credit, both Tom Cronin and Joe Freckelton agreed to stand by the striking drovers.

I decided to try my luck with other stations. Before becoming a boss drover, I had worked for years in stockcamps, including two years on

Alexandria and one year on Glenormiston, both owned by the North Australian Pastoral Company. I wired their Brisbane office and received a reply next day offering me 1500 Alexandria bullocks at five shillings per head; delivery in six weeks time. In accepting the mob, I felt that I had perhaps let the others down, despite the decision of the first meeting.

One of the drovers, who had been on the grog, was told by a town wag that we had won and the strike was over. He hurried back to his camp, packed up and headed for the Territory. When we learnt of his departure, a few of us commandeered a vehicle and set out to bring him back. We did not expect any trouble as we realised he had acted in all innocence, and the bottle of rum we took with us would help dispel any awkwardness created by our action. We caught up with the bolter just through the border fence; he was confused, shame-faced and badly in need of a drink. After a couple of rums, he told his men to take the plant back to his camp, then climbed into the vehicle for the trip back to Camooweal.

The deadlock over the price continued, with no sign of Vestey's agreeing to our demands. Mac advised us that although the company was considering bringing in other drovers, there were still mobs available if we wished to accept four-and-six a head. They had us over a barrel and they knew it. The point of no return for the season's droving was rapidly approaching, with the chances of a successful end to the strike becoming less likely every day.

Despite assertions of solidarity, I was aware of a weakening of resolve among some of the drovers. Many of them had not been successful in obtaining other cattle, and I realised they felt that they were bearing the burden for everyone. Their attitude was not without some justification, and the decision of the first meeting was coming back to haunt us. Gradually, interest in the strike waned. One by one, the drovers accepted the inevitable and headed out West at the old price. The strike was virtually over, but Noel Willets better known as 'The Pic', still held out. We had a yarn the day before I was due to leave for the Alexandria mob.

'What do you reckon I should do?' he asked.

'There's only one thing to do mate; throw the packs on and tell Mac you're going out.'

'I dunno. I don't want to scab.'

'You're not scabbing; the bloody strike is over. Everyone else has gone.'

'Yair, I suppose you're right. I'll see if the Limbunyas are still available.'

The Pic wandered off and I got on with preparations for my own trip.

That afternoon I received a wire advising me that due to an outbreak of three day sickness on Alexandria, all droving had been cancelled. I read the telegram again, and with dismay, I realised its full implication; the plant was shod and ready, I had engaged men and had ordered rations, but what I didn't have was cattle to pay for it all. Mac had advised me early in the strike not to stick my neck out too far as spokesman; in hindsight it seemed like damned good advice, for I felt that the sword of Damocles was about to fall.

I thought things over for a while, then decided the time had come for me to bend the knee and tug the forelock. At the post office, I rang Vestey's Sydney office and asked for the head of the company.

He finally came on the line with a curt 'Yes?'

'Simpson here,' I said, 'the spokesman in the drovers' strike.'

'Yes, I know that. What do you want?'

I gritted my teeth. 'I was wondering if you had any cattle from the West still available?'

'I thought you had Alexandria cattle?' There wasn't a lot he didn't know.

'I did have. The mob has been cancelled.'

'Hold the line.'

I held the line and waited. He was going to make me sweat a little. Fair enough, I thought.

He picked up the phone. 'Can you start out immediately?'

'Yes.'

'There will be a mob of bullocks ready at the Ord by the time you get there. You know the price?'

'Yes. Four-and-flaming-sixpence.'

'Correct.' The line went dead.

I walked over to the top pub. The Pic was at the bar having a quiet drink by himself, so I joined him and told him the news.

'Fair enough. I've got the Limbunyas, so we can travel out together.' I raised my glass. 'Here's to overseas interests and absentee owners.'

Frank Martin, the publican, strolled over and gave us a quizzical look. 'I didn't think you chaps would be celebrating.'

'This isn't a celebration,' said the Pic. 'This is a wake.'

BULLEN CREEK

WHEN I TOOK delivery of one mob of Ord River bullocks, Billy Hart was the only experienced man I had with me; the cook and the other two young chaps I'd employed had never been droving before. The Ords, like most Western bullocks, would rush; however, they seldom split and once you wheeled the lead you usually found you had the whole mob. But wheeling the lead was not all that easy at night, for the Ords galloped hard and fast, crashing through or over everything in their path.

The head stockman and two ringers came with us for two days to give me a hand, but we were on our own, with the bullocks still playing up, when we arrived at Bullen Creek, and Bullen Creek was not a good camp. There were some bad cattle camps that I felt relatively comfortable with, but this was not one of them. Boss drovers are a down-to-earth breed not usually subject to fanciful premonitions, so I found it difficult to explain my feelings about Bullen Creek. In the end I put it down to fatigue and forgot about it.

The cattle camp was on a rather narrow flat with stony ridges on the right, a creek and breakaway gullies to the left and in front, and a jump-up behind. I strung the mob down the jump-up well before sundown, feeding the bullocks along the flat to give them plenty of time to become familiar with their surroundings before dark. At dusk the bullocks came together on camp without trouble, about 10 yards (9 metres) in front of the fire, where the cook was busy with his camp ovens.

I had placed the camp as close as possible to the jump-up so we could take full advantage of the good galloping the flat provided. After talking things over with Billy, I decided the best way to control a rush would be to turn the mob up on to the stony ridge; it would result in the laming of a few beasts but the alternatives left us little option. I told the two lads of the strategy, and advised them that if the mob rushed they should pull out of the road and leave things to Billy and me. I felt sure one of us would have to be on hand all night.

Billy had tied up four nighthorses. Two of them had seen many bad rushes and could be relied on to wheel any lead. The other two were younger but both showed the qualities needed to make top nighthorses. Charm, a clean-legged bay mare, had received her baptism of fire during the last trip. The last horse to be tied up was a big brown gelding I called Brown Harlequin. Originally an O'Hara Gap brumby, he was one of those unique horses that could be used anywhere; he was an excellent camphorse and had taken to nightwork like a duck to water. Sure footed, like all brumbies, his speed and intelligence at night had made him invaluable. He did, however, have one fault; if you let your hands drop onto his wither he would buck a town down. When I was drafting cattle on Gordon Downs he had caught me by surprise and had thrown me very convincingly. Because I knew the brown horse so well, I usually rode him myself.

I did the dogwatch on Harlequin while Billy took the day horses out and hobbled them where he'd left the plant, well clear of any possible trouble. When he returned he had a quick meal with the others then rode out to join me, both of us riding in a clockwise direction on opposite sides of the mob. It was a clear, moonless night with the Southern Cross hanging brightly above the ridges to the south, and despite my earlier misgivings the mob was quiet enough to suggest we may have a trouble-free night.

A little after eleven I decided to go in to the camp to grab a quick meal before Billy was relieved by one of the new chums. I stopped to wait for Billy to ride around to meet me.

'I'll slip in and grab a quick feed while I've got the chance, Billy.'

He nodded. 'I'll be right. I'd like to see a few more bullocks on their feet, but I don't think we'll have any trouble.'

I agreed with his observation; the more bullocks that were awake, the less likelihood there was of a bad rush. Billy had been with cattle all his life and I appreciated that having him in the team offset, in many ways, the lack of experience of the others.

'If they do go,' I said, 'we'll just have to hit them quickly. We've not a lot of flat to play with.'

I watched Billy ride on around the mob, then I turned the brown horse and rode slowly into the camp. I had almost reached the nighthorse tree when Charm woke from a doze and shook herself. Despite having the surcingle over the top flaps and the irons knotted over the saddle, the noise was enough. With a crash like thunder, the mob was away.

I gave the brown horse his head and rode for the lead, knowing that Billy would come around the mob and back me up. Harlequin streaked down the flat in pursuit of the flying lead, with the timber and broken ground close to our left. Although the mob had not had a big start, the lead had almost reached the end of the open flat before we caught it. I rode in hard, shouting to wheel them quickly, taking the risk that the mob would not split behind me. The bullocks hit the ridge at full gallop, sparks flying from the flint stones underfoot while the air was filled with the acrid smell of seared hooves and clashed horns.

At the top of the ridge I swung them to the right again, along and down the slope to join the rest of the mob galloping below. Glancing back, I saw that Billy had kept the rushing bullocks in line behind me. The tail caught up as we held the ringing mob near the bottom of the ridge and gradually, to shouts of 'Whoa bullocks!', they steadied down and finally stood with heads up and sides heaving. The first round had gone to us, but the fight was far from over. It was not yet midnight.

When we had eased the mob down on to the soft ground we found ourselves halfway along the flat and in a far worse position than before. Most mobs can be put back on camp after a rush, but the Ords were not like that; I knew from past experience that they would constantly break back around us if we tried. We were committed to watch them where they were, with only half the flat to wheel the mob in.

Twenty minutes later the mob rushed again. This time we hit them quickly, bending the lead on to the ridge before the wild-eyed leaders had gone too far. The mob continued to take fright and splash and it seemed that the stony hill, although doing nothing to calm the mob's panic, was causing the bullocks to baulk at facing it at a gallop. I hated to think what it was doing to their feet, but needs must when the devil drives.

I noticed that the bullocks were taking fright from within the mob itself and this convinced me that some beasts had broken, dangling horns that were causing them to panic whenever they moved their heads. We could do nothing to remedy the situation until daylight when the injured bullocks would have to be thrown and the horns removed.

Billy and I watched the mob until one o'clock when I decided it was high time we changed to fresh horses as we had a long trip ahead of us. As I rode around the camp side of the mob, something freakish happened: Harlequin trod on what must have been a loose, angled stone and it flew like a bullet, striking a bullock on the edge of the mob. It was on again.

This time there was no stopping them quickly, for the mob took on the flat and the hill with the same frenzied determination. When we finally steadied them up at the end of the flat, Harlequin was lathered with sweat but as game as ever. The mob continued to ring, dust flying from the churning hooves. Then, for no apparent reason, the mob rushed again, and this time the lead stormed down the flat straight for the camp.

Billy, who was riding the fresher of the two horses, set out after the bullocks at a flat gallop. To me, backing him up, it seemed like an eternity before he drew level with the big wild-eyed pikers in the lead, and swung them past the camp and on to the ridge. As Harlequin galloped past the fire, I saw the cook standing there ashen-faced, a fire stick in his hand, 20 yards (18 metres) from the thundering mob. Once the bullocks were wheeled on the stony hill, the fight went out of them. They stood wary-eyed and exhausted, but the muted bellowing that ran through the mob showed they were about as stirred up as it was possible for bullocks to be. It would take very little to start another rush.

After half an hour I got a chance to talk to Billy and sent him in to the camp to get one of the young chaps to relieve him on Charm. While he was waiting for the lad to take over, I rode into the camp and changed horses. I rode back out on Kite, an Undilla-bred bay gelding and a night-horse I was sure would be equal to the task ahead.

The bullocks were now a little to the right of the camp at the bottom of the ridge, and for once I abandoned my firmly held beliefs regarding the double watching of cattle: I felt I could not afford to be on the wrong side of the mob if there was further trouble, so I sent the young chap to watch the far side of the mob while I stayed on the camp side.

The next two hours passed without any major trouble but the mob was still restless, making it plain we were not yet home and hosed. At half past three I sent the young chap in to get his mate to take over from him, reminding him that Harlequin was not to be ridden again. I did not see the new rider come out to the cattle as I was riding away from the camp at the time, but a little later I saw Billy standing at the fire waving to me. I rode over to him and asked him what was up.

'I've just checked the nighthorses. That bloody young fool has Harlequin. He's probably half asleep.'

'Thanks, Bill. I'll whistle him over.'

I turned back to the mob and had ridden only a few yards when I heard the rattle of stones from the side of the hill. The noise was instantly lost in an explosion of sound as the mob roared past the camp. The bay gelding went with them, ears pricked and reefing at the reins. I looked over at the mob. I had little chance of wheeling them before they crossed the flat and as yet there was no lead. The bullocks were galloping in a solid phalanx heading straight for the rough going.

As the mob stormed through the timber and over the gullies, I saw bullocks going down under the weight of the maddened mob, for 1350 fear-crazed bullocks create an almost irresistible force. The mob was still rushing on a wide front, a sea of tossing horns and flying hooves. I had gained a few lengths on the mob and decided to take a calculated risk; shaking the thong of my whip loose, I swung it with all the power I could muster.

The whip-cracks rang out like rifle shots above the tumult and the result was better than I had hoped, for the mob veered sharply to the right, then crashed back in the direction of the flat. I cracked the whip again to keep the rest of the mob turning, then set out after the leaders. The bay horse took the broken ground in his stride but almost went down over a fallen tree. He kept his feet somehow, but in doing so, rammed my knee into a leaning limb, tearing my moleskins and gashing my knee. I felt the blow at the time, but the pain did not come until later.

I saw the lead racing along the bottom of the ridge away from the camp as the bay horse gained the flat. He stretched out after them and caught the vanguard, turning them up the ridge. I thought the mob would steady quickly on the stony ground, but it was as though they knew this was the last throw of the dice: when I wheeled them at the top of the ridge, they fought me all the way back along the slope, dust and stones flying in their wake.

They finally threw it in and stood 50 yards (45 metres) from the camp. They were obviously distressed and many of them were tonguing, but for the first time that night I felt I had the upper hand. There was another rider out with the mob and from his voice I knew it was Billy, but the young chap was nowhere to be seen. Billy waited by the camp for me to ride around the mob to him.

He greeted me with: 'Harlequin came in to the camp riderless as I rode out to give you a hand.'

'Bloody hell,' I said; then added, 'Billy, did you hear a sound on the side of the hill just before the mob went?'

'Yes, I did. If the brown horse threw him—' He stopped.

We looked at one another in dismay. The bullocks had swept over the whole hillside in the last frenzied rush and if the lad had been thrown and injured he would not have stood a chance. I turned Kite without another word and rode up the hill, hoping against hope that we were wrong. I went slowly, zigzagging across the slope, and three-quarters of the way along the ridge I saw something ahead of me. I dismounted to find the lad's hat almost cut to ribbons by the trampling hooves of the galloping mob. It looked as though he had been thrown there; if the mob had gone over him, his body, or what was left of it, would not be too far away.

Leading Kite, I began to search the torn-up slope carefully, and the further I went from the hat, the more hopeful I became. Then I heard it: a feeble cry from the bottom of the jump-up. I mounted and rode over. I found him standing beside a tree about 50 yards (45 metres) from the camp. He looked up at me, ashen-faced with blood seeping from a cut in his head, but by this time my relief had given way to exasperation.

'What the hell happened?'

'I don't know,' he said in a shaking voice.

'Then I'll tell you. You rode the wrong bloody horse. You went to sleep and he threw you. You're lucky to be alive.'

He hung his head and said nothing.

'Why didn't you go to the camp?'

'I was afraid and my head hurts.'

'All right. Go to the camp now. Wake the cook and get him to patch you up. It's almost time for him to boil the billy.'

I rode back to the mob and told Billy the news.

He grinned. 'I'll bet you ripped it into him.'

I nodded. 'We can't afford stupid mistakes like that on the road. Not only did he risk his own life, he put the whole show in jeopardy.'

Billy rolled a smoke. 'I reckon he won't make that mistake again.' He turned away from the mob to light the cigarette, shielding the blaze of the match from the bullocks with cupped hands. When Billy had the smoke going to his satisfaction, he leant down and patted Charm's neck. 'You've got a good'un here. She went through the rough-going like a breeze.' He glanced at the eastern sky. 'Must be time to get the horses.'

The morning star was blazing brightly above the horizon, a welcome herald of the coming day. 'Right you are, Billy. I'll be okay here.'

As he reached the camp, a dingo howled on the top of the jump-up. The long, drawn-out lament cut through the crisp morning air like a knife. The big horns tossed and the bullocks stirred uneasily, but they stayed on camp. Like me, they'd had enough galloping for one night.

The stars gradually paled and at long last the darkness lifted. As I rode in to the camp in the light of a new day, I saw that the surrounding landscape bore clear evidence of the night's feverish activities. I unsaddled Kite and walked stiffly to the fire. I felt no great relief at having held the mob; at that moment I was just too knackered to care.

OUTBACK HUMOUR

THERE HAS ALWAYS been a lot of humour in the outback, and droving certainly had its fair share of wags.

The large steel tanks erected at the mills on the Murranji Track became a medium for charcoal-wielding scribes. Many pearls of wisdom, witticisms and quips appeared that brought answers, denials and additions from other drovers. Unfortunately, most of these were never meant for publication.

I remember one verse on a Murranji tank that was a parody of an old army song. It went like this:

> Goodbye Mr So-and-so
> Farewell Vestey's too
> Since we've been a-droving
> We've been stuffed about by you
> This droving is a failure
> A failure and a farce
> As far as we're concerned you can
> Stick it in your arse.

Drovers had the habit of picking up the bleached skull of a bullock and on it writing a biting obituary to the long-dead beast. Here are a couple of examples:

> Here I lie for my race is run
> Driven to death by 'Twenty-One'.

> My cruel fate was a thing of sorrer
> A bovine victim of 'Wirrawarra'.

The skull would then be placed in a tree beside the stockroute for all to see. Twenty-One and Wirrawarra were the nicknames of Territory drovers; in fact, Twenty-One was my nickname.

Boss drovers, by and large, were a colourful lot; one chap who sported a huge black beard would stalk into a bar and announce himself by roaring:

Steel to the heels and leather to the knees,
Wild and woolly and full of fleas,
Bad women and buckjumping horses
Are all the same to me.

Another chap would introduce himself by singing a sad little ditty to the tune of 'The girl I left behind me':

I'm up to my knees in Mitchell grass
I'm up to my knees in clover
I'm up to my balls in bloody debt
And I'm a Vestey drover.

Bushmen have always been past masters at creating their own entertainment, without the aid of television, portable radios or regular newspapers. When drovers hit town after months on the road, they tended to let their hair down. Pranks like shutting goats in outside toilets, riding horses into the bar, and posing as wealthy graziers for the benefit of the barmaids were, to the perpetrators, nothing but good clean fun.

Townspeople, who saw only the larrikin side of the revellers, resisted any temptation they may have had to ask them home for dinner. Hotels and cafes, however, welcomed the nomads with open arms. As a result, the girls employed at these establishments became the focus of attention. The ardent and often inebriated young Lochinvars from the scrub seldom got to first base, but life was good, the beer was cold, and the West was wide.

THE END OF THE TRIP

THE BIG MOBS of store-conditioned bullocks that walked in from the East Kimberley and Northern Territory stations were of no use to the market until they were topped up on properties known as fattening depots. The Queensland Channel Country was ideal for this purpose, and many store mobs went down the Georgina River route to these stations.

Many other store mobs were trucked away by cattle train from Dajarra to the coastal fattening depots. Dajarra, in its heyday, was one of the biggest trucking centres in the world. Other store mobs were for sale while on the road, and the drovers travelled the stockroutes until the owners managed to sell the mobs.

As the drover was employed on a contract of so much per head per 100 miles (160 kilometres), the final count was very important, since it was on the number of bullocks delivered that he was paid. The final count was either done through the trucking yard, or carried out by the boss drover and the original owner.

Drovers with store mobs were often on the road for four, five or six months, so after delivering a mob, it was not surprising that most of them lived it up a bit.

Ian Tinney

The Dajarra pub, once Mecca for thirsty drovers at the end of a trip, has been quiet since the railway closed but it still serves the locals and the occasional travellers.

At the Trucks

The cook's fire glowed in the drover's camp as the Southern Cross swung down,
Ere the first light spread and the shadows fled from the camp and the trucking town.
They had trucked the tail of the store mob down and bade it a glad Godspeed,
And could hardly wait for the stockyard gate to close on the restless lead.

A thousand miles from the West they'd come, from the land where the runs are wide,
Where the wild donks bray at the close of day from the hills where the pikers hide.
They'd travelled far from the scrubs and hills through the land of the grey galah,
On camp each night in the failing light and awake with the morning star.

A thousand miles from the Kimberleys, where the stockroute miles are long,
They'd wrapped the days in a dusty haze and the nights they'd wrapped in song.
Not the kind of song that a rocker sings who clutches a microphone,
But a song that slips from the watcher's lips in a soothing monotone.

Now the journey's end is a short half mile and wide is the open gate,
While spreading slow comes the dawn's first glow as the drovers smoke and wait.
An engine shrills, it's a sad, strange sound to these drifters born to roam,
And the echo brings, as it sharply rings, a sudden thought of home.

But it's time to go and they quietly start the bullocks up from camp,
As they move ahead, from the engine shed comes the glow of a shunter's
lamp.
The end of the long hard road's in sight and the open gate is wide,
With the plant before so the mob will draw, they move like a flowing
tide.

A dawn wind stirs and the grey galahs rise up from the carbeen trees,
Then the big heads rise and with wary eyes the bullocks sniff at the
breeze.
They baulk and ring, then the mob draws on and the drovers steer them
straight,
Till the leaders go with an even flow through the jaws of the stockyard
gate.

With the last beast through, the gates swing to, and the heavy chain's
made fast,
Then the lads slip in with a cheery grin for the trip is done at last.
The mob runs well and the trucks soon fill, for the coastal depots
bound,
But the sun is high and the men are dry when they climb from the
empty pound.

Now a dusty throat is a thing to note in a land that is parched and dry,
And to die of thirst is by far the worst of a thousand ways to die.
But Milligan's bar is down the street and the beer that he pulls is cool,
There a man might drink till he couldn't wink nor sit on a bar-room
stool.

So they troop away for a round of drinks, just a couple to slake their
thirst,
Things look less grim in the shadows dim and the publican shouts them
first.
The sun goes down on the trucking town with the men still drinking
hard,
But the cook has sunk in the corner drunk with his features slightly
marred.

A dashing ringer, well primed with rum, gives the kitchen maid a hand,
And it's plain he's not now a man forgot in a lonely, forgotten land.
They will whoop it up in the trucking town, and each bush pub along,
The lonely track to the far outback will share in the drink and song.

For this is the life that the drovers live, with none but themselves to
please,
Who bring the stores to our crowded shores from the far off
Kimberleys.
It's God's own country, the drovers say, out there where the pied-geese
call,
Where the reckless thrive, and the fit survive and the others go to the
wall.

To the Barmaids

Six months we've been with Fuller's plant and we have just returned,
Two thirsty Barcoo immigrants, to bust the cheque we've earned,
So barmaids have the beer on the tap, and flex your dainty arms,
Bring solace to our perished souls with beer and girlish charms,
For things are dry on Thunder Lakes and drought is in the air,
But you can pour the glass that makes the old world seem so fair.

The days were hot when first we left en route for Jundah town,
The weather Gods, as if bereft, sent showers drizzling down.
We swam the raging Thomson, mate, with flooded packs and bags,
And dined that might on damper straight, and slept without our swags,
But soon we started on the job with Braidwood's Jundah Jack;
We mustered up a breeder mob, and took them on the track.

We've travelled many miles since then and seen a sight or two,
Been held, and spelled and quarantined, and often shown through.
We've mustered fats on Thunder Lakes, and branded on Retreat,
Watched bullocks in the freezing cold, and drafted in the heat.
Three weeks ago our work was done, we trucked a mob away,
Then headed homewards with the plant from down Yaraka way.

We turned the horses' heads for home, and every stockhorse knew,
And as they moved with eager stride we turned our thoughts to you.
Now past and gone our troubles are for we are back in town,
To skite around the Central bar and drink our quota down;
Our mates they took a ringing job, bull tossing in the scrub,
But that can't hold a candle to bull tossing at the pub.

Though oft we've drunk the waters of the Thomson and Barcoo,
To slake the thirst that we have now we need a stronger brew,
So barmaids have the beer on tap, and flex your dainty arms,
Have cold the amber nectar that deceives but never harms,
For things are dry on Thunder Lakes and drought is in the air,
But you can pull the draft that makes the old world seem so fair.

DROVERS' MAIL

WHEN BANJO PATERSON wrote the famous line, 'Clancy's gone to Queensland droving and we don't know where he are', it was no exaggeration. Getting mail to a drover on the road with stock was at best a hit-and-miss operation. Not that drovers had a lot of letters addressed to them. Most were bills and, despite the time lag in payment, the creditors knew the risks were slight. Storekeepers were few and far between on the outback stockroutes, and no drover could afford to gain the reputation of being a bad payer.

Nineteen fifty four was a census year. When the census form was to be filled in, I was droving down the Georgina, then across and down the Wills River route, with a mob of Territory bullocks, en route to Brighton Downs on the Diamantina. It would be honest to say that my concerns regarding the population of Australia were not, at that time, keeping me awake at night. However, on reaching camp one night, the cook waved a large, important-looking document under my nose and said with a grin, 'You, as the bloody householder, are supposed to fill this bastard in tonight'.

After a quick meal, I dug in the swag and finally found a battered biro; armed with this, I attacked the census form and, amid a great deal of ribald advice, finally completed it. The description of the building caused some concern for a time, but bushman are an enterprising lot. As the cook had told me the form would be collected at Dajarra, I stuck it in the saddlebag and forgot about it.

However, at Dajarra no one wanted to know about it. I made unsuccessful attempts to unload it on the publican, the storekeeper, the postmaster, the policeman, and anyone else I thought may be interested in the population growth of Australia. Finally, I rode back to the cattle in disgust, with the cursed form still in the saddlebag. In Boulia, I had no better luck; by that time the census was old hat, and the form and I rode on.

I finally arrived back in Camooweal after finishing the year with a mob off Chatsworth and flung the census form into a cupboard. The termites immediately laid into it and, pricked by a guilty conscience, I wrote to someone (I forget who) and asked for advice. I never received an answer—perhaps the letter is still being shunted between outback post offices.

The census form is still with me. A dozen times I have been about to burn it and then held back. Some day someone may call and collect it, and then the population figure for 1954 will receive a rightful and long overdue adjustment.

North Australian Pastoral Company

Camooweal to Borroloola Mail in 1916.

HORSE DEALING

FOR CENTURIES HORSE dealers have suffered from what can best be described as a bad press. It is not unreasonable to assume that this dubious reputation has been thoroughly earned, for most horse traders would cheerfully sell their grandmothers for fish bait. Of necessity, at times horse dealers have had to deal with their peers, and on those occasions, it was inevitable that one of them would find himself in the invidious position of being hoisted with his own petard. Drovers, who were inveterate horse dealers, sometimes found themselves the victims of this cruel fate. There was little that could be done, however, other than to accept the blow philosophically, for it was no use crying over spilt milk, or spavined horses.

When heading well down into Queensland with Territory bullocks one year, I was on the lookout for fresh horses, as few of the plant were becoming leg weary. I knew that Byron Nathan had retired on a small block on the Georgina, and Byron had always owned good horses, so I let it be known on the bush telegraph that I was in the market to trade.

In the plant, there was a nice-looking bay filly that I was keen to get rid of. She was out of a pack mare of mine and had been broken in while we camped, waiting to take delivery of the mob. Right from the outset, she developed the habit of bucking with her head in the air, and she dealt out a damn good hand. A horse that bucks like this is difficult to ride, because it is impossible to put any weight on the reins, or to get a feel of what the horse is going to do. The filly had finally settled down due to tiredness, but I knew she was going to be a real problem after she had had a spell.

The day we passed Byron's selection, I saddled the filly and rode over to see him. We yarned for a while, then got down to business. I told Byron the filly was a bit leg weary and I would like to swap her for an older, seasoned horse. He asked me what she was like and I told him she had settled in well to droving but might have a root after she'd been given a spell. Byron nodded, then walked around the filly. He picked up all four feet and checked her mouth, then, turning to me, he said he had a black mare in the yard he was willing to trade.

We walked over to the yard where a fine-looking black mare was standing. She had a good girth, straight clean legs and fine quarters. I looked at her teeth and saw she was rising seven years old; good for at least another five or six droving seasons. With studied reluctance, I agreed to the deal. We swapped receipts, then, leaving the filly in the yard, I saddled the black mare, saluted Byron and rode off.

Before I had ridden 200 yards (180 metres) I realised we had caught one another. The mare had been foundered in front and almost fell twice before I reached the mob. No doubt Byron was smiling to himself, but he was yet to deal with the bay filly after she'd had a spell.

The worst deal I ever made was with the legendary Sam Fuller. I had worked for Sam in the past and we were good mates, but friendship, unfortunately, was never a factor in horse dealing. I had five older horses in the plant that were nearing the end of their working lives, so between Winton and Longreach I swapped them with Sam for three big fat horses. Sam swore they were as quiet as ladies' hacks. God knows where they came from and, knowing Sam, I didn't bother to ask. Within 24 hours, I wished I'd never seen them. They were hard to catch, harder to ride and cleared out every night, giving a clear indication that wherever they had come from was preferable to their present situation. I got rid of them at the first opportunity.

Some time later I ran into Sam in a hotel in Longreach where he was entertaining a crowd in the bar with songs, yarns, lies and his own ingenious method of making music. He greeted me like a long lost brother and bought me a beer. We yarned for a while, then he asked the question I knew he'd have to ask.

'How did you get on with those three horses?'

'Sam,' I said, 'they are three of the best horses I've ever saddled.'

He laughed and slapped me on the back, then, to a chorus of approval from the crowd, he pulled the flap off a tobacco packet and playing it like a gum leaf, giving us a rollicking rendition of the old song 'Ten Thousand Miles Away'. And that, I thought as I drank my beer, would be a bloody good place for his three fat horses.

A STITCH IN TIME

SOME 25 MILES (40 kilometres) west of Camooweal on the stockroute stands a stone building reputed to have been a customs house prior to Federation; it is a spot that has seen its share of tragedy over the years. A particularly brutal murder is supposed to have been committed there, for which the killer was later hanged. Some years later three people, two men and a woman, died of thirst in the area. It was an oft-repeated story in the outback of people ignorant of bushcraft trying to walk to water.

None of the place's gloomy history bothered the drovers, who often camped there with empty plants on the way to pick up mobs from further out in the Territory. There was a wire yard used for station branding close by the old stone building. One year I camped there and decided to break in a clumper mare that had adopted my horse plant. No one seemed to know who owned her, so I decided I might as well get some work out of her before her owner turned up. As soon as I caught her, I realised she had a vicious streak in her a mile wide. It was also evident that someone had tried to break her in before and had given it up as a bad job.

She was an ideal type for a packhorse, so after lunging the mare and teaching her to lead, I hobbled and sidelined the uncooperative clumper and strapped a packsaddle on her back. I had a halter on her with a short halter shank, but to remove the sideline I lugged her and prevented her from seeing what was going on. I then got Ronnie Condon to undo gently the hobble strap that fastened the sideline chain to her near hind leg. After a few dry runs, during which the mare never moved, he undid the buckle and started to straighten up and move away. He never made it. The mare lashed out, kicking him full on the forehead.

The clumper mare then turned on an exhibition of bucking, with the sideline chain still swinging from her front leg. Concerned she would trample the unconscious man, I let go of the halter shank and kicked dust at her to get her out of the way, and then dragged Condon out under the bottom wire of the yard.

He looked in a bad way, so I called for help, and we carried him into the stone hut, where we surveyed the damage. Condon was still out cold, and the wound on his forehead looked as if it had been caused by a blow from an axe. Grabbing a double handful of flour, I poured it on the wound to staunch the bleeding, then placed a towel round his head. It was obvious to me that the situation was beyond the limited scope of my first aid kit, which was geared more to the treatment of horses than it was to the alleviation of human suffering. Leaving the unconscious man in the care of the cook, I caught and saddled a chestnut gelding that at one time had raced in Mt Isa and started the ride to Camooweal.

The most comfortable and natural gait for a horse is the trot. A good trotter will cover a long distance without knocking up, and do the trip in smart time. I reached Camooweal in just under two-and-a-half hours. At the hospital I found the sister who ran the place (a doctor from the Isa visited once a week) and told her the story. She rang the auxiliary ambulance bearer, who picked me up at the Ringer's Roost after I let the chestnut go there, and we drove out to the scene of the accident.

Condon had regained consciousness, but was still a bit dazed. However, he insisted on sitting up in the ambulance and walked unaided into the hospital when we arrived there. After giving the patient a tetanus shot, the sister cleaned the wound up, then suggested that Condon be taken to Mt Isa to have the gash stitched up. When I queried the need for this, she admitted she had never stitched up a wound.

I looked at her in amazement, then said, 'Look Sister, I can't think of a better opportunity to learn. I've stitched up a few horses and I'll give you a hand if you need it.'

After some hesitation, she agreed and the job was completed to everyone's satisfaction, but she insisted on keeping Ron in hospital overnight for observation. Before leaving, I saw Ron tucked up in bed, and congratulated him on being responsible for furthering the cause of medical treatment in the drovers' town. I checked on my horse, making sure he had feed and water, then went to the pub for a rum and a meal.

Next morning, after organising a ride out for Ron, I rode back to the camp. A week later I removed the stitches from the wound with the aid of a castrating knife and a pair of stake pliers. In the meantime the clumper mare had settled down to pack work and was earning her keep in the plant. Later that year I lent her to a drover who was short of packhorses. I never saw her again.

SHOEING ON THE ROAD

THE SHOEING OF plant horses was an absolute necessity when droving, as during a season, plant horses often travelled more than 2000 miles (3200 kilometres) over all types of terrain. The way we shod was called cold shoeing and was quite different from the work done by blacksmiths, who made the shoes with the aid of a forge and anvil, then fitted the shoes hot.

Drovers bought the shoes already made up in sets of four, comprising two front and two hind shoes. Although they came in a range of sizes, from size two (for a pony) upwards, they still had to be cut and shaped before they could be used. To cut the ends off the factory-made shoes, most drovers favoured an old axe head and a short-handled one pound hammer. Unlike stockcamps, drovers could not afford to carry an anvil, due to its weight. However, a short length of rail track made a satisfactory substitute on which to shape the cold metal.

The balance of the shoeing kit comprised a light shoeing hammer with a small head, a hoof rasp, a pair of heavy pincers and a steel pritchel to enlarge the nail holes in the horseshoes. Some drovers also included a pair of hoof cutters in the kit. Horses' hooves keep growing after being shod,

Shoeing on the road using a collar rope.

and by the time the shoes had to be replaced, there was a growth of hoof or toe to be cut away before the new shoes were fitted. Hoof cutters made this task faster and easier.

Drovers and ringers on stations always liked to shoe horses 'up on their toes', as this made the mounts more agile and less likely to fall. To achieve this desired result, the horse's heels were only lightly rasped down to level them, while the toe or underside of the front of the hoof was cut back as far as possible. A good shoer always shod a horse with the hoof in the air, never on the ground.

Experienced road horses seldom gave trouble when shoeing was in progress; however, fresh horses in the plant were often a problem. At times during a trip, a drover would buy horses or swap tired ones for fresh mounts that had never worn shoes. Shoeing them in front never posed many difficulties, but they tended to play up—and sometimes kicked like blazes—when hind shoes were being fitted. The standard procedure, then, was to use a kicking strap on the horse.

The kicking strap was simply a wide strap that was placed around the horse's neck, and to this was fastened a long strap that was passed around the horse's hind leg below the fetlock, then back to a patent buckle at the shoulder. When the strap was pulled, the hoof was drawn forward and up, preventing the horse from kicking. The same result could be achieved with a collar rope made by fitting a neck loop in a greenhide rope with a bowline knot.

Occasionally we owned horses that could only be shod on the ground. The easiest way to throw them was to make a double collar rope by tying a loop in the middle of a greenhide rope with a bowline on the bite. The ends of the rope were then passed around both hind legs and back to the neck loop. As the ropes were pulled the horse sat down on its rump, and was eased over on its side by a man holding the head.

The shoeing, or rather cueing, of road bullocks was at one time a common practice. Fat cattle, because of their weight, were particularly susceptible to lameness on rough routes. Cueing enabled the drover to deliver these valuable beasts in good condition. As cattle have cloven hooves with a very thin shell, cueing was quite different from shoeing horses. The shoes used were worn-out horseshoes called slippers. These were cut in half before being shaped to fit the animal's hooves, then tacked on with the light nails used with racing plates. If no suitable yard or cueing pen was available, the beast had to be thrown before the job could be done.

Shoeing was at best an onerous and back-breaking task, by no means a favourite occupation with ringers. Nevertheless, they took pride in their work those days, and shoeing was no exception. I once worked on a station with a head stockman who had a rather warped sense of humour. We had just finished a three months' muster without a day off and at the fire that night he looked us over, then said, 'Well, lads, you've done a good job. We'll have a holiday tomorrow and reshoe the horses.'

HORSE STEALING

THE WELFARE OF a drover's horses was vital to his successful operation; a man who neglected his horses never lasted long as a contract drover. After a long trip, it was essential that the horses were given a spell on good feed to ensure they would be fat and fresh at the start of the next droving season. When droving from the West, it was not unusual for plant horses to travel over 2000 miles (3200 kilometres) during a trip, and the drover's job was not finished until he had turned his horses out in a secure, well grassed and watered paddock or town common.

Security was a consideration, although genuine horse stealing was rare and, unlike poddy-dodging, was usually condemned. The reason for this was simple—most horse owners were drovers or battlers, not wealthy station owners. A less serious and sometimes practised offence was horse 'sweating', drovers would 'borrow' horses for a trip, then return them to where the owner would find them.

The Camooweal common was without a doubt the pick of all the spelling areas; the horse feed was Mitchell and Flinders grass and the common ranger kept an eye on all that went on there. Some years I delivered bullocks well down inside Queensland and rather than walk the horses all the way back to Camooweal, I left them at places like Fort William, just above Boulia, or on the Kynuna common. The security was not the best at these places, but the only time my plant horses attracted the attention of a true horse thief was when I had taken the plant back to Camooweal.

After trucking Ord River bullocks at Dajarra, late in 1956, I walked the plant back to Camooweal in easy stages, to find the common in very poor condition. After pulling the packs off on the bank of the Georgina, I rode into town to see Jack Dally, the common ranger. Jack was an old-time bushman, who, in his heyday, had been a mate of Galloping Jones, a legendary figure in the Queensland Gulf. I liked Jack and respected his opinion. He told me that the common had been flogged with cattle, and that there was little likelihood of rain before the following February. Although the common would hold my horses, he said, they wouldn't get fat. As long as I kept an eye on them, my horses would be better off at Split Rock, where there was good feed, and agistment available.

With that said, Jack pushed his hat back and added, 'Come in and have a drink of tea, anyway.'

I followed him inside and said hello to Mrs Dally. Jack had married Count Biondi's eldest daughter and despite having a large family, they always extended true bush hospitality to visitors. I found Johnny Ormond seated at the kitchen table with a cup of tea in front of him. He looked up as I entered.

'Lock up your daughters—there's a drover in town.'

Johnny was a mate of mine, and a member of that band of unsung heroes, the bush mechanics. Before going out to the Ord, I had bought an ex-army jeep of World War II vintage and Johnny had patiently given me a crash course into the mysteries of the internal combustion engine. I had two reasons for buying the jeep: firstly, it gave me a handy run about during the slack months, and secondly, I had reluctantly come to the conclusion that courting women from the back of a horse was rapidly becoming passe. Packs were still out on their own on the road, but a packhorse at a picnic was regarded as something of an anachronism.

After yarning for a while, I rode back to the camp, and next morning, jumped in the jeep and drove out to Split Rock. The block was roughly halfway between Camooweal and Yelvertoft Station, on the road and stockroute to Mt Isa. I found the feed to be excellent and the water supply adequate. I returned to Camooweal and lost no time in organising agistment for my horses. After pulling the hobbles and neck straps off them, the next day I took them out to Split Rock, getting Johnny to pick me up in the jeep. I knew I was taking a risk leaving them there, but it would have to do until the Camooweal common improved. In the meantime I decided to check the plant regularly with the jeep. Horses that have been together on the road will continue running with their mates, making it very easy to see if horses are missing. It was a pleasant half hour run out to Split Rock and I never lacked company when checking the horses. I was delighted with their progress—that is, until the horse thief struck.

I heard that a chap I knew reasonably well was bringing a plant of horses out from Mt Isa. He had an interest in a block up in the rough country to the north. Normally he would have come through Camooweal, so when he took a short cut past the town, the alarm bells sounded. Early next morning, I threw some gear in the jeep and got Johnny to run me out to Split Rock. When we arrived at the water, I asked Johnny to wait and, grabbing a bridle, I walked out and caught a horse, jumping on him bareback. I quickly saw there were six of my best horses missing. I put the remaining 38 together on the water and, letting the horse I had been riding go, I caught Harlequin and led him over to the jeep as Johnny jumped out.

'Anything wrong?'

'Yes, the bastard has taken six good horses.'

'What are you going to do?'

'I'm going after them,' I said as I saddled the brown horse.

'Do you want me to go to the police?'

'No, I'll handle it. You could let Jack Dally know the score.'

I slipped into the saddle, told Johnny I'd see him when I returned and set out after the horse thief. The tracks of his plant were easy enough to follow, and as I knew the route he would have to take, I could lap along and take short cuts. I made good time, but despite my advantage, it was almost sundown when I rode up to the culprit's camp. There was no sign of the man himself, however his ringer was hobbling the horse plant 100 yards (90 metres) or so away from the packs. My six horses were standing already hobbled on one side of the mob. The man looked up as I reined in.

'Take the hobbles off those six horses.'

He shook his head. 'No, they belong to boss.'

I tapped the revolver I had stuck in my belt. 'They belong to me. Take the hobbles off now.'

He hesitated a minute, then walked slowly over and did what I had asked. He straightened up and glared at me. 'The boss won't like it.'

'He can tell me that himself. Where is he?'

'I dunno,' he said sulkily, and went back to hobbling the rest of the plant. I pushed my horses to the Camooweal side of the camp and let Harlequin go. I caught and saddled Flight, then led her back to the camp and helped myself to a drink of tea. The ringer finished hobbling up and sat on his swag in silence.

Just on dark, the man I was after rode into the camp. He stopped short when he saw me and stammered a query. 'Are those horses yours?'

'You know bloody well they are mine. A man has to sink pretty low to lift a drover's plant horses.'

'I'm sorry.'

'You're only sorry because I caught up with you. If I hadn't, you'd be thinking what a bloody smart man you were.'

'You won't go to the police, will you?'

'No, I won't, but if you ever touch a horse of mine again, you thieving bastard, I'll have your guts for garters.'

I mounted Flight and headed off with my horses, leaving him standing by the fire. I arrived back in Camooweal at ten o'clock the next morning and put the horses in the yard at the Ringer's Roost. I had changed twice on the way back and none of them looked any the worse for the experience. As soon as it rained, though, I lost no time in bringing the plant horses back to the Camooweal common.

CATTLE HUSBANDRY
ON THE ROAD

THE DROVING OF store cattle from the West entailed far more than merely driving a mob from point A to point B. A boss drover charged with fulfiling the conditions of a droving contract had, in my day, a formidable task ahead of him. To be successful, a drover not only had to know the route—he had to be skilled enough to get the best out of the cattle he was responsible for. A drover who was a good cattleman could read the mood of the cattle and react quickly and correctly to the mob's response to the many and varied situations encountered on the trip. These skills were not learnt overnight; they were gained by years of experience and observation.

Despite their unpredictable behaviour at times, the basic needs of road cattle were simple: feed, water and rest. The last named was as important as the others; road cattle needed rest because, like all ruminants, they masticated their food more than once. It was essential that they were given ample time to rest, so they could regurgitate and chew their cuds.

A drover who was a good cattleman harnessed the natural urges and habits of the cattle to achieve his own ends. The benefits of doing this were threefold. Firstly, the day's stage was covered with the minimum effort—very important if the drover happened to be short-handed. Secondly, the bullocks were kept happy and contented, and contented bullocks lose less weight and give less trouble. Thirdly, it was easier on the horses, and the condition of the horses could be crucial on a long trip. Good drovers ensured that the pace of travel and the distance covered was governed by the weaker beasts on the tail of the mob.

The drover's day started early; the boss drover, who did the last watch, would call the cook and horsetailer well before five o'clock. Ringers on the road were given about half an hour to roll their swags, have a wash, have breakfast, cut their lunches, saddle their horses and take over from the boss.

If the camp was in open country, the mob was moved off camp at first light; but in rough or timbered areas, the bullocks were held back until broad daylight. After being held on camp all night, the cattle were naturally hungry, and were ready to feed as soon as they were on their feet. Good drovers were always prepared to accommodate the needs of their cattle and fed the mob along slowly in the direction the drover wanted to go. At the same time, the bullocks were allowed to spread out, so that the weaker beasts on the tail had the same opportunity as the leaders to obtain unspoilt grass.

Drovers were aware that on the station runs, the bullocks had been conditioned to walking to water from their feeding grounds, and simply waited for nature to take its course. After a couple of hours grazing, the mob showed signs of wanting to drink by walking over grass rather than eating. The mob was then eased together and turned on to the stockroute pads. There, without any urging from the drovers, the bullocks would step out, their instinct telling them there was water ahead.

Most drovers liked to be at the water by ten-thirty, even earlier after a dry day, to allow the bullocks to camp during the heat of noon, and to give them plenty of time to process the grass eaten earlier. Dinner camp also gave the drovers a chance to relax.

If the watering facility was adequate and the cattle not too thirsty, most drovers preferred to let the mob string in to drink at their own pace. If, however, the bullocks had not had water the previous day, or if the drover had doubts about the quantity of water available, the bullocks would be cut into small mobs. These small mobs or 'cuts' were watered individually to make sure that the weaker cattle were not disadvantaged in the struggle to get a drink.

As soon as the mob had drunk its fill, it was put on dinner camp and the drovers boiled their quarts. Each day the man whose turn it was did the dinner watch. Despite it being daytime, bullocks could be lost off dinner camp, particularly on a dry day when bullocks could walk off camp looking for water. When the chap on dinner watch had taken up his duties, the rest of the team could relax over a leisurely meal, then have a rest or take the opportunity to have a shave and a clean-up.

The mob was seldom taken off the water before half past two. The exact hour depended on the heat of the day and the distance to the night camp, which had been selected earlier by the cook and horsetailer on instructions from the boss drover. Before the mob was moved, it was put back on the water to top up with a second drink. As the bullocks were accustomed to walking out from water to the station feeding grounds, the drover would put the mob on the pads and walk the cattle to within feeding distance of the camp. After turning the mob onto the feed, it would be allowed to graze slowly along and would be fed up to the camp and pushed together at dusk. Once the bullocks were on camp, the boss drover or the cook would do the dogwatch, allowing the rest of the men to let their horses go and have a meal.

The routine on a dry day differed only slightly. The periods of grazing could be reduced, as dry cattle feed less than well-watered ones, and the dinner camp was, of course, a dry one. The drovers would fill their quarts from the water bags carried around their horses' necks. On an extended dry stage, great care had to be taken when using water for washing and cooking. I have seen thirsty bullocks ringing madly around a camp when a careless cook knocked over a water canteen, the smell of the wet earth being enough to drive the mob almost crazy.

When cattle lie down, they do so with their bodies upright and with their feet tucked under and to one side. When well fed and watered road bullocks lay down on a night camp, air was expelled from their lungs with a quite audible whoosh. It was a sound that drovers enjoyed hearing, for it signalled full and contented cattle.

When bullocks moved off a night camp, they left behind clear evidence of the drover's husbandry. Weeks later a good cattleman could ride past the camp and tell at a glance how the mob had been faring. Small, dark dung that was almost nodular in composition indicated the mob had been having a hard time, while large, light-coloured, flattened pats clearly showed all was well.

Back in the days when cattle were walked to their destination, instead of being trucked as they are today, there were three types of mobs on the stockroutes: fats, breeders and stores. Drovers often specialised in one class of cattle droving and were described in conversation as being of that ilk.

The droving of fat cattle from the fattening depots in the Channel Country to the railheads provided work for a large number of drovers. The trips were short—weeks rather than months—and the mobs were restricted to about 700 head. The big, placid fats seldom gave trouble and after a few nights, most fat cattle drovers gave watching away, merely camping behind the mob. All in all, the job of droving fats was regarded as something of a sinecure, although it was essential to nurse the mob along and deliver the cattle in prime condition.

The droving of breeders, or cows and calves, was, in my opinion, sheer drudgery. Circumstances forced me once to take on a mixed mob that included cows in calf, and it was a mistake I vowed never to repeat. The long-suffering characters who followed this type of droving usually had a conveyance called a calf cart in which they put the newly born calves for transportation to the next camp. No self-respecting cow and calf drover would be without his calf cart, for without one, the calves would have to be knocked on the head and the mothers thrown and hobbled each night until they forgot about the unhappy event. Cow and calf droving was not for me, but I suppose someone had to do it.

Store cattle drovers were a breed apart. Many of them were larger than life characters who had a lot in common with the wild restless cattle they brought down the unfenced stockroutes. Despite their often reckless behaviour, those of them who were successful were all top cattlemen. If they regarded themselves as an elite group—if they dismissed other forms of droving with cynical amusement—it is perhaps understandable.

STOCKROUTE CHARACTERS

NORTH-WEST QUEENSLAND and the Territory were at one time full of hard cases—men who drifted to the outback, there to find scope for their unique individuality and general acceptance of their most outrageous behaviour. Among them were the adventurers, the drifters, the ne'er-do-wells, and those reckless characters who left wherever they came from in haste and for a very good reason. There was an unwritten law in the Territory—you never asked a man about his past. If he talked about it, well and good—otherwise his anonymity was respected. Many an outback character took his past to the grave with him.

In the outback the use of nicknames was common. These were, as a rule, descriptive, colourful, and not without humour. Here are a few examples: One Potato Tom, Wirrawarra Mick, Jerida, The Dancing Duck, The Gilgai Crab, The Blue Bull, Beef Eye, The Territory Tick, Up and Down the River Jack, Cornbeef Jack, Shortstop Turner, The Pregnant Goat, Twenty-One, The Pic, Robbo the Lair, Robbo the Horsetailer, Looking Glass Joe, and Knock 'em Down Tommy.

Droving, because of its mobility, attracted many of these characters. They were colourful, larger than life figures who thrived in an environment where the social graces and conventions meant nothing, but where guts and self-reliance were essential for survival.

VALE RUSTY REAGAN

Old Rusty Reagan's cashed his chips
No more he'll go on droving trips,
And no more grog will pass the lips
    Of drunken Rusty Reagan.
He died of drink, or so they say,
Or pure neglect, but anyway
The sands of time have slipped away
    For luckless Rusty Reagan.

Although he camped upon the flat,
The bar was his true habitat,
And home was underneath the hat
    Of drifter Rusty Reagan.
There's none to say from whence he came,
Not sure, in fact, if that's his name,
To Rusty, though, it's all the same,
    Dead finish Rusty Reagan.

No relatives with reddened eyes
Will weep at Rusty's sad demise,
No lowered flag at half-mast flies
    To honour Rusty Reagan.
We'll miss perhaps his ugly dial,
His raucous voice and toothy smile,
We'll miss him for a little while,
    Then forget Rusty Reagan.

Perhaps somewhere someone will wait,
A mother, sister, brother, mate,
Who'll wonder as they vainly wait
    For absent Rusty Reagan.
I'd like to think some tears might fall
For Rusty's ilk, no-hopers all,
Who answer that last trumpet call
    Unmourned like Rusty Reagan.

THE STOCKROUTE DIPS

OVER THE YEARS Australia has had many problems with introduced pests: rabbits, prickly pear and cane toads, to name just a few. One of the major threats to the cattle industry in this country had its beginning in 1880 when cattle ticks were brought in on Asian cattle imported to Glencoe on the Adelaide River. From there the ticks spread like wildfire.

The ravages of this blood-sucking parasite have been dealt with in detail elsewhere. It is sufficient to say here that they cause serious debility in stock, and are carriers of red water fever, a bovine disease that virtually wiped out some stations in the early days of Top End development. Tick infestation led to serious restriction of stock movement and the introduction of tick lines, as well as tick-free areas.

The main method used to stem the spread of ticks was to put travelling stock through plunge dips containing an arsenic solution. In an attempt to keep the cattle tick out of Queensland, a plunge dip was constructed at Lake Nash, on the Northern Territory–Queensland border, in 1907. The walls and floors of this dip were built of puddled clay and are a monument to the enterprise of outback Australians.

It soon became apparent that cattle had to be dipped more than once before they could be guaranteed to be free of ticks. To avoid holding cattle at Lake Nash, dips were put in at Austral Downs on the Georgina and at the Rankine in 1918. From then on, cattle going down the Georgina to Queensland were dipped three times, with at least one week between dipping. Later still, dips were built at Wendy Bore on Anthony's Lagoon and by the Queensland authorities at Camooweal. Dipping at Austral was later abandoned.

In response to the huge movement of stock walking to Queensland after World War II, a number of actions were initiated. The Territory was under martial law during the conflict and in 1945 the army ordered that all drovers' horses travelling to Queensland were to be sprayed for cattle ticks. In 1949 an additional dip was constructed at No. 7 bore near Elliott, and by the 1953 droving season, another dip at Connell's Lagoon, between Brunette and Alexandria, was ready for use. This latest addition to tick control prompted an old-timer to growl: 'The bastards will have us swimming the bloody bullocks to Queensland soon.'

The early 1950s saw a large increase in the number of Northern Territory stock inspectors and this took some of the load off the shoulders

Ian Tinney

The now abandoned police station at Anthony Lagoon.

of the Territory police, who had previously done a great deal of the work relating to travelling stock. In the early 1960s the old dip at Wendy Bore on Anthony's was relocated to No. 1 bore on the stockroute between Anthony's Lagoon and Eva Downs.

The introduction of compulsory spraying for drovers' horses caused immediate protest and ongoing bitterness that was not helped by the actions of the character in charge of the dip on Anthony's Lagoon, who plunge-dipped some horses. Drovers had good reason for concern: after spraying, horses cut up badly in the cold south-easterly winds that swept across the tableland.

Many of the road mobs were difficult to yard for dipping and drovers who put the horse plant up front to lead the bullocks in found the horses becoming as yard shy as the cattle. Dips were never popular with drovers, who, while accepting them as a necessary evil, cursed them whole-heartedly for what they did to the cattle. At best, dipping knocked the road bullocks about and stirred them up, causing bad nights and rushes well into the trip; at worst, if the arsenic solution was too strong, cattle could be driven half mad.

One of the worst nights I ever experienced on the road was after dipping at the No. 7 bore near Elliott. When the lead split off and got away, it was close to daylight and our nighthorses were exhausted from a night of hard riding. My brother Jeff, who stuck with the leading mob, did not get back to camp with them until eleven o'clock in the morning.

The day I dipped Willeroo bullocks at Anthony's Lagoon, the late 'Wogga' D'Arcy put his mob of Mallapunyahs through behind me. Wogga was quite a character; the eldest son of George D'Arcy, he was reared with the rest of the family on Mallapunyah Springs, the family property. He was a big man, big enough, some said, to hold a bull out to piss, and he had huge feet. So large were his feet in fact, that he never managed to get boots that would fit him—so Wogga went through life quite happily without them. A good all-round man, he never let the lack of boots inhibit his riding ability; he hung his spurs on his bare heels and put only his big toe in the stirrup irons.

That night, after dipping, Wogga camped about a mile behind me, with the turpentine scrub at his back. Near midnight the Willeroos splashed, and soon after, the Mallapunyahs rushed and hit the scrub. I heard Wogga bellowing at them as he crashed through the turpentine on a nighthorse. It must have been hell on his feet, but next day when I met him he seemed none the worse for the experience.

The Eva Downs bullocks were usually good on the road, but they could turn it on if things went wrong. One mob I took got a bad fright after dipping at Connell's Lagoon and for the next few weeks they kept us on our toes, as the rather laconic entries in my 1958 diary show.

16TH JUNE. Camped out from Plain Bore. Mob rushed at daylight.

17TH JUNE. (No entry)

18TH JUNE. (No entry)

19TH JUNE. Dipped 1395 bullocks Rankine.

20TH JUNE. Camped back from Coolibah Bore. Mob rushed. Two crippled bullocks shot.

21ST JUNE. Watered. Went out from bore. Bad rush. Two bullocks shot.

22ND JUNE. Went back. Watered at bore. Camped at point of timber. Rush. One beast shot.

23RD JUNE. Watered. Camped at the same camp to settle the mob.

24TH JUNE. Watered and went out. Left crippled bullock.

25TH JUNE. Watered at Bell Hole. Bad night. Little feed. Raining.

26TH JUNE. Horse plant cleared out during night. Took mob on with nighthorses. Camped on ridge back from Five Mile. Horses caught up late. Raining.

27TH JUNE. Weather clearing. Watered at gilgias. Same camp. Bad night.

The mob finally settled down, although it was a rough trip, as the feed down the Georgina was little more than goose picking. Five months to the day after taking delivery, I trucked the mob away at Longreach.

THE WOODSTOCK HILLS

THE CATTLE PADS of the Boulia–Winton stockroute wound their tortuous way through the hills of Woodstock Station; dry, rugged, scrub-covered hills that seemed to us road-weary drovers to be unending. I eased myself in the saddle as I watched the leaders of the store mob pick their way gingerly through the spinifex and stones. They had travelled over 800 miles (1300 kilometres) since leaving Eva Downs in the Northern Territory, and it was obvious that the rough going was not to their liking. All the fire that had characterised their behaviour in the first weeks of the trip was gone, and all that remained was the disciplined resignation of bullocks that had marched 9 miles (14 kilometres) a day for too long.

I rode back along the straggling lines of cattle stretched almost half a mile (800 metres) from lead to tail, and as I rode, I cooeed through the lifting dust to keep them moving. I was short-handed. Two men had pulled out in Boulia, leaving only myself and two Aboriginal stockmen, Splinter and Isaac, with the cattle. With my brother Jeff doing both the cooking and horsetailing, that made four men in all to handle 1350 bullocks and 46 horses. Droving is a hard game at best, but being short-handed meant each man had to work so much longer and harder than normal.

As I rode around the point of a hill, Splinter rode towards me. One of the old school of Aboriginal stockmen, Splinter had proved his worth many times.

'How is the tail travelling?' I asked as he reined in beside me.

'Orright, maluka. Them sore-footed fellers are a bit slow. Mebe a little bit spell help 'im.'

Splinter would never be more direct than that, but I knew him well enough to accept the implied advice.

'Right oh,' I agreed. 'There's a flat just ahead of the lead. I'll block them up there and you can give them a spell while I trot ahead and see where the camp is.'

About 2 miles (3 kilometres) on, I saw where the plant horses had turned off the stockroute. I found the camp over a low ridge, with a fair expanse of open ground to camp the mob on. The eight packs were lined up, with the fire between them and the cattle camp, and behind the packs a sapling had been selected for the nighthorse tree.

Jeff was busy working around the fire as I rode up. I swung down from my horse and tied it to the sapling. Strolling over to the fire, I greeted him with: 'How is it going?'

'How the hell do you think it's going? I've got to take the horses on six miles to water yet, and make a damper before I go.'

I took stock of the situation, agreed it was a dog's life, and got my quart pot from my saddle.

'How about a drink of tea?'

'Look in the billy.'

I sat on my heels and sipped the tea.

'What's the horse feed like?'

The acting cook did not answer at once. He was slamming flour into a mixing dish with careless abandon. Finally, he looked up.

'There's enough for them tonight, about half a mile down the flat. Nothing much for the bullocks, though, apart from spinifex tassels.'

'Well, that will have to do them.'

I put down the quart pot and rolled a smoke. Jeff quickly added rising and salt to the flour, poured water into the mixture, then began to work the dough as though he was intent on belting the bottom out of the dish.

'Take it easy,' I said. 'You've a couple of hours of daylight yet.'

He looked at me. 'I've got plenty of time to do what I have to do, but I don't have time to sit round the fire smoking and drinking tea.'

I said nothing. I knew he was dog tired, for the long hours were taking their toll on all of us. Tossing out the tea dregs, I walked over to my horse and rode over to inspect the cattle camp. In area it was not a lot bigger than a normal size house block, but it would do. Road bullocks can be eased into a surprisingly small camp once they are broken in.

On the way back to the mob I rode past the fire, where my young brother was shovelling coals onto the camp oven that held the newly made damper.

'One thing,' I said. 'If you ever leave the bush, you could get a job cooking at Lennon's Hotel.'

His initial reply was unprintable, but then he laughed. 'Get back to your bullocks, you slave driving bastard.'

I saluted him and rode back to where I had left the mob.

We put the bullocks on camp just on dusk, riding around them and pushing them together until they were in a roughly circular configuration about 5 yards (4.5 metres) in front of the fire.

Jeff, in his capacity as horsetailer, then had to take the horses we had ridden that day on to the water 6 miles (10 kilometres) ahead. I changed to a nighthorse and watched the mob until he had returned and hobbled the day horses out with the rest of the plant.

He nodded to me as he rode out to take over. I tied up the nighthorse and got stuck into a frugal meal of corned beef and damper. I had done half of my brother's watch while he was tending to the horses and I was still sitting by the fire, albeit half asleep, when he was relieved by Splinter.

He came over to the fire for coffee and saw me.

'Why the hell aren't you in your swag?' He shook his head. 'You've got to be on watch at three.'

'It's all right,' I assured him. 'I've been dozing here.'

I lay on one elbow and listened to the corroboree that Splinter was singing drift across the sleeping mob. It had been a hard day, but at that moment I was at peace with the world.

My brother broke the spell. 'I've had droving,' he stated. 'Never again will I work on the road with Territory bullocks.'

'At least you'll be able to tell your grandkids about the time you did two men's work on the road with Territory bullocks.'

'I'll also be able to tell them I did it for one man's wages. Anyway, after the pizzling I've had this trip, I doubt if I'll be able to sire anything.'

I laughed. 'Don't worry, you'll get a fat bonus when we deliver this mob.'

'When we deliver,' he snorted. 'This mob had been for sale ever since we left Eva. I don't think they'll ever sell them and you'll probably end up in Victoria.'

'Oh well, I wouldn't mind. Look, we'll be out of these blasted hills in a few days. When we get to Winton we should be able to pick up an extra man or two.'

'Fair enough.'

He pulled out his tobacco tin, opened it, then put it down in disgust. I was about to throw him mine when he got up and walked to the dry ration pack for a fresh tin.

'I'll tell you one thing,' he said, rummaging about in the packbag, 'you'll never get me back in this part of the world. It must be the last place God made. I doubt if it would carry two goannas to the square mile.'

I looked over at the rugged ridge tops outlined against the starlit sky. 'It's pretty rough all right,' I agreed. 'I might give this route a miss myself in future.'

Fate, however, can play some funny tricks. These same Woodstock hills were to play an important part in both our lives at a later date. Deep under their rough surface were sandstone levels that contained a sparkling treasure: that most beautiful of all nature's gems—opal. In time we would both fall under its spell.

TRIALS AND TRIBULATIONS

HAVING FINALLY LEFT the rugged woodstock hills behind us on what would be an epic journey from Eva Downs Station, the soft going was more to the liking of the bullocks. Feed was still scarce, though, and we were entering an area of closer settlement, and would soon be in the heart of the sheep country. The day before we reached Winton, I camped a few miles out and watered at a bore west of the town.

Being short-handed, all of us were feeling the pinch. After the bullocks had a drink at the bore, I let them lie down around the trough on dinner camp. Splinter and the other ringer lost no time in catching up on some sleep while I did dinner watch. I was sitting on my horse, one leg cocked over the pommel of the saddle, when I saw a car approaching at speed. The vehicle swung around the mob and braked to a stop in front of me. A smartly dressed chap of about 30 stepped out and walked over. I picked him to be a stock and station agent, and soon discovered I was right; I also found him to be a smart alec.

He greeted me with: 'Where's the boss?'

'I'm the boss.'

'How long has your name been Chambers?'

I was in no mood for repartee. 'Look, mate, my name is Simpson, I'm in charge of this mob. If you want the bloody owner, bloody well ask for him, otherwise piss off and don't bother me.'

He ignored my outburst.

'Do you know where Alf Chambers is?'

'No, I don't.'

I uncocked my leg and rode off around the mob.

Later that afternoon Alf put in an appearance. I asked him about my visitor, and he laughed.

'He's a bit of a hard case, but he's no fool. I think he will sell the mob.'

The cattle had been for sale for a long time and had been in the hands of a number of agents. Alf was right about my visitor at the bore. Within a week he would have the mob sold.

Alf and I yarned over a cup of tea for a while, then he suggested we both take a run along the stockroute towards Longreach. The feed got worse rather than better, but in the fenced off-rifle range just past Winton the Mitchell grass was 2 feet (60 centimetres) high.

The rifle range was seldom used, but nonetheless it was illegal to put stock inside the fence. On the way back through Winton, I called on the common ranger. I gave notice I would be crossing the common and handed him two large pieces of corned beef. I had ideas about the rifle range and I wanted to keep the common ranger on side. The following day I took a calculated risk and told my brother Jeff, who was doing two jobs, those of cook and horsetailer, to camp in the rifle range. I thought I would be able to get rid of the common ranger before we got to the camp, but in that, I was wrong.

The common ranger was an old drover, and a friendly bloke. The gift of the meat may have been a mistake, for he took a shine to me and stayed with the mob all day. As we neared the rifle range, my mind was working furiously.

Suddenly the common ranger reined in his horse. 'The camp's in the rifle range.'

'What the hell does he think he's doing? He must have misunderstood me. Mind you, he's just about dead on his feet—he's been doing two jobs for nearly a month.'

'Well, you can't stay there.'

The common ranger had a job to do, and that job was to move the camp. The only chance I had was to take the initiative away from him.

'Of course not. He'll just have to pack up and shift the camp.'

We rode into the camp, with me winking furiously at my brother.

'What are you doing here? We can't camp here—this is the rifle range.'

Jeff ignored my winks. 'You bloody well told me to camp here.'

'Well, I'm afraid you'll have to shift the camp.'

'But I've just cooked a bloody feed, and it's nearly sundown.'

'Sorry mate, but the common ranger says we have to move, so move it is.'

My brother let go a string of oaths, put the boot into a billy of tea and, still cursing, turned towards the packs.

'Hang on, hang on,' said the common ranger. 'Look, leave the camp here, but I didn't give you permission—and I didn't see you here.'

I nodded my thanks to the common ranger, who wheeled his horse and left the scene of the crime at a hard gallop. Grinning, I turned to my brother, to find him looking daggers at me.

'You're a nice type of bastard. You know bloody well that you told me to camp here.'

'Of course, but I tipped you the wink. The only chance we had of staying here was to make him feel sorry for you.'

'I don't need any bastard to feel sorry for me. I reckon you'd sell your soul to the devil to get feed for those f...ing bullocks.'

I laughed. 'I did that a long time ago.'

I left Jeff refilling the tea billy and rode back to the mob feeling rather pleased with myself. The common ranger had disappeared, but he was no fool—he would have known that I had put one over him, and he would have known why, for he was an old drover himself.

Late the next afternoon Alf Chambers ran out to the camp with a cook. He was busy around the fire as I put the mob on camp and the aroma of a stew wafted across the bullocks. When I finished the dog watch, he had done the washing up and was sitting on his rolled-up swag. I nodded to him and helped myself to a plateful from the camp oven and grabbed a drink of tea. When I had finished, I rolled a smoke and looked at the cook. 'That was a damned good feed.'

'Make the most of it—I won't be cooking another; I'm finished.'

'Finished! You've just bloody well started.'

'Well, I'm pulling out. I won't work with packs.'

'I suppose you expect to get paid?'

'No, I've had a feed. We'll call it square.'

Without another word he stood up, shouldered his swag and was gone. I've had some short-term employees, but that cook still holds the belt.

The grass improved quite a bit in the next few days, and when the agent brought two potential buyers out, the mob was on dinner camp looking full and contented. My friend the agent bustled over to me.

'Can you lend these chaps horses to look through the mob?'

'Yes, they can take those,' I said, indicating the horses Splinter and his mate were riding.

'What about yours?'

I was riding a smart chestnut mare. She was one of four I had bought back in Boulia. She was still fresh and was a bit lively to mount.

'She's a bit hard to get on. They would be better to use the others.'

'Oh, if you can ride her, this chap will handle her,' he said, nodding towards one of the buyers.

I dismounted and handed the reins to his client, who looked far from confident. The moment he reined up the mare, I knew he was in trouble. As he swung for the saddle, the mare ducked away, leaving him sprawling on the ground. I caught the chestnut mare and rode around to the back of the mob, leaving them to sort things out for themselves.

Despite the bad start to the inspection, the partners bought the mob and advised me that they would be trucking the bullocks from Longreach. Alf Chambers was of course delighted, the agent had his commission, and the buyers, who came from Jericho, seemed pleased with the deal; it was, in fact, happiness all round. The only cloud on the horizon was the trucking date. The first available one was three weeks away. At the normal rate of travel, it would only take me eight or nine days to reach the trucking yards at Cramsey. There was little feed for the mob there, so I decided I would have to waste time on the route.

Store bullocks are supposed to travel 9 miles (14 kilometres) per day, and the stockroute ranger is employed to see this is done. Stations along the route also send men, usually jackaroos, to see you don't leave the stockroute. Despite the attentions of these characters, it is still possible to take things easy: a day's spell here and there because of lame bullocks, a few days held up because of lost cattle while a man rides back along the route on a wild goose chase—and then there is the organised rush.

It is very easy to step a horse over a sheep fence; horsetailers do it all the time to get feed for the horses. A sheep fence is not very high. If you take your belt off and tie the wires together, a horse can step over the fence very easily. When organising a rush, a drover uses this method to take a horse into a well-grassed paddock after dark. Most drovers have a horse that will pull with their tail; with a horse like this, it is an easy matter to hook a rope on to a post and pull 20 or 30 yards of fence out into the paddock. The bullocks are then driven through the gap and scattered far and wide. The drovers then return to camp for a good night's sleep.

When, the next morning, a jackaroo would bum-trot up to see the mob along the route, I always would make a point of galloping about in the pretext of mustering the bullocks. The 'roo usually took one look and galloped back to the station, giving me additional time to scatter the mob. By the time the furious sheep cocky had arrived and I had explained about the rush, the bullocks were as full as ticks and starting to camp. I explained then that it would be easier to muster them onto the water, and all hands started on the job. By the time the mob was pushed back through the gap, it was usually late afternoon and the bullocks had paunches on them like poisoned pups. The moment they saw the camp, they went over and lay down. I always gave the cocky a hand to put the fence back up and invited him to camp with us if he was worried about a reoccurence. It was an offer that was never accepted.

I had no compunction about doing this, for as far as I was concerned, drovers who pinched grass were only getting a bit of their own back. Many graziers regarded the adjacent stockroute as part of their property and used it as an extra paddock early in the season. By the time the first mobs moved down the route there was little grass left.

By devious means such as this, I arrived at Cramsey with the mob the day before I was due to truck the bullocks. Over the next two days I sent them east by stock train to their new home.

FURTHER IN

On the road with Eva cattle we've at times had quite a battle,
But we've struck good grass at last past Winton town;
All the squatters look us over: 'Just another drunken drover',
As we're heading down through Queensland further down.
It has been a sad old story since we left the Territory,
Old man drought has had the country by the tail,
But the grass is growing sweeter, and the jillaroos we meet are
Getting fairer as we travel on for sale.

We have seen the stubble blacker than our native trade tobacco,
And the drought, some say, is worse than 'fifty-two;
What with trials and tribulations and the squatters' altercations,
'Twas the OP rum alone that pulled us through.
Now the bullocks look in wonder at the sound of muffled thunder,
As the boundary rider passes in his jeep;
For the gates are coming quicker and the 'pills' are getting thicker,
And it's plain enough the country carries sheep.

Oh! the gates are crazy tangles, swung a dozen different angles,
And the source of many blasphemous tirades,
For a bloodhound soon would find us by the hide we've left behind us,
On those blasted, buckled, twisted barricades;
Some are mantraps made of wire that a trapper well might hire,
Should he wish to catch the bear that hibernates,
They're of wood and steel and cable and we shut them when we're able,
Oh! they keep us pretty busy with their gates.

It seems these blanky squatters look on droving men as rotters,
As one fellow said who found us on his run;
Oh! his manner grew quite shirty and the words he used were dirty,
But we told him that we took it all in fun.
Oh! their boundary riders haunt us, but they very seldom daunt us,
And the stars alone look down and see us pass,
With a fortnight still to squander, we must let the bullocks wander,
And it keeps us pretty busy pinching grass.
We've a camp of native ringers and they really are humdingers,
At wolfing red-hot rib-bones off the coals,
Now our killers are all eaten, but a drover's never beaten,
For a drover is a man of many roles.
They of course prefer goanna in their ancient tribal manner,
But a stock of them is rather hard to keep,
Tho' at first they wouldn't try it, now they're on a mutton diet,
And they keep us pretty busy pinching sheep.

Oh! this droving game is chancy, there's no cop in being Clancy
If you're not awake and haven't any clues;
For your friends are few, if any, and the pitfalls they are many,
Though old Eva Downs of course pays all the blues.
Up to date we've dodged the rangers, but we're wary still of strangers;
Being caught, we're told, is far the greatest sin.
But the grass is growing sweeter, and the jillaroos we meet are
Getting fairer as we travel further in.

Yes, the worst of it is over and we'll really be in clover,
When we truck the mob away at Longreach town;
Then like modern guided missiles we'll head straight to wet our
whistles,
And we'll toast the little steers bon voyage down.

CATTLE DUFFING

CATTLE DUFFING HAS always been prevalent in Australia. When one considers the number of poachers and sheep stealers transported to this country, it is not surprising. Add to that the influx of people with an inherited antipathy toward the landed gentry, together with the opportunity created by the bush, and the result was inevitable.

It is a fact of life that Australian bushmen have always regarded cattle duffing with a sneaking respect. Take the case of Harry Redford, the greatest cattle duffer of them all: the evidence was overwhelming, the judge's summing up damning, yet the jury, without hesitation, found him not guilty. In reading the report of the case, one almost gets the impression that the members of the jury stood and applauded Redford as he left the court.

The attitude of bushmen to cattle stealing probably rose from two facts: firstly, the theft, as a rule, was from big stations; secondly, those stations were usually owned by southern or overseas interests.

The stealing of stock falls roughly into three categories: killing other people's beasts for beef; stealing unbranded stock, called poddy-dodging; and the stealing of branded stock, or cattle duffing.

The first type of offence has always been widespread. There's an old story that the only time a station owner knows what his own beef tastes like is when he visits a neighbour. The second of the above was, in the past, common practice, and many a respected cattle baron got his start by poddy-dodging. The third, and most serious, offence is cattle duffing. It is a risky business, to say the least, but at times it still goes on.

I was involved for a short time in a poddy-dodging block with Looking Glass Joe Dowling, who was one of the smartest men with wild cattle I ever met. Looking Glass Joe got his nickname because he was a bit of a dandy; shaving daily was something of a ritual with him and he spent a great deal of time admiring himself in the mirror-like inner surface of his tobacco tin lid—rolling a smoke was usually a leisurely exercise for Looking Glass Joe. Recognised as a top cattleman, he was also a notorious poddy-dodger. Mind you, he had never been convicted of the offence, and he remained in the eyes of the law a cleanskin, like the cattle he lifted.

I did not take our venture into the cattle business too seriously, and perhaps that was just as well, for it had many of the elements of a second-rate theatrical farce. The owner of the property was in gaol in Alice Springs, but he had agreed to sell the place to Looking Glass Joe, and also agreed to let us have possession of the run while the sale was being finalised. Joe, who believed in the old adage 'The early bird catches the worm', moved in, and we began mustering at once. Looking Glass Joe was totally uneducated, but he was no fool.

The block had some unusual land formations on it as well as quite good grazing country. Out on the edge of the desert there was a rather strange spring that ebbed and flowed with the phases of the moon like a tide; when the moon was full, the spring ran out for at least a mile, then gradually dried back as the moon waned. When the new moon put in an appearance, the process was reversed. The block lay south of Newcastle Waters, not far from the Powell Creek telegraph station, and west of Helen Springs. Newcastle Waters was a big station and always good for a few poddies, so Looking Glass Joe reckoned we had it made.

He did, however, have one problem; neither of us had a Territory cattle brand. I had a Queensland brand—no use at all for our present circumstances—and Joe had never held a brand, as all his past efforts in poddy-dodging had been for other people. He had made application to have the property brand and earmark transferred to him after the sale went through, but with his reputation, that was no certainty. Looking Glass Joe, however, did not seem to be worried, so we mustered merrily on.

Stations had a long-standing agreement that whenever country near a boundary was to be mustered, both stockcamps would be involved. Looking Glass Joe sent word to Newcastle Waters that we would be mustering around Powell Creek on a certain day, then made sure we were there two days before the given date. The evening before the Newcastle camp was due to arrive we had a small mob of cattle in hand in which was a fat barren Newcastle Waters cow that Joe decided would make good eating. He had just ridden to the camp for the rifle when out of the timber jogged the Newcastle horse plant.

In charge of the horses was a jackaroo who told Joe that the head stockman, who was coming along behind with the rest of the ringers, had decided to get to Powell Creek before us. Quite undaunted, Looking Glass Joe handed him the rifle, pointed out the cow and got him to shoot it. By the time the Newcastle Waters camp arrived the beast was butchered and we were wolfing into rib-bones freshly cooked on the coals.

The property had a rough but fairly comfortable homestead on it, so Looking Glass Joe arranged for his wife to join us. She had been a nursing sister at the Quilpie hospital before she met Joe on his last trip into the Channel Country.

By this time we had close to 300 head of cleanskin cattle mustered, but still no brand, and no news of the sale being finalised. Looking Glass Joe and his wife decided to go into Renner Springs to pick up the mail and to try to find out what was going on, while I rode the horse paddock fence where we were holding the cattle.

They returned late that afternoon looking as miserable as bandicoots. Looking Glass Joe handed me a letter advising him that the deal was off. Whether the owner received any help in changing his mind was debatable, but in any case, we were up the proverbial creek without a paddle. Next morning we opened the horse paddock gate and bushed the cattle that were to have been the nucleus of our herd. Looking Glass Joe and I rode off the place with nothing—at least, I got nothing. A few days later Looking Glass Joe received a broken jaw from the head stockman from Newcastle Waters, who apparently took umbrage at our activities, regarding them as a personal insult.

That was the closest I ever came to becoming a cattle king. However, Looking Glass Joe eventually obtained a run in the Top End. Sadly, his wife was killed off a horse soon after.

GALLOPING JONES

Where the Gulf rivers run, in the days that are past
The runs that bred cattle were fenceless and vast,
The stockriders mustered while e'er there was light,
But the duffers of cattle rode only at night.
They were reckless and daring, a larrikin band,
They took what they wanted and rode where they plann'd.
The troopers who chased them, though chafed to the bones,
Were sure the ringleader was Galloping Jones.

Many sovereigns have sat on a great many thrones,
And the King of the duffers was Galloping Jones.
His throne was his saddle, his realm it was vast,
The horses he rode were sure-footed and fast.
He travelled by starlight, unchallenged and free
To colour the pages of Gulf history.

He would go to a ball and he'd dance half the night,
Then be forty miles distant before it was light,
With a nice mob of poddies he quickly would sell
To a battler, then back to Kajabbi Hotel.
The tired troopers knew by the smile on his face
He had done them again, for they hadn't a case.
He took what he wanted and rode where he pleased,
The troopers who cashed him were taunted and teased.

Now the cattlemen argued the troopers are fools
We have got to do something to alter the rules.
They employed a sharpshooter on cattleman's pay
To hunt the wild duffers and keep them at bay.
But the message he got from the duffers was clear,
They stalked him at midnight, and shot off an ear.
He resigned very promptly and said, 'I'll refrain
From combat in future', then caught a fast train.

Quite a legendary figure was Galloping Jones,
Though the cattlemen viewed him with curses and groans.
He was straight in his dealings, a good mate in strife,
A friend of the battlers the whole of his life.
Though the police had been told: 'Bring the Galloper in',
He greeted them all with a wave and a grin.
He could ride, he could fight, and he galloped at will,
Now in legend and story he's galloping still.

Many sovereigns have sat on a great many thrones,
And the King of the duffers was Galloping Jones.
His throne was his saddle, his realm it was vast,
The horses he rode were sure-footed and fast.
He travelled by starlight unchallenged and free
To colour the pages of Gulf history.

Now the duffers have gone from the Gulf and the West,
And old Galloping Jones has been called to his rest.
But up in the Gulf, when the mist's on the ground—
When the night wind is stirring the treetops around—
It is then you may see them as wraith-like they go
With cleanskins in front, with the troopers in tow.
The stars pale and shiver, the dark forest moans
As fast flies the spirit of Galloping Jones.

A Letter 'Inside'

No doubt, perforce, you've settled down to prison's grim routine,
But I suspect you often think of how things might have been.
For one so used to distant hills it must be very hard
To find horizons shortened to a crowded prison yard,
But you have seen hard times before—have struck a snag or two
And though the going may be rough, you'll doubtless see it through.
I meant to write you long ere this, but you know how things are,
With us who live the same old life by bit and stirrup bar.

Although of late you've found that fate can play a fickle game,
Back here beyond the Queensland fence things still are much the same.
The Wet has come and gone once more and in the drovers' town
The same old crowd have had their fun and drunk their quota down.
Out bush it's like a garden now, the weather's fine and fair,
The scent of turpentine in bloom drifts on the freshened air,
The waterholes have overflowed, and on the blacksoil plain
The Mitchell grass and Flinders grass are tall and sweet again.

The travelling stock are rolling down the old Georgina route,
And I am on the road again with stores from further out;
As to the shaded dinner camps the bullocks slowly string
I wonder what you'd give just now to ride upon the wing—
To watch the mob these autumn nights on timbered camps starlit,
And feel a good and willing horse again upon the bit—
To yarn around the fire again as stockmen always do,
While close beside the feeding bells there mourns the lone curlew.

A mystic spell the outback weaves beneath the Milky Way
That ever holds a horseman's heart though half a world away.
And when the slate is clean at last, as it must surely be,
You'll find the old life waiting here, the same old company,
And on the day you meet old mates upon the blacksoil plain
You'll know the firm and friendly grip of bridle hands again.
Though men must bear misfortunes cross, and bow to unkind fate,
Unchanging, loyal to her own, the bush will always wait.

Maloney's Luck

Once a battler named Maloney owned a run so rough and stony
That the only way to prosper was by quietly pinching calves.
Now this very crafty codger was an expert poddy-dodger,
One who never cruelled his chances or did anything by halves.
With a conscience never troubled and a herd that quickly doubled,
It appeared our friend Maloney was enjoying fortune's smiles.
For the seasons made to order and the cleanskins on his border
And the attitude of bankers seemed reward for all his wiles.

Then alas the good years finished and his fortune soon diminished;
To prevent the wolf from calling, he was almost out of clues.
For his herd was gaunt and bony on his run so rough and stony
And it seemed at last the devil was desirous of his dues.
Now the drought gave him no quarter, he was almost out of water,
Just one soak, a creaking windmill and a tank of many years;
Though the banks had cancelled lending and discouraged wanton
spending,
His appeal to them for money would have moved Shylock to tears.

But Maloney's star was waning, as were chances of it raining,
And Maloney's credit rating now was rather on the nose.
They appeared to think it funny that he'd write to them for money,
So they answered and advised him that they shortly would foreclose.
Well Maloney felt quite bitter, but he'd never been a quitter,
So he reckoned he would front them, he would meet them face to face.
He fuelled up the old Land Rover and he cranked the motor over
And he set off through the dust clouds at a very lively pace.

Now the road to town was shorter by his one remaining water;
There the sight that met Maloney wasn't one to create mirth,
For the tank so badly rusted had thrown in the towel and busted
And had spilled ten thousand gallons on the dry and dusty earth.
All the cattle he had cherished, those of them that hadn't perished,
Were now bogged down most completely in sad and sorry state.
Well Maloney cursed creation and he cursed his stony station
And he wished on money lenders a most agonising fate.

Then he drove his old jalopy through the quagmire wet and sloppy
And he dragged each beast to freedom with a trusty greenhide rope.
Through the bog on foot he struggled, then with clutch and gears he juggled,
For to save his last few cattle was Maloney's only hope.
When the job at last was over, mud had caked the old Land Rover
And Maloney too was filthy from his hard, back-breaking toil,
For his shirt was mud bespatted and his hair was badly matted
And his boots and duds were plastered with a yard of sticky soil.

'Ah, to hell with boots and trousers and to hell with lending houses,
And to hell with bloody cattle,' wild Maloney loudly swore.
'They can take me as they find me, for the devil's close behind me,'
Then he drove to town and pulled up by the bank's rapacious door.
In the bank he grabbed a teller: 'Is the big boss here, young feller?'
And the manager thought quickly: it's far better I am out,
But Maloney wasn't dozing—as the boss's door was closing,
He just put his shoulder to it, striking hard the banker's snout.

Quickly choking back a groan, he cried: 'Come in, my dear Maloney.
That mud's a welcome sight, sir; no there's no need to explain.
I will make no protestations, my sincere congratulations,
It is evident to me, sir, that you've had drought-breaking rain.
Well, that loan will be no trouble, we in fact can give you double;
The interest rate will suit you and the terms will quite astound.
Here, Maloney, have a whisky, some investments can be risky,
But I've always told head office you are one man who is sound.'

Well Maloney never faltered, from that day his fortunes altered;
Soon with assets and investments he was up there with the best,
And today his boundaries wander out across the wide blue yonder,
He's respected, well regarded, through the North and through the West.
But there's always speculation in this region of the nation
On just how Maloney started, on just how he got his wealth,
And his bankers all acknowledge though he never went to college
He has got a head for business, then they drink Maloney's health.

Now Maloney doesn't prattle of the start he got in cattle
Or the lucky reprieve given by a ruptured iron tank;
But the servants who attend him note that mud does not offend him,
For Maloney still remembers it was mud that beat the bank.

Jimmy Charles, left, *and the author with Sam Fuller's plant in 1951.*

BUCKJUMP SHOWS

THE BUCKJUMP SHOW in Australia was the first step in the evolution of rodeo as we know it today, and has always been popular in the outback. Most of the early buckjump show arenas were merely a roped ring with an outer wall of hessian. Spectators stood in the space between. Despite their humble beginning, the Australian buckjump shows have had a long and colourful history, many of them surviving long after the introduction of organised rodeos. Over the years some illustrious names have been associated with buckjump shows: Martini, the Skuthorpes, Thorp McConville, the Gills and the Tulipans. The cry of 'Roll up, bowl up, tumble up, bring your sheila up to the buckjump show' once was an oft heard invitation throughout the land.

Many of the buckjump shows added to their attraction by having whip cracking, sharp shooting and rope tricks in the program. Some even had a pug on hand who was prepared to take on all comers. Probably the last of the buckjump showmen is Larry Dalhunty, a colourful character from North Queensland, who ran a traditional-type show until recently.

Winton Rodeo 1950s. Note the small Australian saddle and stockman's gear used before rodeos became Americanised.

Sam Fuller, a legendary figure in his own lifetime, ran his buckjump shop as late as the 1950s. Sam made Longreach his base, and at that time he also had a plant doing contract mustering and short droving trips. As he used some of the plant horses in the buckjump show, the plant was called to town whenever a show was planned. I put in a season with Sam, and to me, the difference between the plant and the buckjump show was fairly academic.

Sam always had good buckjumpers and the first I remember was Send 'em. When I was with him, his top horses were Depot Glen and Wait and See. He also had two creamy mares, Wattle Bough and Icecream. As the hour to start the show approached, Sam would stand outside and bellow: 'Prizes for riders and busters for windbags, just a few canvas chairs left.' There were as many chairs in the show, however, as there were feathers on a horse.

Sam Fuller was a born showman and a good horseman. Among his stunts were playing a mouth organ as a horse bucked, and riding a buck-jumper he knew whilst blindfolded. Most of the showmen used a long flank rope, which they held as a horse bucked. Sam's own men were given the nod to jump off before a horse was bucked out, but if a rider from the crowd backed himself to ride a horse for money, Sam had no scruples about helping to unseat the rider with the aid of the long flank rope.

The buckjump shows remained traditionally Australian to the last and did not succumb to American influences as rodeos did.

TALL STORIES IN VERSE

THE TALL STORY is an important part of our outback folklore. I doubt if there is a single facet of bush life that has escaped the outrageous attention of the spinners of tall yarns. Such stories are another example of how isolated people created their own entertainment. Whether it was around a gidgee fire, on a stockroute, or in the bar of a bush pub, the teller of tall yarns never lacked an audience.

DUCKABROOK DAN'S RIDE

In legend and story we constantly read
(Until we're emotionally spent)
Of tales like the man and his suffering steed
Who galloped from Aix to Ghent.
For love and for honour men galloped pell-mell,
They galloped for better or worse,
The Light Brigade charged to the entrance of hell,
As Tennyson told us in verse.

The man from the Snowy, a tedious lout,
Is very well known to us all.
With galloping yarns there is never a doubt
Most epics we clearly recall.
We all know of Phar Lap and old Peter Pan,
They raced with and humbled the best,
But who's heard the story of Duckabrook Dan
Who once raced a storm in the West?

It was out at the ten mile the contest began,
It was run at a furious pace,
A wild western storm and old Duckabrook Dan,
One gut-busting hell of a race.
Dan was riding that evening his favourite steed,
An ancient and flea-bitten grey,
Dan swore that the horse had a fair turn of speed
Though he'd once known the shafts of a dray.

Old Dan was enjoying an afternoon nap,
Unconscious of peril or rain,
When the wild tempest struck with a great thunder-clap
And the noise of a runaway train.
Dan leapt to the saddle and gathered his wits,
He whistled his dog to his side,
As the mill on the dam bowed down to the blitz
Dan started his marathon ride.

Ahead and beside them the lightning would strike,
Behind was a curtain of rain,
Dan wished for a moment he'd ridden his bike,
Then spurred over Bandicoot plain.
The grey galloped on with his blaspheming load,
The lightning had made him near blind,
But he kicked up the dust on the deep-rutted roar,
With the dog only metres behind.

To get to the station Dan knew was a must,
The old grey was still going strong,
The storm wind blew harder, a cyclonic gust,
A tail wind that helped them along.
The thunder boomed out through the scrubland beside,
The wind shrieked a fiendish refrain,
Behind came the rain like a billowing tide
And never a foot could they gain.

At the four mile the old horse was covered with foam,
He was spavined and short of a feed,
Dan crouched on his back like an oversized gnome
And prayed that they stayed in the lead.
At the two mile the grey seemed to break in his stride,
He had thrown off one of his shoes;
Dan swore to the saints if he finished the ride
He'd give up bad women and booze.

Dan wished he'd been born with the wings of a dove
As down went the grey on his knees,
The wild wind that roared through the timber above
Blew the fauna right out of the trees.
To be killed in a storm is a terrible fate,
It preyed on old Duckabrook's mind,
But they finally lurched through the horse paddock gate
With the dog only metres behind.

Old Dan asked the grey for an effort supreme,
The station was looming ahead,
The grey crossed the yard as he ran out of steam
To stop in the stable near dead.
But old Dan was the winner, he never got wet—
Was not even damp from the spray,
He had beaten the tempest by three lengths and yet—
The dog had to swim all the way.

MURRANJI MICK

Now old Murranji Mick was a tiger to talk,
A rough Territory stockman as wild as a hawk,
He would booze and he'd bellow and blaspheme and fight
And talk a blue streak without pausing all night.
He was rugged and rough and addicted to drink,
And could wreck a bush bar-room before you could wink.
He was ugly and sinful and fond of a brawl,
With a temper as short as his stories were tall.

He proclaimed he was born in the midst of the Wet
On a dark Monday morning he'd never forget,
The North-West monsoon had made things rather damp,
And at midday the flood rose and covered the camp.
When his crib sank beneath him, the outlook was grim,
He had one chance, he reckoned, and that was to swim.
So he floated and swam till he reached higher ground,
And was nearly a month old before he was found.

But he got by all right, eating crocodile eggs
And the Burdekin ducks that he caught by the legs.
Mick was good in the bush, he would calmly relate
How he ran mustering camps long before he was eight.
But he shot through soon after to go to the war,
And exceedingly strange were the sights that he saw.
But he won fame and honour and seven VCs,
And he soon had the enemy down on his knees.

When the fighting was over, Mick headed back quick,
Swimming most of the way just to get into nick;
His renown as a fighter was well known of course,
He'd a punch in each hand like the kick of a horse.
He was tougher than greenhide—as quick as a cat,
And he'd once flogged a bunyip to death with his hat.
He had challenged Jack Johnson, and Johnson turned white
And pleaded with Mick that he'd no wish to fight.

But his hardest fought battle, he said to us, was
When he went fifteen rounds with the Wizard of Oz;
They fought and they struggled and tore up the ground,
And Mick took an eight count in the very first round.
When the Wizard was cornered, he'd just disappear,
Then hit Mick from behind on the butt of the ear.
In the end Mick had wheeled him, but only because
He had pointed the bone at the Wizard of Oz.

'Twas an art he'd been taught by the Bullwaddi blacks,
But the thing he excelled in was following tracks,
He could track a black ant down a bitumen street
And then tell you what grass seeds it took home to eat.
On a horse that could buck Mick would stick like a flea,
When he rode Curio he'd been pretty to see;
He got on her blindfolded with saddle reversed,
But he'd thrown that away when the surcingle burst.

There are some who claim Mick is a terrible liar—
And some say that the devil himself was his sire,
But to question the truth of his tales is unwise,
As the sceptics have learned to their painful surprise.
Now if Mick ever dies, and of that there's some doubt,
I wonder sometimes just how things will turn out;
Where he'd finally end up isn't hard to foretell,
But they'll hear throughout heaven the uproar in hell.

THE TERRITORY ROUSEABOUT

Now Brumby George was broke and sick and looking for a job—
A week before he'd snatched his time and left a travelling mob;
He'd had his spree, and sober now his troubles had begun,
Far from home and stranded in this town of Hughenden.

For Brumby George was born and bred where scrubs are deep and dense,
In God's own land where pikers roam across the border fence.
He'd cut his teeth on bronco ropes, at breaking colts he'd played,
His greenhide whip and Wave Hill spurs were hallmarks of his trade.

And many a ride he'd had at night, when troopers were abed,
Thru distant runs on business that is better left unsaid.
But Brumby George grew tired of life where poddy-dodgers ride,
So with a droving plant he went to 'look about' inside.

And as he tramped those dusty streets from whence all joy had fled,
A shearing team prepared to leave to start at 'Blowfly' shed.
The agent glowered in his door, his thoughts a bitter cup,
In vain he'd tried all over town to find a picker-up.

Just then o'er Brumby's doleful face his searching optics ran,
And as he called the bushman in, he knew he had his man.
The cunning agent rubbed his hands and spoke of added pay,
'Out there,' he said, 'they eat the best and work an eight hour day.'

Now Brumby listened, to his woe, to what the agent said,
Next morning saw him signed and set to start at Blowfly shed.
'Your duties are,' the classer said, 'as shown by the award,
You bring the fleeces here to me and sweep the shearing board.'

Just then the board-boss rang a bell and with a hungry shout,
Five shearers sprang into the pens, each dragged a wether out.
No doubt to Brumby's startled eyes it was a crazy sight,
And then the fleeces light and loose were off to left and right.

Like falling snow the stubborn wool slipped thru his horny hands,
And soon a foot in depth it lay in drifts about the stands.
The classer cursed and screamed for wool to fill the empty bins,
Until devoutly Brumby wished that he'd been born twins.

In high-heeled boots and beaver moles he sprinted down the board,
While 'wool away' and 'tar boy, tar' the grinning shearers roared.
With growing wrath yet icy calm, he let them have their fun,
Until alas, the last straw came, when halfway thru the run.

It may have been a trick of fate, or yet a studied plan,
No one ever found out where the root of it began.
Perhaps the shearers weren't to blame (though shearers mostly are),
Five fleeces all came off at once, and each man yelled for tar.

Then something snapped in Brumby's head, for Brumby went berserk,
He tore a top rail off a pen and with that went to work.
They say that shearers like a stoush where freely flows the gore,
They never had a bolter's chance when Brumby went to war.

He stacked the shearers in a heap, put jackaroos to flight,
The classer, struck behind the ear, was outed like a light.
The 'bogis' freed from nerveless hands went clattering o'er the board,
And like a Scot at Bannockburn, old Brumby smote and roared.

Fresh-shorn sheep went flying by like signals of distress,
In mortal fear the presser-bloke sprang headlong in the press.
Quite calm, the expert grabbed a wrench, he looked a worthy foe,
As Brumby charged with levelled lance, as knights did long ago.

His aim was good, without a doubt the blow was neatly dealt,
The expert with a gentle sigh collapsed across the belt.
The air was thick with oaths and screams and fleeces torn to bits,
When Brumby deftly felled the boss, and cried: 'We'll call it quits.

'I'm going back to Camooweal, and then to further out,
No more I'll tramp your crimson board as ruddy rouseabout.'
And there today old Brumby toils where scrubs are deep and dense,
In God's own land where pikers roam, across the border fence.

Although he's no philosopher, his views have stood the test,
He sticks to beer and bullocks, and to blazes with the rest.
And in his whole vocabulary, without the slightest doubt,
The most soul-searching epithet is 'ruddy rouseabout'.

North Queensland Register

'Old drovers never die, they just keep meeting at reunions.'
Bruce Simpson and Les Teece.

THE TRANSPORTS
TAKE OVER

MARION DOWNS IN the Channel Country introduced road transport for cattle as early as the late 1940s. However, other stations were slow to follow, and droving continued to boom during the 1950s.

Drought and higher cattle prices finally saw the introduction of road trains throughout the cattle industry, and in the early 1960s the long trips from the East Kimberleys to the western half of the Northern Territory stopped forever. Droving did continue, on a drastically reduced scale, on other routes, and today a few mobs still walk into Queensland from the Barkly Tableland.

Disease control has cleaned up herds on the outback runs, and today the demand is for younger beef. As a result, cattle moved now are little more than weaners—a far cry from the big wild store bullocks that once came down the Murranji and other routes in their thousands.

The mechanised replacement for drovers:
a road train at the Victoria River.

And Yet Sometimes . . .

Now the droving is done and no more from the scrub
Come the drovers to camp by the Newcastle pub.
They are gone from the routes with their horses and packs
And the tall grasses blow o'er their deep trodden tracks.
Now there's never a campfire the stockroute along,
For the transports have silenced the night-watcher's song.
And yet sometimes on nights filled with thunder and rain,
In my dreams I am back on the stockroutes again
With a wild restless mob ever ready to rush,
On a camp mid the ant beds and dry underbrush.

'Twas a grim hundred miles down the Murranji track
Where the night camps were bad and the scrublands were black,
A vast wasteland unwanted that seemed without end
From the scrub-covered jump-up to Bucket Creek bend.
Then we prayed for fine weather—a clear autumn sky
When we entered the scrubs of the grim Murranji.
And we doubled the watches and cursed long and plain
When the Murranji met us with thunder and rain,
For when big mobs rushed there, there was little recourse,
Save to trust to your luck and to trust to your horse,
And there many a drover when things went amiss
In the Murranji scrublands faced grim Nemesis.

And the big bullocks knew, for they gave us no rest
As they grudgingly walked from their runs in the West,
For they sulked and they pined for their far distant hills
And they scorned the long troughs at the Murranji mills.
They would moan soft and low for their pandanus springs
And they watched us like hawks from the lead and the wings.
But they'd ring in rebellion and baulk in dismay
When the Mitchell grass plains stretched ahead and away.
Now there's never a campfire the stockroutes along,
For the transports have silenced the night-watcher's song.

There is bitumen now where the big diesels roll
And the dead men grow lonely by Murranji hole.
Now the shy curlews wail and their sad chorus swells
As though missing the music of Condamine bells,
For the droving is done and the drovers no more
String their mobs to the lake by the Newcastle store.
They have hung up their whips and like me settled down
In a job that's secure mid the comforts of town,
And yet sometimes on nights filled with thunder and rain
In my dreams I am back on the stockroutes again,
With a good horse beneath—with the timber a-crack
'Round a mob of wild stores on the Murranji track.

Travelling Stock—1969

Southward the road trains thunder,
*   On through the hours of light,*
Never a halt this morning,
*   Never a rest tonight.*
Hollow, and gaunt and hopeless,
*   Dusty, and dim of eye,*
By night and day on their weary way,
*   The travelling stock go by.*

On through the noon day silence,
*   On through the dust dry air,*
Away with the drought time harvest,
*   The loadings of dumb despair.*
Weary, and weak and wasted,
*   Famished, and sinking fast,*
Two tiers high 'neath a brassy sky,
*   The travelling stock go past.*

PET FOOD

I was passing by in the blazing heat,
Past the transport parked in the empty street,
When I saw the grey in the pet food crate
With a brumby mob that would share his fate.
He appeared to be of the game old breed
With an honest eye and a turn of speed;
We had known the type, we had known their worth
In the cattle country that gave him birth,
But they'd sold the grey, and without regrets
Had consigned his flesh to the city's pets.
Then the truck moved off with its sorry load
And was lost to sight on the Longreach road . . .

That was long ago, but I can't forget,
For the old grey stockhorse haunts me yet,
Standing there betrayed in the heat and flies
With a look of trust in his weary eyes,
With his dumb brute's mind that could never know
Of the lengths to which human greed will go.

Don Dawson, a horse tailer for Jimmy Charles.

DEATH ON THE BARKLY

ONE OF THE worst droughts experienced in the Territory was in 1952. Early in the year I left Camooweal with a packhorse plant en route to Eva Downs. Despite knowing that the Tableland had claimed the lives of many, the trip held no terrors for me; I was confident that I knew the area fairly well, as I had worked for just on two years in the stockcamp on Alexandria and had crossed the Tableland on the stockroute. I had a good mate with me, Bruce Hanson, whom I had worked with on Glenormiston. He was a good ringer but had been away from the game for a few years— and he was no tracker—so it was always my job to do the horsetailing and find horses that were away from the main mob.

With the season being so dry and horse feed so scarce, this was necessary almost every morning. We worked as a team; my mate would be throwing the packs on while I went after the strays. This was not a problem until I developed sandy blight about the time we got to Lawn Creek on Alexandria. Sandy blight can be a real curse in the bush. Every morning it took me a few minutes with a handkerchief and a quart pot of warm salty water to get my eyelids separated. My eye became progressively weaker and reacted strongly to bright sunlight, making tracking lost horses something of a torment, and I found I constantly had to dismount to check tracks.

Horse plant crossing the Barkly River.

I hoped to get something to relieve the curse from Dick Carter at the Rankine store, but he could offer me nothing to relieve the condition of my eyes. When needs must the devil drives, so we kept going. I tied a handkerchief over my eyes and rode blind behind the horses as we moved from camp to camp. Bruce had a go at finding missing horses, and he did his best, but if horses cleared out, Bruce did not know the country, so I decided to carry on.

We camped one night out from a stockroute bore. Next morning there were four horses away. After a quick breakfast of corned meat and damper, I helped Bruce start to pack up. Then I noticed he had a horse we called Match Box tied up. He was usually hard to catch and, being in a hurry most mornings, we had not ridden him a lot. I decided he was over-due for a bit of work and told my mate I would take him to look for the missing horses. I saddled Match Box then filled a waterbag and hung it around his neck.

I told Bruce to go on to the next water when he had finished packing the rest of the horses. As I was confident the strays would not be too far away, I said I would catch him up. I then gave my eyes a quick bathe and rode off. Half blind as I was, it took me the best part of half an hour to pick up where the missing horses had left the main mob. Normally horses that split off will feed around and finish up not too far from the main mob. These four horses, however, seemed to have a definite destination in mind. Their tracks led off almost due west in a fairly straight line. This did make tracking them fairly easy, although I still had to dismount every few hundred metres to check their tracks. I used these moments to bathe my eyes from the waterbag.

After following the tracks for some seven kilometres, I dismounted and, satisfied the missing horses were still ahead of me, I wet my hand-kerchief from the waterbag and squatted down to clear my eyes, a rein lying loosely across one arm. Being hardly able to see, I did not notice the small goanna lying doggo beside me. When I moved, it took off and ran straight up my horse's front leg. There is nothing calculated to give a horse a bigger fright, and Match Box was no different. He pulled away, wheeled around and galloped off, leaving me sitting on the ground clutching a wet handkerchief.

I cursed, stood up and looked for the horse. I could see nothing. The sunlight danced like coloured lights through my misted vision. I scrabbled at my eyes with the hankie and looked again. I still could not see my mount.

I forced myself to remain calm and, crouching down, tried to pick him out against the wavering horizon. With a cry of relief, I saw the dim shape of the horse moving some 200 metres away to my right. He seemed to be heading back the way we had come. I stood up and realised I was still in a dangerous situation. I had to catch Match Box or I was in real trouble. My mate would be off to the next camp and would not miss me until late afternoon. He probably would not take any action until after dark or my riderless horse caught up with the plant. Realising the futility of trying to find me himself, he would be likely to ride to the nearest station for help. Tomorrow would be the earliest a search party could be organised and that could well be too late for me.

It was now almost midday, the sun was nearly overhead, and I was in no condition to walk a hundred metres in a straight line. I had to catch the horse, that was my only chance. I crouched down again and, yes, there he was, still walking back towards the camp we had left. I rose and started walking on a parallel course. I dared not go directly towards him lest he take fright and start trotting. I stumbled on, slowly gaining on my loose mount, resting now and again to clear my eyes with the rapidly drying handkerchief. It took me over half an hour to draw level with the horse. He had thankfully found a little dry grass, so that stopped his progress for a while.

Sandy blight is a debilitating condition, underfoot was loose, dry ground and I was beginning to feel the pinch. I decided it was now or never and I angled in towards the horse, which was still some distance away. Match Box looked at me and walked on. You bastard, I thought, this is a game of life or death and you're playing with me. I began talking to him and gradually edged a little closer. I knew it would be fatal to move quickly, and I was not sure how long I could keep up the pursuit. One eye was almost closed with the strain of looking into the glare. I cursed myself for a fool in riding a horse that I had known was hard to catch.

After a period that seemed like an eternity, I found myself in front of the horse. He was still about 30 metres away, and was looking at me. I sat down and caught my breath. I knew with this particular horse, one false move would undo all my good work.

Finally I stood up slowly and, trying not to stumble, walked slowly forward. Thankfully Match Box stood there until I quietly caught him. I patted him and lent against his shoulder. I was feeling done in and I knew for sure I would have been in trouble getting back on foot.

I bathed my eyes, had a drink of water and again cut the tracks of the missing plant horses. About an hour later I found them in a hollow in the downs. It was almost dark when I got to camp. I kept my misadventure to myself but it was a salutary lesson I never forgot.

Throughout the history of the Northern Territory, living conditions and lifestyle have taken a huge toll of human life. There have been shootings, spearings and other violent deaths inflicted by Territorians on their fellow beings. The Territory was an isolated and inhospitable frontier and, like all rough frontier regions, it attracted hard and often violent types of men.

It was accidental death, however, that claimed the greatest number of victims in the development of the Northern Territory. Of all the ways for a person to die, perishing from thirst is the cruelest. One area of the Territory, the Barkly Tableland, had a grisly reputation for visiting this form of agonising death on the unwary. People died of thirst in many parts of Australia, but it was the Tableland that was the undisputed killer.

On 29 August 1883 a bullocky named Joseph Martins was killed by Aborigines. It was the beginning of a chain of events that would result in the death by thirst of six members of a police party, a catastrophe that sent shock waves through the administration of the Territory. The murder took place at Lawson's Springs, north of Powell's Creek. Martins and his mate John Rees, together with an Aboriginal boy named Gumen, had unyoked the bullocks and had taken them into the spring to water them. After watering the bullocks, they decided to stay at Lawson's Springs that night. A small group of bush Aborigines, who appeared to be friendly, were also camped there.

At about 10.30 p.m. Rees was awakened by a disturbance. He heard Gumen shout out in alarm and, jumping from his swag, saw an Aborigine standing over Martins with a heavy firestick. He fired his revolver at the man, who disappeared. Going over to Martins, Rees found that he had been bludgeoned to death. No motive was reported for the murder. A native woman may have been involved, although the Wagata tribe, whose country encompassed the Attack Creek area, had been known to kill before.

A punitive patrol was organised, led by Mounted Constable Shirley. With him were a number of trackers, as well as John Rees and A.W. Giles, from the Overland Telegraph station at Powell's Creek. Giles, who had a reasonable knowledge of the local Aboriginal language, acted as interpreter. The trackers attached to the patrol picked up the tracks of the suspect group on 22 September. These tracks were followed to north of Newcastle Waters.

While the patrol was temporarily halted on 1 October, the Aborigines attacked. Boomerangs and spears were thrown and were answered with rifle fire. No casualties were inflicted on members of the party and the Aborigines slipped away into the thick Bullwaddy scrub. Rees and Gumen recognised some of the attackers as men wanted for the killing of Martins. The tracks of the wanted group then led south towards Attack Creek.

It was at this point that a rumour concerning the murder of a party of whites began to gain credence. On 5 September Harry Redford, J.F. Uhr, P. Kelly and a man named Macansh had left Attack Creek to travel to Corella Station. The men, all experienced bushmen, had started out at 2 p.m. and faced a dry stage of some 90 miles (144 kilometres). Nothing had been heard of the party since, although this should not have been surprising considering the lack of communications in that part of the world. The commissioner of police was concerned, however, and advised Mounted Constable Shirley to abandon the pursuit of the Aborigines who had killed Martins and investigate the possible murder of Redford's party. On 29 October an enlarged police patrol gathered at Attack Creek. With Constable Shirley were John Rees, A.W. Giles, John Hussey and brothers Arthur and George Phillips. Two police boys were included as trackers, making a total of eight. From this point on the story of the disastrous episode is based entirely on the report of A.W. Giles, the only white survivor.

Shirley intended to follow the tracks of Redford's party, and to shorten the dry stage he went out on the 30th with Rees, Giles and a tracker to try and find water east of Attack Creek. They took two packhorses with them; one of these, an aged horse in poor condition, carried water canteens. The small party travelled about 25 miles (40 kilometres) but found no water, so made a dry camp. Next day, Wednesday 31st, Rees found a native well 6 miles (10 kilometres) past the night camp. There were also some crabholes, or gilgais, around the well. This well became known as Rees's well, and played a major part in the tragedy. The party camped there that night, minus the water canteen horse, which had died during the day.

On Thursday 1 November, Shirley went back to Attack Creek and brought up the rest of the police party. The full patrol then camped at the well. Shirley apparently decided to spend 2 November in a reconnaissance of the area. More crabholes were found 2 miles (about 3 kilometres) to the east of the camp, and Redford's tracks were cut. On the 3rd he moved the patrol out to these crabholes and camped there. The patrol was now over 30 miles (48 kilometres) from Attack Creek. There had been plenty of horse feed around the camps and the patrol should have been in good shape to cover the dry stage ahead.

On Sunday 4 November Shirley led the patrol out from the crabholes and followed Redford's tracks for some 35 miles (56 kilometres). At 7 p.m. the party settled down in a dry camp. The next day, the 5th, things started to go wrong. The patrol left camp at 6.15 a.m. and proceeded along Redford's tracks. Later these tracks were lost and at 3 p.m. the patrol began searching a line of coolabahs in the hope of finding water. Shirley made camp at 5 p.m., having travelled only 25 miles (40 kilometres). In camp he advised the members of the party that he intended to return to Rees's well. There were only 3 gallons (13.5 litres) of water left.

In a very good season a large lake system forms in the Barkly region, covering parts of Anthony's Lagoon, Brunette Downs, Eva Downs and Rockhampton Downs. When these lakes dry back, it is very difficult to get to them; in a bad drought, it is impossible. In 1952 I took a job with the Chambers Brothers on Eva Downs. Most of the lake country was then dry but was covered in blue bush; this is excellent cattle feed. In an attempt to save the Eva herd, the Chambers boys decided to put down bores in the dry lake country. I helped Bill with the boring, using an old percussion plant. I then did the horsetailing, as Alf built the earth tanks with a horse team. It was astute management; the Eva Downs herd was saved. In a good season those bores were metres under water.

Had Shirley known the area, he would not have wasted time looking for water. Before turning back, all swags, heavy gear and the bulk of the rations were placed in trees to lighten the load on the packhorses. At 6.30 p.m., taking only the water and some light rations, the patrol set off to travel all night on the return journey to Rees's well. The party ran into thick scrub and Giles was convinced that Shirley was heading too far to the south. In the early morning he confronted the constable with his belief. After some argument, in which the other members backed Giles, Shirley turned more to the north. The party travelled another 10 miles (16 kilometres) and at 8 a.m. they reached the edge of the plain. Shirley decided to wait there until evening.

The patrol started off on the evening of Tuesday 6th and travelled north-west to try and cut the tracks of their outward journey. Four horses had already died and all the packs were abandoned, together with rifles and other gear. From that point on it must have been a trip through hell. The men struggled on through the night heat of November, with horses collapsing every mile. When there were only three left, Shirley, Giles and George Phillips rode on, leaving the last of the water with Hussey, Rees and Arthur Phillips, who would continue on foot. At around 1 o'clock on the morning of Wednesday 7th, the party's outward tracks were found. All the horses were by then dead. Giles sent one tracker ahead to bring back water and Shirley sent the other Aborigine on the same mission. Giles thought they were still about 14 miles (22 kilometres) from Rees's well. Giles, Shirley and George Phillips struggled on along the tracks on foot.

Giles managed to go on a little way before collapsing under a small bush. He saw no sign of the others and later had little recollection of that day. In the evening he recovered a little and went on about 3 miles (5 kilometres). Hearing a voice, he discovered Shirley under the shelter of a small bush. Shirley was in a bad way. He told Giles that he thought George Phillips was lying dead about 300 metres back. Neither of them had the energy to check. While they were discussing the situation, they heard a faint cooee, and Hussey limped over and joined them; he had been camped close by during the heat of the day. All three men were close to complete exhaustion, and tormented by a terrible thirst. Shirley said he was unable to continue and no amount of encouragement could persuade him to rise. Giles and Hussey shook hands with him and struggled on towards the well, still 11 miles (17 kilometres) away.

Early next morning Giles could see timber about 2 miles (3 kilometres) ahead. Hussey, however, had collapsed and could go no further. Giles made it to the scrub line at about 6 a.m. and there lost consciousness. He came to as the tracker poured water over his head and face. After a drink, he and the tracker faced the last stage into Rees's well. Two miles from the water Giles had to stop and rest. He finally made it into camp at 5 p.m. on Thursday 8 November. It was just five days since he had ridden out from there with the patrol.

Giles had another drink, a wash and a sleep. At 1 o'clock on Friday morning he and the tracker took water back to try and save Hussey and Shirley. Five miles (8 kilometres) out from the well they both could go no further, and after cooeeing without any answer, they returned to the well. At 2 o'clock on Saturday morning Giles and the tracker started out for Attack Creek. They made it in three days. On Tuesday 13 November the wires of the Overland Telegraph Line ran hot with the news of the disaster. Five white men and one tracker had died of thirst. Ironically Redford and his party got to Corella with no difficulty.

It is easy to be wise after the event; however, if Giles's report is to be believed, then the unfortunate Mounted Constable Shirley should never have been in charge of the patrol. The causes that contributed to the debacle are obvious. The water carried by the patrol was inadequate for a party of eight, and more importantly, Shirley was a poor bushman who had little idea of how to cross a dry stage. To have travelled only 100 kilometres in two days and a night in country without water for horses was to invite disaster. As mentioned above, the leader of the patrol wasted hours of valuable travelling time on the second afternoon in a futile effort to find local water. Had he gone on, the patrol would have reached Corella the next day. Instead, with the bulk of the dry stage already behind him, Shirley decided to go back. It was the wrong decision, made worse by his poor navigation that night.

It may be said that having to follow Redford's tracks slowed the progress of the patrol. Perhaps, but that is not hard country. Even after two months had elapsed, any reasonable tracker should have been able to track a mounted party. It was a black week in the annals of the developing Territory, and a stern and early warning that the Barkly suffered fools not at all.

Some 65 years after the death of the six men, the remains of a saddle and two stirrup irons were found on Rockhampton Downs. I believe that Cecil Teece, who was head stockman there at the time, still has one of the irons in his possession. It is almost certain that these relics were part of the gear used by the ill-fated police patrol.

By the 1890s there were a number of cattle stations established on the Tableland. They were dependent, however, on surface water that was not always reliable. In January 1893 an early pioneer of the Tableland named David McKay died of thirst on a dry stretch between Alroy Downs and Brunette. His body was found some 25 kilometres from water. All his horses were dead, and he left a will in the form of a letter to the manager of Brunette.

The turn of the century brought a lengthy drought to the Territory. The Katherine to Anthony's Lagoon mailman, a man named Stibe, perished together with another white man named Hehir and an Aboriginal woman on this treacherous mail run. Harry Redford found the bodies beside holes they had dug with their bare hands.

The waterless stage across the Tableland, from Renner Springs to Eva Downs, was over 100 kilometres, with the only water available at Eva being from a well containing brackish water. To raise this water to the surface, the mailman had to manually work an ancient windlass. I have never tasted water from this well myself, but Alf Chambers told me that the well never improved and was still brackish until abandoned.

The last stage of the mail run was from Eva Downs to Anthony's Lagoon. This stage, although shorter, is just as dry. It was on this leg that Stibe and his companions died of thirst. This hazardous mail service was done by packhorse eight times a year. No wonder the 'Fizzer', who took it on after Stibe's death, was in fear of perishing.

In *Frontier Country*, Glenville Pike tells of another party that perished in January 1902. Four men left Powell's Creek to go to Anthony's Lagoon. The party was travelling in a four-in-hand buckboard, and took along spare horses. The men appear to have strayed off the mailman's track, which is not surprising, for it would not be all that well defined. They were reported missing, and a police search found the vehicle and perished horses about 50 kilometres south of the mail road. The bodies of the men were found some weeks later.

Two drovers, a father and son named Hopkins, perished on the western side of the Rankine River only 6 miles (10 kilometres) out from Shady Camp, a good waterhole that is known to drovers. There is a bit of a mystery about the deaths of the Hopkins. They were drovers and presumably reasonably good bushmen. They must have known the river was east of them, yet when less than 10 kilometres from water, they cut their horses' throats to assuage their thirst—and perished. I have heard rumours that the Hopkins may have been the victims of foul play, and that their deaths were made to look as though they had perished from thirst. It is said they had not long before been paid for the delivery of cattle.

There have been others, too, men who have died horrible deaths alone. A pumper on Alexandria rode away to his death when Jimmy Fowler was running the camp there. Pumpers were employed to look after the diesel engines that drove the pump heads on the sub-artesian bores. This chap's name was Robinson. He had a horse plant at the bore he was looking after, and it is thought he got slewed, lost, looking for horses that had strayed. Despite a prolonged search by Fowler and others, Robinson's body was never found. Another pumper perished on Gallipoli, an outstation of Alexandria. He walked away from the bore in very hot weather when the manager was absent in Camooweal. It was a tragedy that many thought should not have happened.

One man I knew only as 'Spinifex' perished when he was almost in sight of the Georgina River. He was bringing a plant of horses up the river to Camooweal at the end of the year. It is believed Spinifex had been on the grog at Urandangie and this may have contributed to him becoming disorientated. The two big factors in this kind of death are panic and disorientation. Panic prevents clear thinking, and adds to the feeling of disorientation. People who have become lost and disorientated have been known to do crazy things. Their tracks have shown that they have ridden or walked over roads or creeks, and have even climbed through fences, without appearing to realise that each of these could provide a path to safety.

During the 1940s two double tragedies occurred on Rockhampton Downs in the heart of the Barkly Tableland. In the first, which shocked the Territory, a young doctor named Straede, from Tennant Creek, perished together with his wife while travelling on the station to attend a sick woman there. The train of circumstances that led to the double tragedy was a direct result of wartime measures.

Among the evacuees from Darwin after the bombing was a Mrs Jones. Her sons had been at boarding school with the Easey lads from Rockhampton Downs and had spent the school holidays as guests of the manager, George Easey, and his wife. It was natural, then, that Mrs Jones chose to visit the station when she was evacuated. Mrs Jones, however, was suffering from a duodenal ulcer. During her stay at Rockhampton Downs, she haemorrhaged badly and was in urgent need of medical attention. The flying doctor base at Cloncurry was contacted, but there was no plane available: the Qantas planes used by the flying doctor service had been pressed into coastal surveillance duties. Neither Rockhampton Downs nor Cloncurry had direct phone contact with Tennant Creek, the nearest hospital, so the call virtually had to travel around Australia for medical help to be reached.

Dr Straede set out in the afternoon to drive to Rockhampton Downs, taking his young wife with him. The doctor had little or no experience in the bush; however, he did take a 1 gallon (4½ litres) container of water with him. The pair never arrived at Rockhampton Downs.

Due to the torturous nature of communications, George Easey was not aware that the pair was overdue until the afternoon of the next day. He immediately set out in a utility truck, taking his young son Ron with him. The road to Rockhampton Downs ran past a station watering facility named No. 3 bore. The tracks of the doctor's car were not picked up until they were identified arriving at this bore. A large number of cattle were watering there and for a distance of over a kilometre out from the bore the road was obliterated by cattle pads.

After some trouble, they picked up the tracks of the doctor's car leaving the bore. Then began the difficult task of tracking it through the tall grass and rough going. The manager drove while his keen-eyed son stood on the running board and directed his father. A number of times the tracks were lost, but finally, just on sundown, the searchers found the doctor's small English model car. It had a broken petrol pipe.

It was with dismay that George and his son saw the tracks of the doctor and his wife walking away from the vehicle towards No. 3 bore. The tracks were at least 24 hours old and it was getting too dark to attempt to follow them. In any case, as the pair had not reached the bore, George believed it would have been futile. It was apparent to him that the pair had already perished. He decided to return to the station and organise a search the following day.

The authorities in Tennant Creek had been notified at the same time as George Easey. That night the police, plus a friend of the missing pair, arrived at the station. At daylight next morning a full scale search was organised, and Aboriginal trackers found the bodies of the doctor and his wife late that morning. They died 3 kilometres from water at No. 3 bore.

The tracks told the sorry story of the tragedy. Having failed to find the road where it left No. 3 bore, the young doctor headed off in an effort to try and find it. The going was exceedingly rough, with large tussocks of bull mitchell grass and potholes. Doctor Straede drove around in a desperate attempt to pick up the road, but instead of circling back to the bore when he failed to find the road, he drove off in an almost straight line to the north.

It must have been a sickening blow to the young couple when the car's engine stopped. The petrol pipe had snapped, marooning the pair 12 kilometres from the bore they had left earlier. Due to ignorance of bush lore, the unfortunate pair then broke the fundamental rule of survival. They walked away from the vehicle. By then it would have been late afternoon, but it was February and the temperature on the open downs would have been still in the forties. They never stood a chance.

It was a tragedy that would have been averted had they stayed with the vehicle instead of panicking and walking off. There was drinkable water in the radiator of the car, and it would have been cool by the time the water they carried was exhausted. This was adequate, had they remained calm, to last them until rescued. Ironically, there was another station bore under 5 kilometres from where the car had broken down—its sails could be seen through the trees on a supplejack ridge.

The doctor and his wife were buried in Tennant Creek. Mrs Jones was finally airlifted from Rockhampton Downs, but the unfortunate woman died later in the Brisbane Hospital.

I spoke to Ron Easey about the tragedy. It is almost 47 years since Dr Straede and his wife perished, but Ron's memory of the events are still clear and concise. He believes this is because of his age at the time, and the magnitude of the tragedy.

Towards the end of 1949 Rockhampton Downs saw another double tragedy. The Aboriginal women from the homestead decided to go on walkabout, taking with them two young girls of the tribe. The girls were sisters. Londa, the oldest, was about 14 years of age and her sister was a few years younger. The Aborigines expected to find water in a native well or waterhole they knew. When they arrived there, though, there was nothing but dried mud. Ignoring this warning, the party decided to go on further to another well where they were confident they would find water. Their confidence was misplaced, however, for there was no water at the second well either. The party was now in a parlous situation. It was mid-summer and the sun blazed down unmercifully on the scorched earth. The only chance the women had was to make it back to the station bore they had left on their inadvisable excursion.

The women found the going difficult enough, but for the two young girls it was just too much. When the youngest could go no further, she was left beside a wild orange bush. The bush was laden with fruit, but the wild orange does little to assuage thirst. The rest of the party struggled on, the women hoping to get the older girl to the bore. It was futile, however. Londa collapsed less than 2 kilometres from water and by the time the older women returned with some, she was dead.

Possibly because they felt responsible, the women seemed loath to tell what had happened to the two missing girls. When it was finally established that the girls had probably perished, George Easey, the manager, organised a search party and set out to find the bodies. The body of the oldest girl was found first, and later that of her younger sister.

The Tennant Creek police were notified and a constable arrived two days later, together with an official from the Aboriginal settlement at Phillip Creek. The bodies, which had not been disturbed, were inspected and buried where they were found.

I was working in the Gulf when the tragedy occurred. Cecil Teece, who I had known quite well in the Territory, told me about it later. Although some years had passed, I could see that he felt deeply about the tragedy. At the time, he was head stockman on Rockhampton Downs and had a young family himself. Londa had helped his wife with the children.

Peter Treloar, who was jackarooing on Rockhampton Downs when the tragedy occurred, was a member of both the search and the burial party. I met Peter under quite different circumstances. Ray Drummond, a friend of mine at Caboolture, asked me if I would like to help with a bit of branding. I jumped at the chance and we went up to a small cattle place on Delaney Creek. The place was owned by a mate of his, and the mate turned out to be Peter Treloar. After the branding was done, we repaired to the homestead verandah for a cold stubby. As we had all worked on cattle properties, the talk soon turned to cattle. Peter mentioned Rockhampton Downs and I asked him if he knew anything about the girls' deaths. He nodded, passed me another cold one and told me of his involvement as a young jackaroo.

Peter also told me of the narrow escape of a head stockman on Rockhampton Downs before Cecil Teece took over the camp. This chap came very close to perishing when he became lost. He was found in a very bad way, stark naked and burnt almost black by the sun. The shedding of clothing is a common phenomenon in cases where Europeans are almost at the point of dying of thirst.

Most of the people who perished on the Barkly Tableland were adults, and many were bushmen. It was an area that earned its sinister reputation, for it seldom gave a person a second chance.

THE TANK

In the blazing summer of 'eighty-one,
A musterer vanished from Mulga run;
'Twas a tragic story, an oft-told one
Then in the further out.
They found the spot where his stockhorse died,
With a twisted leg in a hole beside;
But to track the rider in vain they tried;
He perished without a doubt.

Thirst-crazed and limping, his stockhorse gone,
With senses reeling he staggered on,
Mocked by a phantom lake that shone,
Where a rough ridge met the plain.
Keep going, keep going, his fevered mind
Urged, keep going you've got to find
Water ahead, there is death behind;
And the mirage gleamed again.

And then as the rough ridge veered askance,
As the heat waves whirled in a fiendish dance,
He staked his all on that final chance,
And, losing, he had to pay.
For then, as always, the mirage lied,
There was nought but mud that was cracked and dried,
In a shallow creek by the ridge's side;
Then sobbing he crawled away.

With bleeding fingers he tore the ground,
Where the twisted roots of the gidgee wound,
But there wasn't water the stockman found,
Where the age-old ridges wait.
And the dingoes knew as they slunk close by,
While the black crows mocked at his strangled cry,
With ghoulish interest they watched him die,
Lest they, too, should be tricked by Fate.

Out there on the black-soil plain today,
Where heat waves shimmer and whirlwinds play,
Mirages beckon and show the way,
To water beside the hill.
And a man might follow it eager eyed,
With dry lips swollen and stumbling stride,
Not seeing the figure in step beside,
To splash there and drink his fill.

For they came to the spot where the stockman prayed,
O'er a dusty hole that his hands had made;
And there with tractor and scoop and blade,
They threw up a giant tank.
The ridge top crowned in dusty wreath,
Flung back the echoes as gleaming teeth
Tore down to the virgin clay beneath,
By the side of the growing bank.

Unknowing they raised ere they went their way,
An incongruous monument formed of clay,
A rippling gem in a glasp of grey,
It stands by the gidgee hill.

WHERE THE PELICAN BUILDS

The horses were ready, the rails were down,
But the riders lingered still—
One had a parting word to say,
And one had his pipe to fill.
Then they mounted, one with a granted prayer,
And one would with a grief unguessed.
'We are going,' they said as they rode away,
'Where the pelican builds her nest!'

They had told us of pastures wide and green,
To be sought past the sunset's glow;
Of rifts in the ranges by opal lit,
And gold 'neath the river's flow.
And thirst and hunger were banished words
When they spoke of the unknown West;
No drought they dreaded, no flood they feared,
Where the pelican builds her nest!

The creek at the ford was but fetlock deep
When we watched them crossing there;
The rains have replenished it thrice since then,
And thrice has the rock lain bare.
But the waters of Hope have flowed and fled,
And never from blue hill's breast
Come back—by the sun and the sands devoured—
Where the pelican builds her nest!

Mary Hannay Foott

WHERE THE
PELICAN BUILDS

DURING THE FIRST half of the last century opinions regarding the centre of our continent differed widely. Many believed it held an inland sea; others, including some men of note, believed it to be a well-watered region, a veritable land of milk and honey, where that ubiquitous bird, the pelican, built its nest. This opinion persisted despite the reports of explorers Edward John Eyre and Charles Sturt. The journeys of John McDouall Stuart in 1861–62 bisected the continent from south to north and his reports did a lot to dispel the fanciful ideas of an inland utopia. In the 1870s Ernest Giles, John Warburton and John Forrest explored west from the centre, while Frank Scarr and W.O. Hodgkinson travelled west from the limits of settlement in Queensland. These expeditions finally wrote finis to the dream of an inland paradise.

In 1877 a trio led by the redoubtable Nat Buchanan travelled from the Buchanan Creek to Attack Creek, then on to Powell's Creek. It was an outstanding feat. On the way from the lower Buchanan to Attack Creek, the party discovered the lake system into which most of the Barkly Tableland streams flow. Surrounded by blue bush and coolabahs, it was a poor substitute for an inland sea, but the closest to it anyone was to find.

Mary Hannay Foott wrote the touching poem 'Where the Pelican Builds'. It was published in her anthology *The Wide Brown Land* in 1885. The verses clearly illustrate the earlier held belief of there being a fertile inland region. Mary was a Scottish lass who came to this country as a child. She later married a grazier named Foott who took up a run he called Dundoo on Yowah Creek, south-west of Charleville.

Mary Hannay Foott's poem may well have been written about the Prout brothers, who disappeared west of the Georgina early in 1878. Mary may have met them; she certainly would have heard of their failure to return.

Coming as it did just 30 years after Leichhardt's disappearance, the fate of Sydney (Cornelius) and Albert Prout was the subject of great debate throughout Queensland. In some reports the elder brother is referred to as Sydney and in others, as Cornelius; I shall refer to him as Cornelius throughout. Cornelius and Albert were the sons of Lieutenant Cornelius

Prout. The boys' father came to the colony as an officer on the HMS *Warspite*. He left the navy and took up a senior job in the administration of the infant colony. Both his sons were born in Sydney and received the best education possible, growing up as accepted members of Sydney society. Although they had little knowledge of the bush, they both had ambitions of becoming graziers so, purchasing a small herd of young cows and some herd bulls, they set out for Queensland to establish a station.

The Prouts, however, had left it too late. The further they went, the more disillusioned they became. The country had all been taken up. In the late 1860s and early 1870s settlement in Queensland had spread west and north like wildfire. In 1875–76 when W.O. Hodgkinson led an expedition to explore the country between the Diamantina River and the Northern Territory border, a great deal of the area had already been taken up, for the squatters had outstripped exploration on much of the frontier.

In 1877 the Prouts finally arrived at King Creek, a tributary of the Georgina. There they settled on a small block south-west of Boulia. The block on King Creek was not the grand station that the Prout brothers had dreamed of and Cornelius and Albert decided to search further out. Leaving the run, they rode out to the Mulligan River. Beyond the Mulligan was semi-desert populated by unfriendly Aborigines, but at Lake Amaroo, just west of the Mulligan, Herbert Downs had established an outstation. Bitterly disappointed, the Prout brothers returned to their small holding. But the dream of owning a large station still inspired the two brothers.

They decided they would have to go further out past the Georgina and the Mulligan and there, perhaps, they would find what they wanted. When news of Nat Buchanan's successful journey reached the Prouts later in 1877, it may well have motivated them to action. On 2 December 1877 the Prout brothers set out westwards. With them was a white stockman named Baker and an Aborigine from the Diamantina area. They took a plant of more than 20 horses, with adequate rations for some months. They were possibly trying to emulate Nat Buchanan, to find unknown pastoral areas and to establish a route through to the Overland Telegraph Line. However, none of the party had the skills and the experience of Buchanan. Moreover, it was far too late in the year to attempt such a journey. The heat out there in December is a killer. None of the party ever returned.

William Henry James Carr-Boyd was with Hodgkinson's expedition of 1875–76. A commanding figure of a man with a huge appetite for life and

Ian Tinney

Ruins of Amaroo Outstation.

a well-developed liking for rum, Carr-Boyd was an adventurer who revelled in life on the frontier. He had a fine voice, was a renowned campfire raconteur and wrote to the Southern papers using the nom de plume of 'Potjostler'. Above all else, Carr-Boyd was an excellent bushman.

In 1878 Carr-Boyd was at Amaroo helping in the search for a missing man named Greensmith, who had apparently been murdered by Aborigines. When he heard that the Prouts were missing, he wrote to the *Queenslander*, stating that they would be found 140 miles (approximately 225 kilometres) west of Amaroo. He added that for £1000 he would find them if it was at all possible. He stated that he had earlier met 'Sydney' Prout and Baker and advised them to head for Mount Harriet, some 40 miles (64 kilometres) north-west of Amaroo. He also told them where to find water. Mount Harriet is one of two peaks known as twin hills; its sister peak is Mount Kate. There is a waterhole south of the hills named Marked Tree waterhole, which should not be confused with Mark Tree hole on the Georgina. The tree near the twin hills could have been marked by Hodgkinson, and no doubt Carr-Boyd knew the area. Carr-Boyd added that he had found a camp of the party's en route to Mount Harriet.

The disappearance of the Prout brothers caused general concern among the settlers of far western Queensland. In mid-1878 Frank Scarr, a surveyor, and an official with the Queensland Crown Lands Department, led an expedition to establish a route from the Georgina to the Overland Telegraph Line. In his first unsuccessful attempt, he travelled up Pituri Creek, a tributary of the Georgina. At a waterhole approximately 100 miles (160 kilometres) up Pituri Creek, he found evidence of the Prout party. The waterhole is in Manners Creek, a tributary of Pituri Creek.

According to Scarr, it lies approximately 22 degrees 17 minutes south and 137 degrees 40 minutes east. At the waterhole Scarr found a pair of moleskins split up the legs, stained with what looked like blood. He also found a shirt still twisted as though it was being wrung out when dropped. Several bits of a blue blanket, bits of calico and pieces of a felt hat were picked up as well. While he was there, horses came in to water. They had badly marked backs, as though they had been running free while saddled. According to Scarr, it appeared that the saddles had slipped under the horses' bellies and the girths had cut into their backs. These horses were branded C6P and were later identified as belonging to the missing party. Scarr, who obviously had little time for Aborigines, believed that the whites had been surprised and killed. He stated that he thought the 'natives' had eaten the bodies, and later had either burnt the bones or had carried them away.

Scarr then proceeded on his original mission, but was forced back and turned east to the Georgina. He later won through to Tennant Creek on a more northerly route.

Late in 1878 an agreement was reached between Carr-Boyd and Mr P. McGuigan, of Davenport Downs. Carr-Boyd was commissioned to search for the Prouts. The Prouts and Baker had been missing for a little over 12 months—they had expected to return within three months of leaving King Creek. According to Carr-Boyd, McGuigan would have initiated the search earlier but for the presence of two native police patrols in the area. He had expected them to undertake the task. A situation resembling guerilla warfare existed at that time on the Queensland frontier. The same month Carr-Boyd and McGuigan met, a settler named Molvo and his party had been wiped out north of Boulia. Earlier a station hand, Greensmith, had been killed out from Amaroo and James McCromarky, a station manager, had been speared to death at an outstation on the Diamantina. There were, of course, others.

The agreement between Carr-Boyd and P. McGuigan was signed on 29 December 1878 at Davenport Station. For his part, Carr-Boyd was to undertake a seven week search for the Prouts, taking with him one white man and 10 horses. What McGuigan's commitment was Carr-Boyd never spelt out—it may have been the £1000 he had nominated earlier.

Carr-Boyd ignored the condition regarding the white man. He selected instead, John Stokes, an Aborigine. Also with him was another Aborigine named Davey who acted as interpreter. Carr-Boyd wrote in his report that Stokes was reliable and one of the best bushmen he knew, and that he had been with Scarr. Carr-Boyd was quick to point out, however, that the success of the venture was due to him, not Stokes. Carr-Boyd was not renowned for his modesty and he, of course, wrote the report, a significant advantage, as most people would know.

The trip did not get off to a good start. Obtaining the horses proved to be a real headache and valuable time was lost. Carr-Boyd had left Davenport with an authority from McGuigan to pick up 10 horses belonging to the Prouts. These horses were running on an outstation of Glengyle west of the Georgina which was managed by a man called Colvin. The outstation was probably Sandringham. Colvin refused to hand over the horses, telling Carr-Boyd he would have to go to the head station and get permission from Campbell, the manager. Carr-Boyd rode down the river to Glengyle to find Campbell absent and the relieving manager as recalcitrant as Colvin.

Finally Carr-Boyd did obtain three horses from Colvin and another two from a man called McHatter. Carr-Boyd helped him rescue two station boys kidnapped by a group of some 200 Aborigines. He then set out with six horses and headed for Pituri Creek. At Idamea (Glenormiston) he obtained another horse plus a gun and rations. He left there with seven horses, John Stokes and two other Aborigines.

At the end of the first day's travelling Carr-Boyd camped at Lake Wanditta, which he described as being over 3 kilometres long by almost 1 kilometre wide. About 100 Aborigines were also camped there and next morning Carr-Boyd rounded them up and interrogated them. He wanted to know two things: was there any water further up the creek, and did they know anything of the missing party. Davey advised Carr-Boyd that according to the Aborigines there was no water at all up Pituri Creek, and that they had heard white men had been killed up there, but there was no water at the place. Carr-Boyd knew from past experience that there was water 110 kilometres further up in Manners Creek, a tributary of Pituri,

Lloyd Lindon-Smith

Lake Wanditta in a dry season.

and decided further questioning was futile. Carr-Boyd always referred to Pituri Creek and its main tributary as Manners Creek.

Pituri Creek is on Glenormiston Station. In 1947–48 I worked there as a stockman. On a number of occasions during that time I was involved in musters along Pituri Creek and around Lake Wanditta. The lake was not then the pristine body of water seen by Carr-Boyd. Cloven-footed animals have a disastrous effect on the fragile top soil of the inland; silting caused by 70 years of cattle grazing had reduced the capacity of Lake Wanditta. In 1947–48 no Aborigines fished or gathered mussels there—no campfires glowed along the banks and no corroborees echoed across the silent water from the fringing coolabahs. I found plenty of evidence of past tenure, but the proud Wonkajerras, custodians of the Pituri tree, had vanished, leaving behind neither kith nor kin.

Before he left Wanditta, Carr-Boyd persuaded an Aboriginal youth to accompany him. How gentle the persuasion is left to the imagination. Carr-Boyd put him on a packhorse and drove him along with the horses. Three miles (5 kilometres) from the camp the party saw a creek, which Carr-Boyd describes as coming in from the south-west. In his report he said this was Kelly's Creek. He was obviously wrong about this, unless names have changed, for it could only have been Linda Creek. To say it came in from the south-west is a bit puzzling; however, he ran the creek up for 50 kilometres and would have seen its course higher up.

Carr-Boyd's decision to go up Linda Creek was fortunate. On the return journey he found Pituri Creek dry for 80 kilometres above the junction with Linda Creek. Some 16 kilometres up Linda Creek they came to a good waterhole. Another 10 kilometres up was another smaller hole. Here Carr-Boyd decided to dismiss his Aboriginal guide, who he said in his report was full of humbug. The party then travelled another 24 kilometres and camped at a fine waterhole. Next day Carr-Boyd struck out to the north-west and, after travelling 50 kilometres, arrived at a hole in Manners Creek where both Hodgkinson and Scarr had previously camped.

The following day another 50 kilometres brought them to the water-hole where Scarr had found the horses and other evidence of the Prouts' presence. Carr-Boyd searched the area and found a packsaddle near the hole, but found nothing of the clothing and blanket mentioned by Scarr. Carr-Boyd also found a marked tree with the following cut into it: '25/7/78' over 'F. SCARR' over '111' over 'WHITES MURDERED' over '5 HORSES C6P' over 'GOT SUPP' over 'PARTY'. Carr-Boyd then cut his own mark in the tree. It must have been a very big tree.

At this point in his report Carr-Boyd wrote that no explorer need have any fear of the blacks in the area. The secret, he added, was knowing how to deal with them, but did not elaborate. As it seemed obvious that the Prouts had been killed or had perished, Carr-Boyd was keen to obtain help from the local tribe in locating their remains. As no Aborigines came to the waterhole, he set out alone in a westerly direction to find either another creek or to contact 'natives'. He was unsuccessful on both counts and returned to camp. The next day Carr-Boyd sent John Stokes and one of his boys down Manners Creek to see if they could make contact with a tribal group they had seen on the way to their present camp. Stokes came back with the news that a large group had camped 8 kilometres down the creek the night before, but had gone before they arrived. Their tracks led off in a westerly direction. Stokes followed the tracks for 16 kilometres—they came quite close to Carr-Boyd's camp—then Stokes returned.

Next morning Carr-Boyd packed up and set out to track the Aborigines. Picking the tracks up where Stokes had left them, the party travelled another 16 kilometres in a west-south-west direction. They then saw two old Aboriginal women gathering nardoo on the downs. A line of timber was not far off and the women made for this to join the rest of the tribe. Carr-Boyd rounded up the old women, let the rest go, and made a temporary camp for a meal. When questioned, the two women did nothing but yell and howl; Carr-Boyd then let one go and concentrated on the other. Finally she admitted through Davey that she knew of a place where white man's bones were, together with saddles and clothes. It was, she said, a long way away and laughed at the idea of the party getting there that night.

Carr-Boyd was getting short of rations and was keen to get the business over. He packed up, and put the woman on a horse. She led them due west, and after they had travelled 45 kilometres, the downs ended and they came to a gorge. Carr-Boyd described this as being very pretty. The party went up a creek in the gorge and after 4 kilometres came to a waterhole. Carr-Boyd wrote that this water was about the worst he had ever tasted. As it was by this time almost dark, they made camp. The old Aboriginal woman told them that the site where the remains were was not far off.

Next morning Davey told Carr-Boyd that the old woman knew nothing of white man's bones. She had, he said, led them away so the tribe would not be harmed. Carr-Boyd advised her through Davey that if she did not show them the place, he would wipe out the tribe. John Stokes believed that Davey was the problem. He raced at the interpreter with a spear and, grabbing him by the throat, threatened to kill him unless he spoke the truth. Davey saw the light and the old woman led the party on. According to Carr-Boyd, they had only travelled some 5 kilometres up a blue bush flat when he spotted the remains of a camp over to his right. On investigation, the skeletal remains of Cornelius Prout, together with those of a horse, were found. Two packsaddles and packbags, a riding saddle and various camp equipment were scattered about, as well as a blackened billy can that had the words 'no water yet' scratched on it. Among the scattered gear were items identified as belonging to A.E. Prout, and a letter addressed to Albert Prout from his mother. It appeared that a bushfire had been over the camp. Carr-Boyd also found a tattered diary with the last entry dated 26 January 1878, less than two months since starting out.

From the diary, Carr-Boyd gleaned that the Prouts had travelled through a great deal of country previously unknown to whites. Apparently they had been travelling due east for two days trying to get back to Manners Creek. Baker had been there twice before, but the Prouts must have turned south-east and travelled 30 kilometres along a blue bush flat that ran almost parallel with Manners Creek, when they were, in fact, no more than that distance from the creek itself. It had, according to Carr-Boyd, been a fatal mistake. He reconstructed the tragedy as follows. With most of the horses knocked up, Cornelius Prout had stayed at the camp while Baker, and his brother (Carr-Boyd does not mention the Aborigine who was with them) went to look for water. The pair then made another mistake by turning south instead of following the flat down to the creek in the gorge. Carr-Boyd does not say whether he gained this information by following tracks, or by deduction. Had they continued on down the flat, he claimed, they would have reached the hole in Manners Creek within 50 kilometres.

Cornelius Prout's body was identified by its size and a dint in the skull from a previous accident. As Carr-Boyd found no evidence of attack by Aborigines, it appears that Cornelius died of thirst while waiting vainly for the others to bring back water. He must have gone through absolute hell. Few people can imagine the torment of thirst and despair he would have endured before death claimed him.

Carr-Boyd spent half a day vainly searching for Albert Prout and Baker. The Aboriginal woman took him to a creek where she said the bones of two white men had been burned. Carr-Boyd took this creek to be part of Kelly's Creek. As rations had just about run out and the water was foul, he stayed no longer. Carr-Boyd gathered the remains of the elder Prout with most of the personal items and started back to Manners Creek. He reached Idamea in three days, and eight days later Carr-Boyd delivered Cornelius Prout's remains to Mr McGuigan at Davenport Downs as per the agreement.

Carr-Boyd's description of distances travelled and his direction of travel may cause some confusion; for instance, after cutting the tracks out from the camp at Manners Creek, he travelled a total of 70 kilometres to the death site, yet wrote that it was only 50 kilometres back to the waterhole. The discrepancy may be explained by the route taken to get to the site, and by the fact that distance between points was calculated by time travelled multiplied by the estimated rate of progress per hour.

On Carr-Boyd's return, the mystery of the Prout brothers' disappearance had been solved, it seemed, but a lot of unanswered questions remained. Did Albert Prout and Baker die of thirst or were they killed by Aborigines? Was the Aboriginal woman telling the truth about the remains on Kelly's Creek? How did the saddle-marked horses get to the waterhole in Manners Creek? Who was disturbed while wringing out the shirt Scarr found? Did Baker and Albert Prout get to that waterhole, or was it only one of them?

It may seem futile to attempt to answer those questions, yet if the known facts are analysed objectively a clearer picture may emerge:

1. No known white men had been in the area of Manners Creek since Hodgkinson's expedition.
2. The horses at the hole in Manners Creek definitely belonged to the Prout brothers.
3. Two packs were found at the death scene; the Prouts would have had more. A pack was found by Carr-Boyd at the waterhole.
4. According to the diary found by Carr-Boyd, the Prouts had been trying to reach Manners Creek.
5. A partly wrung-out shirt was found at the waterhole by Scarr, together with scraps of blanket and a pair of moleskin trousers stained with what appeared to Scarr to be blood.
6. Scarr stated that the horses' backs were badly saddle marked, as if the saddles had rolled and been that way for some time.

Conclusion: 1. Some of the Prout party did reach the waterhole, and 2. A white man, or white men, had been surprised there and possibly killed by Aborigines in the vicinity.

The country west of Pituri Creek is fairly inhospitable, but Baker was a good bushman who had been in the area before. On the evidence, then, Baker or Albert Prout, or both of them, did reach the waterhole in Manners Creek. If this is so, however, his or their behaviour there raises other questions. Why would anyone spend precious time in washing a shirt when a man dying of thirst was dependent on having water taken back to him?

Here we must abandon fact and rely purely on speculation. A possible explanation could be that the death of Cornelius Prout was already known to whoever was at the waterhole. One could speculate further on how this may have been known, but speculation is, at best, dangerous ground. The facts relating to the final chapter of the tragedy will never be known.

ROCKY CREEK

The rain swept down on the streaming bush as the lightning lit the road,
Where the big truck sped like a charging bull, head down with its
two-tier load.
Young weaner steers from a basalt run en route to the southern sales,
A day and night on the Queensland roads then on into New South
Wales.
The downpour lashed at the cabin glass and the wheel spray billowed
wide
From the runoff water across the road that spread like a rising tide.

The lights of a township gleamed and neared through the wipers' frantic
beat,
And the truckie eased on the brakes and stopped by the pub in the only
street.
He checked his load in the driving rain, then ran from his big machine,
As he crossed the floor the barman saw he was built like a brick latrine.
He shook the rain from his shaggy head as he called for a pot of beer.
'It's nasty weather,' the barman said, 'are you thinking of camping
here?'

'Just a couple of drinks,' the truckie said, 'and then I'll be on me way,
These weaners are wanted in New South Wales and I don't mean
yesterday.
The rain won't worry this rig of mine, when I'm hauling a livestock
load,
She'll plough through water a metre deep as long as there's still a road.'
'Then take it easy,' the barman said, 'when you get down to Rocky Creek,
It's been raining back in the ranges now for almost a flaming week.

'It's one of those creeks you can never trust, as most of the locals know,
The last of the packhorse mailmen drowned in a flood there years ago.
The mails were a sacred trust to him and a duty he'd never fail,
I've heard it said you could set your watch on time with the packhorse
mail.
He lost his life on a night like this, he'd battled through miles of mud,
With never a qualm or a backward glance he tackled the Rocky flood.

'It was running a banker then, I'm told, and it swept with a sullen roar
As the mailman swam with the Royal Mail as often he'd done before.
He was halfway over the raging stream, the current was running strong,
When a tree came rolling down Rocky Creek as a flood crest swirled along.
The man and his horses had no chance, it was curtains for Tom McHugh,
He drowned upholding the service code: "The mail must be taken through."

'They say his ghost can be often seen when the stars wink cold and pale,
As he rides the reaches of Rocky Creek still trying to save the mail.'
The truckie grinned at the barman then. 'That's a damn good yarn, no sweat,
I've seen some sights on the flamin' road but a ghost I have never met.
Well, I'm out of here and I won't pull up 'till I meet with the morning light,
And I won't be swimming that flamin' creek, I will cross by the bridge tonight.'

The truckie settled behind the wheel for a night that would hold no sleep,
The miles slipped by and the rain eased off, but the gullies still ran deep.
The big rig cruised from the timbered ridge to the scrublands down below
As the truckie tapped on the steering wheel in time with the radio.
The airwaves carried a country song, on life 'neath the western sky,
When a man rode out of the scrub ahead with his right arm held on high.

The truckie gasped as he hit the brakes and sounded a warning blast,
But the horseman turned to the speeding truck, with the gap now closing fast.
The truckie cursed as he dropped a gear, then he dropped a cog again,
The gear box heaved as it took the load and it howled like a thing in pain.
He rode the brakes 'till the trailer slewed and some of the weaners fell,
But the man rode straight at the swaying truck like a horseman straight from hell.

With the trailer skidding behind the rig and a madman right ahead,
The truckie knew that all hope he had of avoiding a crash had fled.
He braced himself for the coming prang, but the high beam headlights
shone
Through the ghostly face of a man long dead, then the rider and horse
were gone.
The blood ran cold in the truckie's veins and the cold sweat wreathed
his brow,
But he eased the brakes on the slowing truck and he kept control
somehow.

He kept control with his mind awhirl. If the barman's tale was true,
Then the bearded rider who blocked his path was the spirit of Tom
McHugh.
He drove on slowly around a bend, to be met with a chilling scene,
For a raging torrent in Rocky Creek roared past where the bridge had
been.
He hit the brakes 'till the tyres planed, and he thought of his kids and
wife,
And he prayed as the trailer jack-knifed round, for another chance in
life.

The truck slid on as the truckie's hands froze stiff on the wheel with
fright,
But the big rig stopped on the very brink with the trailer still upright.
The truckie looked at the cold grey flood that almost had been his
shroud,
Then his head dropped onto the steering wheel and the big man sobbed
aloud.
He landed down at the sales at last, though he got there three days late,
And well he knew he'd been guided there by more than the hand of
fate.

He may have imagined the ghost, he owns, for hallucinations can
Play wilful tricks in the dead of night on the mind of a weary man.
He stays down south of the border now, but at times he will quietly
speak
Of the fateful night when his big rig stopped by the torrent in Rocky
Creek—
How he fought the wheel as the tyres planed and he cursed at his
slewing load
When the ghost of a mailman saved his life in the rain on a northern
road.

DANGEROUS WATERS

I REINED THE grey mare up at the bank of the channel. It would be a swim, I knew, but not a difficult one. It was still water, but still or dead water can be more treacherous at times than a strong current. If you swim diagonally across a running stream, the current can help to pull you across, but in dead water the swimmer has to depend entirely on his own efforts. I had every confidence in the mare, however, as I had been swimming her over many such channels for the past week or so and she had demonstrated she was a steady and reliable mare in water.

As in most situations, familiarity breeds contempt, and I put the mare into the water without stripping off my clothing, an omission that has proved critical in many swimming fatalities. The mare negotiated the swim quite well, but on facing the opposite bank she panicked and reared over backwards. I failed to get completely clear and found myself pinned to the bottom with the mare across my legs. She struggled and, in getting up, struck me a heavy blow on the shoulder with one hoof.

When I finally managed to reach the surface, my lungs were bursting, and I crawled up the bank to where my bedraggled mount was standing. The mare's legs were trembling and so were mine, for I realised just how close I had come to drowning. Had the mare struck me on the head rather than on the shoulder, I would have still been at the bottom of the channel.

Two very well known characters in the Northern Territory met their death by drowning. Henry Peckham, the 'Fizzer' of *We of the Never Never* fame, was drowned in the Victoria River in April 1911 and well-known cattle duffer Harry Redford, or Readford, drowned at Corella waterhole on Brunette Downs in the Northern Territory on 12 March 1901. Peckham was doing his first trip on the Katherine to Victoria River Downs mail run. Earlier he had been the mailman on the notorious Katherine to Anthony Lagoon run, a hazardous trip on which death from thirst was a constant threat. Peckham had a terror of perishing in this way, so it is ironic that he met his death in water. The Fizzer was buried at the crossing where he drowned. Later his body was removed and buried in the Elsey Cemetery.

Harry Redford won dubious fame as the man who stole the mob of cattle from Mount Cornish Station near Longreach and drove them to South Australia. At his trial the jury must have considered the feat to be greater than the crime, for they failed to convict him. The theft was

The grave of the 'Fizzer' at the Elsey Cemetery.

immortalised in the book *Robbery Under Arms* by Rolf Boldrewood. Redford's swag and gear, minus a bridle, was found at Corella waterhole by James Hutton on 13 March, the day after he had drowned. On the 14th Harry Redford's naked body was found in the water. He had apparently drowned while swimming across to get his horses; perhaps he got tangled in the bridle. His grave is beside the creek, while the remains of his homestead lie on the low ridge beyond.

Almost all drownings in inland waters have occurred while men have been on the job, or as a result of unexpectedly high floods generated by unusually high rainfall. In late December 1916 and early January 1917 torrential rain fell in Queensland. The ensuing floods resulted in fatalities from the Gulf Country to Clermont, a bush town situated approximately 160 kilometres north-west of Rockhampton. Thomas Humphries, an 18-year-old stockman, was drowned while crossing the Gilbert River on horseback. The Gilbert was just one of the northern streams that rose to record heights in the 1916–1917 floods. Gerado Daimaz, a surveyor's offsider, was swept to his death by the Gilliat River. Torrential rain over four days at Mount Emu sent floods roaring down tributaries of the Flinders River. Five members of the Jenkinson family were drowned when their home was swept away by the waters of Betts Creek. The survivors, two sons and two daughters, were saved by John, aged 22, who knocked

Ted Egan

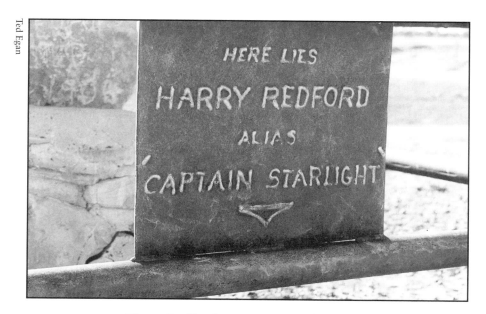

Harry Redford's grave at Corella Creek.

sheets of iron off the roof, giving the others access to it. The building was carried onto trees to which the young people clung until the flood receded.

The Duncans of Rosevale may well have shared the fate of the Jenkinson family if they had not taken the advice of an old Aborigine and spent the night on higher ground. Next morning their home was gone. At Hughenden the flood swept through the streets at record heights, drowning a young girl on the outskirts of the town when she and her parents tried to reach a neighbour's property.

On the night of Wednesday 27 December, rainfall of over 20 inches (approximately 500 millimetres) was recorded in the Clermont and Capella area. Properties were inundated as creeks rose in record flood. A settler on Theresa Creek perished with his family. This creek, which drained most of the rain-affected areas, spread to 7 miles (11 kilometres) wide on its way to join the Nogoa River. At Peak Vale, a station situated near the foot of the Drummond Range, a tributary of Theresa Creek swept through the property in the early morning of the 28th. As the floodwater rose in the homestead, Mr W.R. Tindale, the manager of Peak Vale, together with his wife, six children and Vincent Appleton, a visitor, retreated to the top floor. From that vantage point they watched as one

Ted Egan

Bruce Simpson, left, *and Eugene Costin
at the grave of Harry Redford.*

after another the station outbuildings were carried away in the torrent. Helpless, they saw the men's huts swept away, drowning an employee by the name of Simpson. Finally the family were forced to build rafts, and took refuge on them until the water receded.

Stockmans' Hall of Fame

North of Hughenden flood, 2 January 1917.

At the Glen, a selection about 20 kilometres from Clermont, Miss Lily Anderson had a narrow escape. She was warned to go to high ground by an Aborigine, the only other person on the place, but she disregarded the advice and was in the house when it was swept from its stumps. She survived by clinging to a door for some 13 hours.

It was Clermont itself, though, that bore the brunt of the flood. In one of the greatest disasters in our history, over 60 residents lost their lives. Part of the town was then built in a bow of Sandy Creek, which ran around the outskirts of the town; a lot of the streets were low lying and some buildings were on the edge of a lagoon that was probably once part of the creek's straighter course. The flood of 1870 had caused both damage and fatalities in the low area between the lagoon and the creek. Wolfang Creek joined Sandy Creek just above the bow where Sandy Creek turned northwards around the town. Wolfang Station had recorded 24 inches (580 millimetres) in 14 hours on the night of the 27th. At daylight on the 28th, Sandy Creek was seen to be in flood, but had not then broken its banks.

The Clermont police warned people living in the low areas, but apparently few took notice of this warning until it was too late. A short time later, huge flood crests in Sandy and Wolfang Creeks met and swept through the town to the lagoon and beyond. A man standing on a verandah on the high side of the lagoon saw the huge flood wave and cried out that the sea had broken through to Clermont. To many it must have seemed like this was true. The floodwater rose at the rate of 3 metres an hour, the main street was inundated, buildings were swept away and many people, trapped by the rapidity of the rise, were drowned.

Miss Rose Harris and her father saved the lives of five men by throwing ropes to them from the top storey of their saddle shop as they were being swept down the street to certain death. A number of residents climbed to the ceilings of business houses, crouching there in terror as the buildings shuddered and swayed in the torrent below. Many took refuge on the top floor of hotels. One enterprising horse had similar ideas; it made its way up the stairs of the Grand Hotel and saw the flood out from the top storey. Getting it back to ground level after the flood passed posed a problem, however, until he was finally backed down the stairs.

Few bushmen swam for pleasure. Apart from bathing, outback water-ways held little attraction for stockmen. There is always the exception to the rule, of course, and one tragic instance of this involved twin brothers, both stockmen, who lost their lives while swimming in the Wallam River near Bollon in south-west Queensland. One lad got into difficulties and his brother went to his assistance, resulting in both of them drowning.

The number of bushmen who could not swim has always surprised me, although the ability to swim would not have saved men whose horses caused their death. The list of drowning fatalities that follows is far from complete; however, it gives details of typical outback tragedies.

In 1943 Eric Houghton, a young stockman, drowned while at work crossing cattle at the Georgina River at Camooweal. Vic Stanfield, whom I knew quite well before he became a boss drover, also died in similar circumstances. He was a good type of chap, who, I believe, could swim. When he was a drover in charge of a mob of fat cattle en route to Butru, he was drowned in the Burke River at Picnic Point, just above Boulia. It was not known precisely what happened, but Vic's horse may have got into difficulties crossing the waterhole. When horses panic in water, they behave much like a drowning man and will strike the water, and any object they see, in an attempt to get a foothold. A stockman with Vic saw Vic's riderless horse leave the water and he galloped to the drover's camp, where he told Eugene Costin what had happened. Costin mounted a horse and galloped to the spot where Stanfield had disappeared. There he aided the police in recovering the drover's body.

Most of the inland rivers have claimed victims at one time or another. A young Aboriginal stockman was drowned in the Diamantina when he swam his horse over the river to get some horses that had strayed. A young chap named Fuller, a cousin of the well-known Sam Fuller, was drowned at Abbieglasse in the Wallam. He had ridden into the river after plant horses. The Wallam claimed another victim when a chap known only as 'Buckjump Charlie' drowned near Bollon while swimming his horse over to his camp late one evening. It is believed his horse struck him when it got into difficulties, a common cause of many deaths by drowning.

Linked with outback drownings are the many stories of courageous rescues and rescue attempts. William 'Jack' Oates, aged 35, was a boss drover and a member of a well-known Jundah family. Early in 1956 he was offered a mob of cattle from Bulloo Downs to Broken Hill. When Oates arrived at the station, the mob was not ready, so the drover met the stockcamp on 12 February at Onibootra waterhole. As the drover's plant arrived at the stockcamp, cattle on the opposite side of the hole were disturbed. The Bulloo head stockman shouted to his men to mount up and get the cattle before they got into the thick lignum. Being already mounted, Oates volunteered to help and the party rode down along the waterhole to where it narrowed. It was urgent that the crossing be made quickly, so all the men went into the water fully clothed and with boots and leggings.

The swim was a considerable distance, and halfway over, the horse Oates was riding got into trouble. The drover left his horse as it began striking and plunging, and shortly after, the others saw him disappear. Although fully dressed himself, 17-year-old Bob Findlay left his horse and went to assist Oates. Diving down, he brought the unconscious drover to the surface and started to swim with him to the bank. It was a herculean task and Findlay, although exhausted, refused to let Oates go. The head stockman left his horse to help, but in the changeover Oates slipped away. Findlay came very close to drowning himself, only just managing to reach the bank.

The drover's body was found three days later, caught in the roots of a coolabah tree downstream from where he was lost. The body was removed, placed on a sandhill and covered with bushes to keep dingoes away. One of the stockmen rode into Bulloo Downs Station with the tragic news and the police at Thargomindah were notified. Due to flooded roads, however, the Queensland police could not get to Bulloo, so the New South Wales police at Tibooburra were notified and finally arrived at Onibootra waterhole three days after the body was recovered.

Jack Oates was finally laid to rest on the sandhill. He was buried in his swag and with his boots on. The Royal Humane Society of Australia awarded Bob Findlay its certificate for bravery. Bob now lives at Thargomindah and for some years has been the town's common ranger.

The rivers running into the Gulf of Carpentaria can be death traps in flood, with the fall of these streams far greater than that of inland rivers. Heavy rain on the watersheds of these streams send floodwaters roaring down to the Gulf coast. In 1937 the rainfall was unusually heavy and the Leichhardt, Flinders and other rivers all rose in full flood. In a camp on the bottom end of Clonagh Station, north of Cloncurry, a fencer's wife and two children found themselves trapped by the rising waters of the Corella River. The party phone lines were down and communications were almost non-existent, but word of their plight was received at nearby Cubberoo Station.

Jimmy 'Ringer' Edwards was breaking in horses at Cubberoo and immediately went to the rescue of the stranded family. To bring the fencer's wife and children across the flood, Edwards constructed a boat by upturning a table on a tarpaulin and securing the flaps of the tarp up and over the table. Placing the family in the makeshift boat, Jimmy Edwards towed and pushed the crude but life-saving craft across the flood to safety. It was a fine example of chivalry, guts and bush ingenuity.

At approximately the same time further over to the east, two men attempted to swim their horses across the flooded Flinders River at Black Sam's crossing, just below the town of Richmond. Ted Malone and his mate, another Jimmy Edwards, may have taken the swim rather casually for both were fully dressed when they put their horses into the flood. As in many other cases, the horse ridden by Edwards panicked and began to plunge and strike. Jimmy Edwards disappeared—whether he was struck by the horse is not known, but, being fully clad, he had little chance in a river like the Flinders.

There is a rather tragic footnote to this story. News reached Cloncurry, where the drowned man's family lived, that a Jimmy Edwards had been drowned, but no one knew which one. That is until a few days later when 'Ringer' Edwards rode into the town. One of the children of the drowned man saw Edwards and ran inside crying out that it must have been his dad who had drowned, as he had just seen the other Jimmy Edwards.

All these work-related fatalities occurred when men were swimming horses while mounted. Stockmen have good reason for preferring this method to holding onto their mount's tail and being towed across the creek or river. When stock are being swum over water, they will sometimes start to ring, and stock caught in the middle of the milling mob will inevitably drown. If a man is holding onto the tail of a horse, his eyes will be at water level and he cannot see what is happening, nor would he be able to do anything to rectify the situation if he could.

That is not the only disadvantage to this method. When the far side is reached, the horse has to be caught and can end up amongst the cattle. Not only that, this is a very risky way to cross for anyone who cannot swim, as the tail has to be released before the horse reaches the far bank; not to do so is to risk being kicked. This is exactly how young Colin Cosgrove lost his life. Early in 1957 Colin was working for a drover and on 17 February they began to swim the mob over the Gwydir River. Although he could not swim, Colin elected to hang onto his horse's tail and be towed across. Tragically he held on for too long and was kicked as the horse left the water; Colin slipped back into deep water, unconscious, and was drowned.

Billy Cragg lost his life at a channel crossing on the Stonehenge road. Heavy rain on the headwaters of the channel had sent it roaring down along the Thomson River. Cragg had been horsetailing with a drover's plant that had finished a trip and was returning to Stonehenge. With him were two men, the cook and a young stockman. When they got to the channel, the current was strong and immediately below the crossing the floodwater had gouged out a deep hole in the creek bed that was now a maelstrom of turbulent water. Despite the obvious risk, the three decided to attempt the crossing. The cook, who was driving a horse-drawn wagonette, put the horses into the water, with Cragg riding on the downstream side to keep the team straight. Halfway over the crossing, floodwaters swept the wagonette, horses, and Cragg and his horse into the seething water below. The cook and Billy Cragg's horse managed to escape, but Cragg was drowned, as were the wagonette horses. Billy Cragg's body was later recovered.

Whether at work or pleasure, it is unwise to underestimate the dangers of flooded streams. Billy Ward, a mate of mine, lost his life when he jumped out of a boat that was taking people over the flooded Leichhardt. He

Stockmans' Hall of Fame

Rowley Wall & Company's mail car in trouble at the flooded Thomson River at Longreach in 1923.

J. Kelly

*Horse-drawn wagonette crossing the
flooded Darr River in 1950.*

intended to beat the boat to the other side of the river. Whether he got a
cramp or hit his head is not known, but Billy never made it.

Being reared in North Queensland, I grew up able to swim reasonably
well. However, my elder brother, Keith, was a far stronger swimmer.
While he was still a teenager he saved a chap named Les Millard from
drowning in Owen's Creek. Millard had attempted to cross the creek with
a two-in-hand buckboard; the current swept horses, vehicle and driver
downstream. Keith, seeing Millard's plight, went in and brought him out.

Early in 1969 two large groups from Rutland Plains Station and
Mitchell River Mission on the Gulf of Carpentaria met at the mouth
of Topsy Creek for a day's fishing. The group included the manager of
Rutland Plains, Richard Kriedeman, his wife Marion, daughter Margaret
and son David. Kerry Kendall, a stockman, and Norm Smith, the station's
camp cook, also went along to wet a line. Arthur White, the overseer of
Mitchell River Mission, was there with his family, together with a number
of Aborigines from both the station and the mission. Topsy Creek was on
the boundary of the two properties, and the combined party settled down
to fish after being ferried over to the Rutland Plains side of the tidal creek
by Arthur White. Arthur had an aluminium dinghy powered by a small

Kerry Kendall

The mouth of Topsy Creek, where the ill-fated
fishing party met in early 1969.

outboard motor, and it took a number of trips to complete the crossing. Apart from being a favourite fishing spot, the mouth of Topsy Creek was also known to be the haunt of saltwater crocs and sharks, but that did not bother the group, at least not then.

The day passed pleasantly enough, the whites fishing for barramundi with rod and reel, while the Aborigines employed their traditional method using fish spears. As the afternoon shadows lengthened, the tide began to ebb and it was decided to ferry the party back to the road side of the creek. On the second last trip the tide was running strongly and the water became very rough. In the boat were Richard Kriedeman, nursing four-year-old Margaret, Kerry Kendall, with David, aged two, on his lap, Norm Smith and two Aborigines, with White at the motor. When the dinghy was about a third of the way across the creek, disaster struck. The boat capsized, throwing the occupants into the water. Kriedeman and Kendall held onto the children and placed both on the bottom of the overturned boat. Both men were fully dressed and wearing sandshoes, and handicapped as they were—supporting the youngsters—they found it impossible to take off their shoes. The men realised that there was a danger of the tide taking the boat out to sea, and the decision was made to swim back to the bank they had left.

Swimming with one arm and supporting a child in the other, Kriedeman and Kendall set out for the bank, with Norm Smith swimming between them in case they needed help. It was touch and go, but they finally reached safety, both close to exhaustion. There would certainly have been a tragic end to the day's fishing had not every adult in the dinghy been a reasonably good swimmer. The rescue of the two small children was a commendable act of bravery on the part of both men. Kerry Kendall is a very modest chap who says he just did what had to be done.

Another example of selfless courage was demonstrated when Gordon Davidson, a stockman on Mirrambeena Station, north-east of Charters Towers, developed appendicitis. It was early in 1965 and heavy rain had been falling for some time. Despite the weather conditions, Alec Corbett decided to get his mate Gordon to Dotswood Station, where it would be possible to get medical help. However, Keelbottom Creek, a tributary of the Burdekin, was in full flood and would have to be crossed, as Dotswood was 24 kilometres away on the opposite bank. Undaunted, Alec fuelled up a tractor, the only vehicle he thought might be able to negotiate the boggy conditions. He made Gordon comfortable and set off, hoping to attract attention when he reached the creek bank opposite Dotswood.

The dice seemed to be loaded against the attempt, for they had not gone far when the tractor became bogged to the axles. Alec was not a man who gave up easily, though. Leaving his mate with the tractor, he walked back to Mirrambeena, caught and saddled two horses and hastened back to the sick man. He helped Gordon to mount the spare horse and they set off again towards Dotswood. Gordon was by this time very sick indeed and Alec had to support him in the saddle. Eventually the pair reached a spot on the creek bank opposite Dotswood and Alec managed to alert the station of the situation.

Alec knew it would not be possible to swim the horses over the flooded creek, as he would not be able to support the sick man once the horses were in the water. While he considered his options, the manager of Dotswood got a young chap who was a strong swimmer to cross over to give assistance. Realising that Gordon needed urgent medical attention, Alec took two stirrup leathers off his saddle, and buckling them together, he slipped them on like a bandolier. He put one of the patient's arms through the strap, then entered the water, swimming with one arm and supporting Gordon with the other. Bernie Mossman, the chap who had swum over to help, started swimming with Alec, but the current took him well downstream while Alec swam almost straight across.

The sick man was put to bed at Dotswood and the flying doctor contacted. Thanks to the courage and determination of Alec Corbett, Gordon Davidson made a full recovery.

It is always a traumatic experience for families when isolated by floodwaters. Typical of the parlous situation many families have faced is the one Lucky Forrester found himself in during mid-August 1954 while managing Maramarai Station. Heavy rain fell on the headwaters and tributaries of the Condamine River and Tchanning Creek, and banked up by floodwaters downstream, surrounded the homestead that was situated on a sandhill. This situation would not normally cause concern, but Lucky's wife Eileen, who was eight months pregnant, and his two-year-old daughter Irene were alone with him on the place.

It was impossible for a plane to land on the flooded property and the only phone contact the family had was with a neighbour. As the time for Eileen's confinement grew closer and the floodwater showed no signs of receding, Lucky realised he would have to get the family out on horse-back, which involved wading and swimming for over a kilometre. That should have been straightforward enough, although risky, but therein lay a problem. Lucky had only two horses in hand: one was a very poor swimmer—the type that kept plunging down to feel for the bottom—and the other one, although a good swimmer, was prone to buck.

Lucky overcame the problem by leading the touchy horse into the floodwater before helping his wife into the saddle. Once in the water, the horse forgot about playing up. Lucky took his daughter on the poor swimmer, and the couple set out to cross the flooded claypans and channels. Every time Lucky felt his mount start to dive for the bottom, he told his little girl to take a deep breath. Apparently his daughter thought it was all quite good fun. The family finally reached dry land none the worse for the ordeal and Mrs Forrester was taken to hospital in Miles, where shortly afterwards the couple's son David was born.

I doubt if there is a better example of the combined beauty and menace found in the Australian bush than the Burdekin River. Its tributaries drain a huge area that is subject to heavy seasonal rain. During the dry periods

Kerry Kendall

— 1899. —
LEICHHARDT.
ROPER.
GILBERT.
CALVERT.
MURPHY.
PHILLIPS.

Bushman Mick Perks at the monument erected on the bank of the Burdekin in honour of Ludwig Leichhardt and his party.

of the year, it is a tranquil and beautiful stream, its crystal clear waters gliding gently past sand shoals and rocky outcrops. The first white men to encounter the Burdekin, Ludwig Leichhardt and his party—who were on their way to Port Essington—travelled north up the river, feasting on the fruit from the native plum trees as they went. In the wet, however, the great river changes character. Huge volumes of floodwaters from the Belyando and its northern tributaries roar down, turning the Burdekin into an immense and turbulent torrent.

The Burdekin has been responsible for many deaths since white settlement. In his book *North Queensland Cavalcade*, Fred Bagnell lists the names of some 70 people who have drowned in the river or its tributaries. Many of the victims, children among them, lost their lives due to misadventure while swimming, or at outings and picnics. Others were drowned during floods. Fate can be cruel, as we all know, and it proved to be so in the case of Laurence Bryant, a stockman who lost his life when crossing the Burdekin in 1947. Laurence's grandfather, Harry Bryant, a teamster, had drowned in the Burdekin in almost the same spot, not far from Burdekin Downs Station, in 1899. One of the victims claimed by the Broughton River, which joins the Burdekin below Sellheim, was the head stockman on Fanning Downs, Jack Williams, who drowned in 1964 while trying to remove cattle from the river.

Every wet season the Burdekin River isolated North Queensland, cutting both road and rail between Home Hill and Ayr. The low level rail bridge built in 1913 was totally ineffective. This structure, called the Inkerman Bridge, was 732 metres long and just 3 metres above water level; it rose to the river bank at a 1 in 33 gradient. In 1917, in 1923 and again in 1940 this bridge was destroyed by raging floods. During these periods rail passengers were ferried over the swollen river by a small boat with an outboard motor.

Twice I made the hazardous boat trip over the flooded Burdekin, which stretched for some 700 metres from bank to bank. The first time I was only three years old, but the memory is still quite vivid. In 1926 my father went north to inspect a property he was thinking of buying. He took his family with him, and at Home Hill the Burdekin was found to be in full flood. When our turn came, we stepped gingerly into the boat and headed for the northern side of the river. I wasn't too worried until I looked at my mother; she was as pale as a ghost and obviously terrified. Fear can be contagious and when we disembarked I found that my pants were wet. I'm afraid floodwater was not to blame.

North Queensland Register

*The remains of the Burdekin bridge after one of
the many floods that cut the line to the North.*

My second ferry ride over the flooded Burdekin, in the mid-1950s, was far less stressful. I had been on holidays in Brisbane and caught the Cairns Mail, planning to head west from Townsville on the train to Mount Isa. A mate of mine, Tidly Treffett, had also been holidaying in the big smoke and I was pleased to meet him at Roma Street, also heading north. Tidly was a bit of a larrikin and great company, which resulted in a thoroughly enjoyable journey north. At Bororen we indulged ourselves in the meat pies that had made the little town famous. They were, Tidly pronounced, 'The best bloody pies ever made.' When the train stopped at Rockhampton the pair of us made for the refreshment room and ordered beers; we had both sampled the local brew before and knew its reputation for being virtually undrinkable at times. We looked at one another ruefully and agreed there seemed little improvement; we ordered another round nevertheless.

At Home Hill we discovered the old Burdekin problem had reared its ugly head again. A disembodied voice advised us to leave the train with all luggage and line up beside the tracks to wait for transport by boat over the Burdekin. Tidly and I grabbed our swags from the luggage compartment and climbed down. The sight that met our eyes was disconcerting. We had been in the last carriage and ahead of us now was a queue that stretched for hundreds of metres.

North Queensland Register

Flood damage to the bridge over the Burdekin, March 1945.
Taken shorly after the train disaster that took two lives.

Tidly, however, was not a man to accept inconvenience if he could do something about it. Shouldering his swag, he turned to me and said, 'Let's get going.' He then marched along the line of passengers, with me following. Tidly completely ignored the glares of the long-suffering travellers, and we got to the bank of the Burdekin just as the boat pulled in. Without hesitation, my mate heaved his swag into the little craft and followed it. I joined him, rather expecting to be thrown out again, but neither the train guard nor the boatman said a word. After a few other passengers had climbed aboard, the boat set out for the Ayr side of the Burdekin. As the little boat fought its way across the turbulent floodwaters, I thought about my first crossing. As then, our freeboard was no more than 10 centimetres. My mate was quite unconcerned, but I pulled my boots off just in case.

Shortly after, we were seated in a pub in Ayr with a cold beer in front of us. 'People are like sheep,' Tidly said sagely. 'They'll jump through any hoop, as long as some clown in authority tells them to do it.' I believed his judgement of our fellow passengers to be a trifle harsh but nodded agreement. At the same time I thought to myself that if the world was full of hard cases like Tidly, life could become rather interesting, if at times chaotic.

During the wet season of 1945 the Burdekin claimed two victims. Shortly before 4 a.m. on 8 March a mixed train on its way south pulled into the Ayr railway station. The train consisted mainly of empty wagons but had six wagons full of bullocks, totalling about 100 head. There was also a carriage for passengers and, of course, a guard's van, manned by railway guard Jim Ford. There were already three passengers aboard when the train pulled into Ayr. Cecil Felstead had been on the train since Cairns and was travelling to Mackay. Two brothers, Jack and Leslie Swensen, had also come from further north.

Three other passengers joined the train at Ayr to travel to Keebah siding, south of Home Hill. They were George Pemble, aged 16, Neil Christensen, in his mid-20s and Norman Linton, aged 22. Before leaving Ayr, Bill Thomson, the driver of the train, and the guard were advised that the Burdekin was in flood and the water was about 1 metre under the Inkerman Bridge. The train proceeded south and started across the bridge. At that time there was still no water on the line, but there was

Stockmans' Hall of Fame

A train crosses the old bridge over the Burdekin—the floodwater is just below the track in the middle.

debris deposited by earlier rises in the river. Halfway over the bridge, a piece of this debris ruptured the Westinghouse brake lines between the engine and the tender. This slammed on the brakes of the whole train, bringing it to a grinding stop. It was a situation fraught with danger, for the river had begun to rise. Bill Thomson and his fireman, Errol Gregory, uncoupled the engine and tender and set out to the Home Hill side of the river to effect repairs. By the time they reached the southern bank, water was beginning to cover the line in the middle of the bridge. The rest of the train, stranded on the low middle section, was now in real danger of being swept away by the rising floodwaters.

Realising the danger, Christensen and some other passengers, including the Swensens, decided to try and walk to the Home Hill side. Froth and debris were now being swept down with the flood crest, forcing them to crawl along on the trucks. On arriving at the end of the train, they saw that walking out was impossible due to the current, and returned to where Jim Ford was calling for help to release the cattle. Christensen started opening the doors of the front cattle truck when the front part of the train was swept from the bridge. He turned to see the two brothers flung into the water. The whole train then began to go over and Jim Ford and the rest of the passengers were hurled into the turbulent wall of water that was sweeping down the Burdekin.

The doors on three cattle trucks had been opened before the train was swept off the bridge. Most of the men in the water were able to grab onto the tails of bullocks, an action that saved their lives. Amid the confusion and debris, Christensen finally managed to get hold of the tail of a bullock that was heading downstream. After being towed along for some distance, the beast became stuck in the fork of a huge log that was being borne along by the torrent. Christensen decided to abandon the tail in favour of the log. Some time later Ford, Linton and Felstead, who came by on bullocks' tails, joined him on the tree trunk. At one time during their journey on the log they had to fight off bullocks that were trying to share their haven.

The huge log finally became fouled in trees some 8 kilometres below the bridge. A rescue boat with Sergeant Linnane in charge picked them up from there. Pemble was also rescued, by a boat manned by Constable Lewis and two volunteers. The two Swensen brothers, who went into the river with the front part of the train, were drowned. Had it not been for the cattle, the death toll would probably have been a lot higher.

The Burdekin continued to cut links to the north until 1957, when a new high level bridge was finally constructed and the turbulent waters of the Burdekin were tamed at last.

Late in November 1951 Jack O'Loughlin, a 25-year-old stockman, lost his life in tragic and unusual circumstances. He and his mate Laurie Hansen had worked on a number of cattle stations in North Queensland, and they spent the last part of the 1951 stock season on Van Rook Station. I knew both of them quite well, as they came from the same area as I did, west of Mackay. In fact, Laurie and I were connected by a terrible accident that occurred when Laurie's father was commissioned by my father to transport lumber to build a house on his recently taken-up selection. As a result of an accident with the team, Laurie's father lost half of one foot and my father lost all the timber for the house.

After the cattle work finished on Van Rook, Jack and Laurie were employed at the station. On Monday 26 November Jack O'Loughlin was working on a saw bench with an Aboriginal offsider. Laurie, with another Aborigine, was some distance away collecting firewood in a dray. At 11 a.m. Jack started to cut a twisted and forked log when the circular saw jammed and a large piece of timber flew back, striking him in the face. He

Kerry Kendall

Laurie Hansen, left, *taken with Bruce Simpson in February 1999 at Finch Hatton, Queensland.*

received serious facial injuries and was unconscious for some time. When he did finally recover consciousness, he seemed dazed and lacked coordination. The Cairns Aerial Ambulance was called and the plane, a Dragon Rapide, was dispatched at 1.40 p.m. with Captain Neville Hicks at the controls. Ambulance bearer Keith Howarth accompanied the pilot.

The plane landed at Van Rook, 254 miles (406 kilometres) west of Cairns, O'Loughlin's injuries were dressed, and he was placed on board the aircraft. As the pair had decided to return home for Christmas, Laurie Hansen asked if he could travel to Cairns as well. Captain Hicks had no objection and the plane took off at 5 p.m. with the four men on board.

North Queensland was very dry at the time and smoke from bushfires and low cloud made navigation difficult right from the start. The pilot got his bearings from Wrotham Park Station, and advised Cairns that his ETA was 7.25 p.m. However, as the aircraft got closer to its destination, visibility became worse until finally the terrain became completely blanketed with smoke and cloud. Landing at Cairns under those conditions, Captain Hicks felt, was impossible; the closeness of the sea and the high mountains behind the town gave little room for error. The time was now half past seven and the pilot had no course of action other than to circle around in the hope of the visibility improving.

At that point both the pilot and ambulance bearer were in the cockpit, O'Loughlin was lying on a stretcher with a strap over him and Hansen was sitting on a lower seat. Fuel was getting low and Hansen's recollections are that radio contact had been tried unsuccessfully for some time. With the fuel almost exhausted, Captain Hicks decided to ditch the plane in the sea. Keith Howarth came back and told Laurie and Jack what the situation was, then showed them how to release the strap on the stretcher and open the escape hatch above it.

As he didn't know how close he was to the ranges, Captain Hicks decided it was better to err on the side of caution, and put the aircraft into the water some 3 kilometres from land. There can be no doubt that Captain Hicks' decision was correct, nor any doubt that the ditching was skilfully handled. Despite reports to the contrary, however, Laurie Hansen is positive the plane sank almost at once. By the time he had released his seatbelt, water was rushing in from the plane's ruptured side, and he had to wait for the water pressure to stabilise before getting out. He remembers having to swim upwards for at least two strokes to reach the surface. As he swam towards the other three, he bumped into a floating seat cushion, which was given to Jack O'Loughlin when he joined the others. All four of the men on board were shaken and slightly hurt in the ditching, and the already seriously injured O'Loughlin was now in a bad way, dazed, disoriented and fighting efforts to help him.

It was now dark and the men were not sure how far out to sea they were, nor in which direction the coast lay. Laurie still remembers the struggle he had pulling off his boots and getting out of his jodhpurs. He almost drowned in the effort. The three who were relatively fit had to support O'Loughlin, who was a poor swimmer at the best of times; now badly injured, he could do little to help himself. The visibility at water level was not much better than it had been in the air. All that could be seen on the horizon was a dim smudge, until Laurie, a good bushman, saw the evening star above the haze. Some time later the lights of cars could be seen on the coast road. The party set off swimming towards the coast, with Jack O'Loughlin being supported on the cushion. All three of them could swim, but the task of controlling the semi-conscious O'Loughlin made progress slow and difficult.

The knowledge that the waters off Cairns were the haunt of sharks made the struggle to reach safety a nightmare. Finally it was decided that Laurie Hansen, who was the strongest swimmer, should go on alone and try and get help. He set out, leaving Jack on the cushion being helped by Hicks and Howarth, who had stripped down to their underpants. After five hours in the water, Laurie heard breakers and shortly afterwards he thankfully crawled up the sand of a beach north of Cairns. Initially he had difficulty in standing, but after a few minutes he set off and came to the Cook Highway. He turned south and continued on in the hope of finding help for his mate and the other two men still in the water. Unknown to Hansen, Captain Hicks and Keith Howarth were now swimming on their own, having lost O'Loughlin some two hours into the swim.

Meanwhile the aircraft had been reported missing, but the authorities had no idea where it might have come down. An RAAF fix put the aircraft near Mareeba, and a call for assistance was answered by many motorists, who lit up the Mareeba aerodrome with their headlights. The Cairns police were notified and Inspector W. Peters decided it might be worthwhile taking a run up the Cook Highway.

At 11 p.m. he set out with two constables and at 2.45 a.m. the police party met Laurie Hansen walking towards Cairns. He told them of the ditching and asked for a boat. As there was none available, the inspector drove on and later picked up Captain Hicks and ambulance bearer

Howarth. The three men were taken to Cairns hospital suffering from shock and minor injuries. Next morning an aerial search was organised to try and locate Jack O'Loughlin's body. Unfortunately this was unsuccessful—his body was never found.

PAST INVERWAY

Oh! the West seemed full of promise
And the bush asked little from us,
When we rode the track that led us
Out to where our future lay.
And we left but few hearts grieving
At the prospect of our leaving,
Like the wild geese heading westward,
Further out past Inverway.

With the plant shod up we started
On our pilgrimage, light hearted,
With the hobble chains a-jingle
And the loaded packs a-sway.
But we'd little more to guide us
Than the faith that rode beside us,
When at first we travelled westward
Further out past Inverway.

Then the wattle scent was spreading
And the boughs their blossoms shedding
Made a golden fairy carpet
Where the dappled shadows lay.
Then the wet had not long ended
And the grass like wheat extended
From the old road heading westward,
Further out past Inverway.

When we camped the evening found us
With the virgin bush around us,
While the horses grazed in hobbles
lest they wander off and stray.
Down the flat their bells were ringing
As the Southern Cross was swinging
Up above the darkened timber,
Further out past Inverway.

As the night wind softly blowing
Set the back-log embers glowing,
We yarned of future triumphs
Where the last frontier lay.
We awoke each dew-drenched dawning
To the music of the morning,
As the bush birds gave us welcome
Further out past Inverway.

Then we had no qualms not knowing
What awaited us, when going
Out to where the wild geese gathered
And the brolgas danced at play,
For the sap of youth was flowing,
And our spirits soared when going
Out to Kimberley, our mecca,
Further out past Inverway.

AFTER BUCHANAN

NAT BUCHANAN AND the other early overlanders left a legacy of outstanding droving achievement. After their departure others took up the challenge of overcoming the natural hazards and the tyranny of distance that stood between far-flung stations and the markets. They were to prove worthy successors to the men who opened up the country.

To many people in Australia, droving is no more than a rather romantic interlude in our past—a chapter that was romanticised by poets like Ogilvie and Paterson. In truth there was little romance in droving, but it was one of the most important industries in this country. Since early settlement Australia has depended largely on its pastoral wealth. No station could have been established or could have operated without the help of drovers, first of all to stock the runs and later to take the stock to market. Prior to the early 1960s, each year thousands of mobs of cattle and sheep travelled the vast network of stockroutes that crisscrossed this country.

No, droving was no romantic interlude. For over 150 years it was one of the mainstays of our nation. During that period everyone who sat

The lead of a mob of Manbulloo store bullocks
crossing the Rankine Plain.

down to a meal of chops or steak, or carved a Sunday roast, had a drover to thank for his or her meal. The railways in Australia did not extend into the vast cattle country as they did in America, where they put an end to routes like the Chisholm trail after just 28 years of operation. The Kimberley and Northern Territory stations established by Buchanan, the Duracks, the Farquharsons and others remain as isolated from markets today as they did back before the turn of the century.

In an attempt to open a stockroute from the Kimberley runs to the West Australian goldfields, A.W. Canning, a government surveyor, set out in 1906 from Wiluna and travelled north to Billiluna. Two years later he opened the route that still bears his name. Water was scarce and Canning opened and deepened Aboriginal waterholes to provide stock water. The nomadic Aborigines of the area resented the intrusion of whites into their tribal lands, and in 1910 when the first mob attempted to travel the Canning, they struck. A small mob of about 200 head was started down to Wiluna. With the cattle were drovers Thompson and Shoesmith and one Aboriginal stockman. Late one afternoon when the men were in camp, they were attacked by Aborigines and all three were killed.

Tom Cole (not the author) took a small mob down the torturous track the same year and got through. Later Wickham and McManus followed. The Canning route then fell idle until 1930, when Canning again opened it up to cattle. Men like Dick Rowan and later Wally Dowling took cattle down to Wiluna, using whips, a system of ropes and pulleys harnessed to a camel, to draw water from the wells. Dowling used camels successfully during his trips on the Canning. However, the route was never used to any great extent.

The meatworks at Wyndham, established during World War I, did a little to ease the burden of isolation by providing a limited market closer at hand. Mobs of forward store bullocks (bullocks in good condition) from the East Kimberley region and from the western part of the Territory walked to the works at Wyndham. Vestey's huge meatworks, also built during World War I, was a white elephant, however. Erected at Bullocky's Point near Darwin, it closed down in 1919. Many claimed the company built the works with an eye to securing grazing leases rather than the processing of meat. Whatever the motive, the white ants took over and the stations continued to be forced to send their store bullocks down the long and lonely stockroutes to Queensland.

The boss drovers who brought the big store bullocks in were for the most part tough characters. Hard conditions breed hard men; the

Ray Hulbert

Victoria River Downs bullocks watering at the East Baines River on their way to Wyndham meatworks. Drover John White was in charge.

stockroutes of the North-West were no place for cream puffs. Boss drovers bore a heavy responsibility, having the welfare of cattle, horses and men on their shoulders. It has been said that there was no one above them to pass the buck to but God. They were an un-Godly lot, however, who spoke to God but seldom and then never in a manner likely to engender a sympathetic response from their maker.

Droving trips of 1600 kilometres were common during the period between the turn of the century and the early 1960s. Drovers took store bullocks from the East Kimberley stations to the trucks at Dajarra or to fattening properties in Queensland. Bullocks from the Northern Territory runs followed the same route, while cattle from stations in the Queensland Gulf often walked the stockroutes down into New South Wales and at times into Victoria.

One would need a complete book to list all the outstanding droving feats of those days; a few typical examples will suffice here. In 1930 legendary Kidman drover Jim Laffin drove 1250 bullocks from Alexandria in the Northern Territory to Glengyle Station in the Channel Country of Queensland. After a week's spell he took the top 500 of them to the trucks at Marree in South Australia. Sam Cousins and his sons picked up a mob of bullocks from Wave Hill, Northern Territory in the 1930s. After travelling the stockroutes of the Territory and Queensland for almost 3000 kilometres, the mob was delivered at Clive Station near Marlborough, only a short distance from the Queensland coast. It was reported that some of the mob from Wave Hill had previously walked there from Yeda and other stations on the West Australian coast. If this is correct, some of the cattle delivered at Clive had walked across Australia from west to east.

In the 1930s Bob Iles, later a boss drover himself, worked for Billy Hall. Hall took delivery of 1500 store bullocks from Dalgonally Station in the Queensland Gulf Country; eight months later he delivered the mob at Cubby near Bourke in New South Wales. During a drought year Jack Jackson, a boss drover from Barcaldine, took delivery of a mob of store bullocks from Avon Downs in the Northern Territory. The mob was put on the road for grass, Jackson taking them down the Georgina, then on to Birdsville. With a five-in-hand team of mules, Jackson then crossed into South Australia over the sandhills at Haddon's corner, the only drover ever to do this. The mob was taken on down the Strzelecki Track. Jackson then turned the mob back on advice from the owners, and from Birdsville he travelled the mob down to the border with New South Wales. Crossing

George Ellis

Bruce Simpson, right, *with 92-year-old ex-Kidman drover Jim Laffin (Snr).*

Group of ex-drovers and ringers at Camooweal, 1997.
Left to right (back): *Herb Huemiller, George Booth,*
Ernie McCarthy, Blue Ellis, Alf Champers, the author,
Ian 'Spud' Tait; front: *the late Bob McDonald*
and the late John Gardner.

the border, Jackson finally trucked the bullocks away at Walgett after 41 weeks on the road.

In 1954 boss drover Bob Iles took delivery of 1500 head of dry cows from Newcastle Waters Station in the Northern Territory. The mob was travelling for sale. Iles travelled the mob down to Augathella, where the cows were spelled for a month. Iles then picked the mob up again and crossed over into New South Wales, taking the mob to Bourke, then on to Walgett. With the mob still unsold, Iles crossed back into Queensland, then south again. At Brewarrina the mob was at last sold. The travelling time for the trip was 10 months.

The above are just some of the droving trips done in the past by the men who followed in the footsteps of the early overlanders. There are many other stories that could be told: tales of Tom 'One Potato Tom' Starr, of Paddy Conway, called 'Beef Eye' by the Aborigines, of Walter Cowan and Jack Carroll, drovers who took cattle off Rocklands Station for 49 years and 50 years respectively, of that legendary drover of later years, Noel 'Pic' Willetts, the last drover to bring cattle through the notorious Murranji track.

Typical of the top men who worked for boss drovers is Tom Cusack. A veteran of the notorious Birdsville, Strzelecki and Murranji tracks, Tom knew every stockroute in the North-West like the back of his hand. He worked for a number of old-time drovers and in 1962 he was droving with Paddy Fogarty. After delivering a mob at Clifton Hills Station in South Australia, Fogarty was offered two mobs off Billiluna Station, just south of Hall's Creek in Western Australia. Paddy was advised to take his plant to Marree and go by train to Alice Springs. At this time he was using a truck and trailer to cart his droving gear. In due course, men, fresh horses and vehicles arrived in the Alice. Fogarty's droving team consisted of his father, Lloyd Snr, and his sons Lloyd, Stan and Jack, with Tom making up the normal crew of five men and the boss.

The plant horses were trucked up the Tanami track to Mount Doreen Station, the destination of the first mob, then driven over the West Australian–Northern Territory border to Billiluna. When Paddy and the others arrived with the plant, the mob of 1860 store bullocks was not yet fully mustered. The drovers agreed to hold the mob in hand as the muster progressed. It was the first time a large mob would ever attempt to travel down the Tanami track. The year before a small mob of 400 had travelled down as a test run, but it was the mob from Billiluna that would really open the route.

Things did not go well for the drovers during the muster. First young Jack developed appendicitis and was taken to Balgo Mission, and from there by the flying doctor to Derby Hospital. Shortly afterwards Stan broke his arm when his horse fell while mustering around Lake Gregory. Paddy was two men short and the trip had not even started. When the mob was ready, however, the manager of Billiluna lent the drover two Aboriginal ringers for the trip.

They took delivery of the bullocks and started off, facing a dry stage of nearly 130 kilometres. Now, a dry stage of that magnitude can be a problem with broken-in road bullocks; to negotiate it with fresh cattle is a formidable task that calls for expert cattle work. Against the odds the mob was taken through safely, the truck delivering water for the horses at each camp. After a week on the road the mob started rushing (the Australian term for stampede), and continued to rush for up to four times a night during the whole trip.

Spud Tait

Tommy Cusack at the
Camooweal reunion, 1998.

As Paddy and Tom were the only members of the team with experience with rushing bullocks, they got little rest at night, but were able to snatch a bit of sleep on dinner camp. At Lake Alexandria (a dry lake) they found themselves dealing with a very bad rush, with the bullocks almost going over the camp. Next morning there were bullock tracks hurdling Tom's swag.

One of Tom's jobs was to track around wide of the ground where the mob had been the night before. If tracks showed bullocks had got away, he tracked them and brought them back. On one occasion he was away for three days getting bullocks that had cleared out.

There were many dry stages to cross and because of slow water supply the drovers were forced to use the pump they carried to augment the flow from bores. But after dust storms, dry stages and constant rushes, the mob was finally delivered at Mount Doreen. Paddy Fogarty was sometimes known as 'Piebald Paddy' because of his liking for coloured horses, but he was no mug with galloping bullocks and he had a top man with him in Tom. The Tanami track was open.

After a couple of days' spell the drovers headed back to Billiluna to pick up the second mob. En route they enjoyed the hospitality of Father McGuire and the nuns at the mission. Again the mob numbered 1860 store bullocks. Paddy's two sons, now both fully recovered, joined the drovers. This time the mob was destined for Mount Riddock Station, north-east of Alice Springs, a trip of over 1200 kilometres. It was far from the longest droving trip, but the nature of the route made it an epic. The same 130 kilometre dry stage had to be faced, and again the bullocks rushed almost every night and there were problems with the water supply.

After counting the mob at Chilla Wells, some of the bullocks strayed into the timber. As he rode over to turn them back, Tom noticed what looked like a white tarpaulin some distance away. Closer inspection revealed the tarp was over a Volkswagen, and on the back seat was a dead man. A hose from the exhaust into the car appeared to be the cause of death. In due course the police were notified and Tom went back with them to show them the vehicle and body. Later Tom learnt that the body in the car was that of an English journalist, who had apparently chosen to drive out into the desert to end it all.

At Amburla the drovers found short green feed and herbage. If cattle have been on dry feed for a long time, grazing on this type of feed will cause them to bloat; that is, there will be a large build up of gas in their stomachs. The condition, if not treated, is usually fatal. The old bush remedy is simple—a pocket knife blade is driven into the paunch at the right place and out whistles the gas; the small wound quickly heals. Fourteen of Paddy's mob went down with the bloat, but Paddy and Tom, being experienced men, put the old method to work and saved all but four.

It was now starting to get late in the season and the temperature often soared above the 120°F (49°C) mark; the ground reading would have been around 160°F (71°C) or 170°F (77°C). Tom recalls seeing 'phantom rain' on more than one occasion. This phenomenon only occurs in extremely hot weather in dry desert country areas: rain can be seen falling from clouds but evaporates before it reaches the ground.

Although still rushing on some nights, the mob had settled down a bit when the drovers turned the bullocks up the Plenty Highway towards Mount Riddock Station, where they were delivered on 27 October.

Both droving trips were regarded as epics and received quite a lot of publicity. Sadly there are now only three survivors of those outstanding trips. Lloyd and Jack Fogarty both live in Winton, Lloyd has a small business while Jack works for the electrical authority. Tom Cusack, his droving days far behind him, now works on Mittibah Station in the Northern Territory. One of his greatest enjoyments in life is meeting his old droving mates at the drovers' reunion held at Camooweal in August each year.

They were tough characters, the old-time drovers, but great Australians who brought the beef to the tables of our city dwellers. There is still some droving done today, but the days are gone when the great mobs stretched down the stockroutes, a day's stage between them, for hundreds of kilometres. It is estimated that in 1953, 150 000 head of cattle went on the road in the North-West. To move that number, over 100 drovers with their men and horses would have been required. I am proud to say that I was one of those drovers. During the first 60 years of this century the stockroutes of Australia were alive with movement; the sound of hoof beats and stock whips, of horse bells and hobbles, was music to a horseman's ears. Droving was a tough job; we ate rough tucker and slept on the ground in thin swags, yet even if I could I would not change a day of my time on the stockroutes.

THE DAYLIGHT WATCH

The daylight watch is a graveyard shift,
From three till the dawn comes stealing,
While a billion stars in the heavens drift
To the planet's steady wheeling.
The cross hangs low in the southern sky
As the last watch slowly passes,
No bullock stirs as my horse goes by
Hooves quiet on the dew-damp grasses.

I ride on watch with a loose-held rein,
My tryst with the darkness keeping
Round the cattle camp on the narrow plain,
Where the big store mob is sleeping.
I ride and sing lest the mob take fright
And rush like a torrent flowing,
To smash forever the calm of night
In the wake of their frantic going.

I watch and wait for the glow of dawn
That will herald the coming morrow,
But night holds sway and the curlews mourn
Like souls in the vale of sorrow.
It's an eerie shift for a man alone
Ere dawn when the night is dying,
A chill wind blows and the gidgees moan
As ghosts of the past come sighing.

The Lament of a Cow
and Calf Drover

Mixed cattle thirteen hundred head, they spread across the plain,
We pause a while to curse our fate then start them up again.
With waterholes at every turn and feed at every stride
The bloated breeders walk so slow you'd think them petrified.
It's little use, we realise, to flog or rave or stamp,
The lead departs, the wings expand, the tail decides to camp.

A thousand miles we brought the plant, it spelled down at the 'fort'
A thousand long and lonely miles for bullocks, so we thought.
We would have welcomed weaner steers, or stags, or even both,
As every ringer here declared upon his crimson oath.
But cows and calves! Our hearts rebel and with one scorching breath
We wish on every cow and calf a fate far worse than death.

The bovine birth rate's on the rise—a packhorse drover's blight,
Each morn we curse the newborn calves, arrivals of the night.
The old night horses that would fight to catch a flying lead
Go round the mob with grudging step to turn the strays that feed.
Eight miles a day they've put us on, eight weary miles a day
Along the green and watered road that passes Inverway.

The billabongs are brimming full, the bush with music rings,
The grass is blowing tall and sweet from here to Helen Springs.
The coolibahs are fresh and green, and bright blue are the skies
And with a lively mob of stores we'd call it paradise.
But cows and calves! We grind our teeth and gibber in our sleep,
A man should give the North away and go a-droving sheep.

Oh! one must be a stoic born to stay sane and succeed
At droving blasted cows and calves that have a bullock lead.
Still I suppose things could be worse, the springs could all go dry—
The bores could all be broken down across the Murranji,
The ringer lads could catch the blight—the nags catch 'walkabout'
The publicans along the road could all forget to shout.

So *we will bear our bovine cross, although we cannot grin.*
And do a spot of penance now for some forgotten sin.
We'll keep the old hides plodding on along the pads and ride
Like demons down the spreading wings to stem the bawling tide.
We'll tear our hair and curse our fate here where the road dust clings
And dream of that delivery date ahead at Helen Springs.

Bob Gordon

Lake Nash bullocks on the road in the early 1930s.

Barlow Jackson's plant taking Avon Downs cows across the flooded Alice River, Queensland in 1950. The drover in charge was Claude Burns (in overcoat at edge of river).

Men with Barlow Jackson's plant in 1950.
Left to right: *Alan Bunt, Bricky Hayes, Barlow Jackson, Herb Huemiller, Ian 'Spud' Tait, Jack Jackson (Jnr) and Claude Burns.*

TROUBLE WITH THE COOK

DURING THE TIME I was droving, I often found myself short handed. On one particular trip there were only three of us with 1350 bullocks and 45 head of horses. My brother Jeff did both the cooking and horsetailing jobs, while John Schonrock and I were with the mob. Being so short handed—down three men—made life rather difficult, as each of us had to do a three-and-a-half-hour watch each night. This situation continued for about six weeks, and to make matters worse the mob developed contagious bovine pleuropneumonia, a lung disease commonly called just pleuro. As a result, the authorities had to be notified and a stock inspector met me and ran his eye over the mob.

Most drovers regard stock inspectors as a damned nuisance, but I found this bloke, Jack Travers, to be all right. In fact, Jack and I became good mates and have remained so ever since. As a result of his visit, my mob was ordered to stop travelling and was quarantined at the Buchanan River. As he was leaving, I asked Jack if he could find me some men to relieve the situation. He promised to do what he could when he got to Camooweal.

When Jack returned a few days later to check the mob again, he had failed to get me any ringers, but he had brought out a camp cook. He looked like a typical bushman—lean almost to the point of emaciation—but I was to realise later that his physique was due more to a drink-affected liver than to the rigours of outback life. After three days of very indifferent cooking, the new man complained about the lack of rations, which was an accurate enough assessment of the situation. He suggested he catch a ride into Camooweal and bring back some stores, and also mentioned that he knew a couple of ringers who were looking for work. I took him at face value and gave him an open cheque for the goods.

When he hadn't shown up at the end of the third day I began to have misgivings about placing trust in a man I hardly knew. My doubts were confirmed the next day. I cursed myself for a fool when the cook arrived as full as a boot, clutching a bottle of rum. There were no rations and no ringers. I impounded the bottle, and the cook, after staggering around, crashed in his swag. He was still there at sundown, forcing Jeff, who loathed cooking, to knock up a meal for us. Light rain fell early in the night, causing the bullocks to drift off camp, and holding them kept both my brother amd me busy for some time. When things had settled down a little, Jeff rode around to me with a worried look on his face.

'One of us had better go into the camp. The cook is having a fit by the fire.'

'Stuff the cook.'

'Stuff him if you like, but he's likely to roll into the fire.'

I looked at my brother. 'Well, if he does, I hope the bastard burns well—we're short of wood.'

My brother rode away shaking his head. I had not really meant what I said, but felt a great deal better for having said it. When I finally went into the camp, the cook had returned to his swag without augmenting the wood supply.

We started travelling again next day and planned to go out about 4 miles (6–7 kilometres) after watering the mob. The cook took no part in getting breakfast or in packing up. He looked so close to death that I took pity on him and gave him a stiff rum. I doubt if he would have made it to the next camp without it. As it was, Jeff had to help him onto a horse.

When I put the bullocks on camp that night, the cook was in his swag and Jeff was doing the cooking—and in a foul mood. Next morning the patient looked reasonably fit but refrained from lifting anything heavier than a knife and fork. I got the distinct impression that my brother was beginning to regret that the threatened immolation of the cook had not in fact taken place.

We were crossing the Rankine Plain, a treeless expanse of some 50 kilometres with one bore approximately halfway across. That day I planned to dry day the mob, camping a few kilometres short of the bore. The mob neared the camp as a wild-looking storm approached. I fed the mob along as fast as it was possible, to be close to the camp when it broke. I could see a strange vehicle in the camp but took little notice of it until it was driven along the stockroute road and pulled up opposite the mob, blowing the horn. As I rode over, I could see it was an old ex-army truck with no doors. I could also see the cook sitting in the front seat with the camp rifle across his knees.

'What's up?' I asked as I reined my horse up.

'We're going to kill,' said the cook, who was obviously drunk again.

'Like bloody hell. Can't you see that storm? There's plenty of corned beef left in the packs.'

'It all went bad. I threw it out.'

'Well, go back and bloody well pick it up. We're not killing.'

The cook half fell out of the truck. 'We're going to kill,' he insisted. 'I promised me mate some fresh meat.'

'Tell your bloody mate to take you back to the camp, then roll your swag. You're fired.'

The cook levelled the rifle at me. 'If you won't kill for your men, you miserable mongrel, I'll kill you.'

I had no idea if he was bluffing or not, and did not intend to sit around at point-blank range to find out. Slipping out of the saddle, I ducked under my horse's neck and relieved him of the rifle. As the driver was starting the engine, I stuck my head in the cabin of the truck.

'What the hell do you mean by bringing grog into my camp?'

He jerked his thumb at the cook. 'He told me it was his camp.'

'Well, now you know differently. Get the hell out of here and take this bloody ratbag with you.'

The cook had struggled to his feet and was trying to get back into the truck. I helped him with a none too gentle hand. Once seated, he glared at me. 'What about me wages and me rum?'

The truck took off before I could answer. I sat on my horse and watched the truck head across to the camp. It pulled away again as Jeff returned from watering the horse plant. Still carrying the rifle, I rode back across the Mitchell grass to where the mob was feeding along. Thunder rolled and the bullocks' heads went up as they caught the smell of rain on the storm wind. It would not be an easy night. As I pushed the mob towards the camp, I cursed all cooks, my last one in particular. The only one I could think of as being worse was a character called O'Duff, who once cooked in a Gulf stockcamp.

THE BALLAD OF DIRTY O'DUFF

I once worked on a run where the old Leichhardt flows,
Where the dark tangled gidgee and snappy gum grows.
We were working all hours, we were mustering fats
From the scrub-covered ridges and silver box flats.
Though the work was no worry, conditions were crook,
For the stockcamp was minus the skills of a cook.

So we gritted our molars and pulled our belts tight,
Each cooking in turn when we finished at night.
But one day to the camp came the old station truck
And it seemed fate had granted a change in our luck,
From the cabin there tumbled a hungover slob,
Who in loud tones advised us, 'Cooking's me job.'

'I believe,' said the wreck, 'things have been a bit rough,
Well, you're in for a change or me name's not O'Duff.'
He was famous, he told us, a cook of repute,
And had gone fifteen rounds with Jack Hassen to boot.
But conditions got worse in the camp just as soon
As this fat reprobate got his hands on a spoon.

For he washed very seldom and smelled like a drain
And he soon had us clutching our stomachs in pain.
He was greasy and slack with a liking to spit
Anywhere, not concerned in the least what he hit.
Now bush babblers at best are a difficult crew
But this fellow was dirty, and dangerous too.

With some awful bait-layers my life has been cursed
But without any question O'Duff was the worst.
Now a stockman's a fellow who'll seldom complain,
He will work like a dog in the heat and the rain,
And the tucker he'll thrive on, as everyone knows,
Is enough to make town people turn up their toes.

But all ringers will bail if you push them enough,
And the end of our tether we reached with O'Duff.
For he gave us the trots and quite often the spews
With his villainous curries and sinister stews.
The insides of his dampers were gluey and raw,
With a crust that would fracture a crocodile's jaw.

'Now don't get downhearted,' was all O'Duff said,
'You'll be howling for more when I turn out me bread.'
But disasters in dough were the things that we got,
While the flour bags emptied and tempers grew hot.
First he blamed it on flour, then he blamed it on yeast,
Then he blamed the cold nights as our hunger increased.

'Why this hoon can't boil water,' the head stockman said,
'I'll ride bareback to Bourke if he ever makes bread.'
How we watched him each morn as he gazed in surprise
At inert sullen dough that seemed never to rise,
It would sprawl unrepentant and sometimes it shrank,
Then he'd hurl the whole batch down the steep river bank.

Down the bank every day went the dough that was flat
Until every wild pig on the Leichhardt was fat.
There they'd gather each evening in hoggish delight
And they'd gourmandise loudly far into the night.
In swinish abandon they'd gorge on the stuff,
Their porcine praise swelling to honour O'Duff.

Well, this stirred the head stockman, at last got his goat,
For he sprang from his horse, grabbed O'Duff by the throat.
'You unnatural disaster—you poisonous swine,
Just once more on our bread will your bloody mates dine—
Just once more let them feast and they'll have you, by God,
For I'll strangle you outright, you bait-laying sod.'

Well, our dough roaster spluttered and quickly agreed
That no more feral pigs on his dough would he feed.
We rode campwards that evening with visions of bread,
To be greeted as ever with damper instead.
There we ate with reluctance, no cook was in sight
And no sound of a pig broke the Gulf Country night.

Then we sat around smoking, not caring to talk,
Till the head stockman said he must go for a walk,
For the calls of old nature were sudden enough
On the culinary crimes conjured up by O'Duff.
He had only just left us when rending the air
Came the horrified cry of a soul in despair.

While our flesh crawled, we stood there, aghast and afraid,
Then, fearful hearts thumping, we raced to his aid.
In a monster's foul grip he was trapped to the thighs,
And the grey evil 'thing' seemed to quiver and writhe.
When at last he was freed from his devilish foe,
We found that the 'thing' was a pit full of dough.

But the pigs hadn't dined, O'Duff's promise was sound,
Like a doctor, his failure he'd put in the ground.
And away in the Gulf where the wild Leichhardt flows—
Where the dark tangled gidgee and snappy gum grows—
Where the stockcamps still muster and living is rough,
Many still curse the memory of Dirty O'Duff.

SAM FULLER'S THOROUGHBRACE

Sam Fuller's was a well-known face on stockroutes yesteryear,
And Fuller bought a thoroughbrace to shift his droving gear.
A spanking coach it once had been in days of Cobb and Co.,
That carried mail on roads between the 'Reach and Jericho.
Converted to a wagonette, Sam Fuller thought it grand
Despite the fact he'd still to get a team of five-in-hand.

We loaded on the gear and swags, we roped them into place,
Then culled the plant for likely nags to pull the thoroughbrace.
We draughted five from Fuller's mob, the progeny of sin,
Then readied tackle for the job of breaking outlaws in.
'We're wasting time,' Sam Fuller cried, 'we're shifting camp you know,
We'll have some fun with them un-tried, we'll break 'em as we go.'

The Boss's word was law, of course, somehow the job was done,
We caught each wild, unbroken horse and harnessed every one.
We battled hard to keep control, then placed as Sam decreed
Two snorting brumbies in the pole, three others in the lead.
As ringers held each horse's head—five timebombs all alive,
Sam Fuller turned to me and said, 'They tell me you can drive?'

In shaking hands I took the reins with, 'Steady, whoa there, whoa!'
Then five mad horses hit the chains as Fuller shouted, 'Go!'
At a reckless pace away we sped, the horses running blind—
Escape they knew was up ahead while hell was close behind.
They bolted out towards the track, the bits between their teeth,
The dust and grasses billowed back, the stones flew underneath.

They held to scorn the heavy load, the smoking brakes were spurned
And when we reached the Jundah road we all but overturned.
The Jundah track was fast and dry and faster grew our speed
For not a hope in hell had I of pulling up the lead.
I held the reins in hands that grew white-knuckled with the strain,
As hooves beat out a mad tattoo and gravel fell like rain.

The leaders bowed the spreader bars, with harness all a-flail
They cleared the road of motor cars and scattered them like quail.
The thoroughbraces pitched and rolled, the camp gear rattled free
Like cargo in a clipper's hold that braves the stormy sea.
I rode the wildly swaying seat, one foot upon the brake,
As ringers yelled, 'You've got 'em beat' and galloped in our wake.

We thundered through a flock of sheep, the polers shied in fright,
But Lady Luck chipped in to keep the wagonette upright.
I waited for the pace to ease, I knew it couldn't last,
But still the dusty gidgee trees like phantoms flitted past.
I saw at last the chains go slack beside the heaving flanks
And as I reined the leaders back I said a prayer of thanks.

The weary horses ceased to fear the vehicle at their backs
And with the brake-shoes riding clear they trotted on like hacks.
They swept past distant station roofs and by a stony hill,
With arching necks and drumming hooves now bending to my will.
What seemed at first a hell-bent trip was now a Sunday drive
As sceptre-like I raised the whip above the team of five.

The big wheels sang the same refrain they'd sung in days of yore
With dust clouds following in train and flying heels before.
The 'braces gently rocked the load and oh! but life was grand
When spinning down the Jundah road with Fuller's five-in-hand.
In fancy's flight I rode with men who drove for Cobb and Co.,
Oh! I was young and foolish then but that was long ago.

The bush is not the same today for time has turned the page,
And out Stonehenge and Jundah way trucks roll on every stage
Long gone is Fuller's wagonette—long gone the plunging team,
But memories that linger yet enshroud me like a dream,
Once more I feel the 'braces sway as at a cracking pace
Down distant roads I'm borne away on Fuller's thoroughbrace.

PRIZES FOR RIDERS

'PRIZES FOR RIDERS and busters for windbags.' Sam Fuller's call to action beckoned loudly as we sat at the back of the hessian-walled buckjump show with the horses. We looked at one another and smiled wryly; Sam was in full flight, drumming up business for the show that was scheduled to start in half an hour. We sat in a rough circle on the ground; Sam didn't waste money on the unnecessary. There was Banjo Hunt, a top rider; a chap named Dawson; myself; and Sam Albury, who fought all comers, to add variety to the show.

'Step up a little bit closer,' Sam roared, 'and you won't be so far away from the best buckjump show in Australia.' He paused for breath. 'Just a few canvas chairs left,' he advised the growing crowd. There was, of course, not a canvas chair to be seen on the inside of the hessian wall, nor, for that matter, was there a chair of any sort. That did not worry Sam. No chairs meant a bigger crowd, for chairs took up space.

Sam Fuller's buckjump show was austere to say the least. A roped ring into which the horses were led was surrounded by a hessian wall, with a reasonable space left for spectators. It was quickly erected and just as quickly pulled down. Sam liked to keep on the move. He had always combined his buckjump show with his droving activities and was not above putting a long flank rope on a plant horse if he thought it had potential. I had been horsetailing for one of his plants, and a big brown horse I had broken in to nightwork had been pressed into service at an earlier show. The horse had acquitted himself well, but every day after that he thought the droving plant was a buckjump show. That night he stood with the other horses, his ears pricked at Sam's spruiking.

Sam Fuller was a hard case and a charismatic character. At one time he drove a taxi in Longreach as well as having two droving plants on the go. A taxi ride with Sam could be an interesting affair. He was not above letting the car idle along in first gear, then, when passing a pub, opening his door and stepping out, leaving his startled passenger to carry on alone. Sam had a rather outrageous sense of humour and could at times get away with acts that would attract censure if perpetrated by others.

The latter part of Sam's life was spent in Longreach, the home of the Stockmans' Hall of Fame. There is, however, no mention of the legendary Sam Fuller in that august establishment. Perhaps Sam was not polished enough for the 'powers that be' at the Hall.

One of a large family, Sam was born in 1900. After the death of his grandmother in England, Sam's grandfather left the UK and brought his teenage son out to Australia. Before the turn of the century they settled in Mitchell, in the Central West of Queensland. Sam's father grew up and married there, and the town has been 'Fuller' country ever since. As a lad, Sam went bush, and he never looked back. He worked on stations and with drovers, earning a reputation as a buckjump rider. During the 1920s and 1930s he got his own plant together, doing droving and picking up buckjumping horses wherever he could. Sam loved rough horses; it was a passion that stayed with him all his life. He was always ready to turn his droving plant into a buckjump show, for Sam was, above all, a showman. People all over Queensland and various parts of New South Wales have heard the Fuller cry: 'Prizes for riders and busters for windbags.'

People often gave Sam bad horses that were too much trouble to work, and he never knocked them back. In fact, if he took a shine to a buck-jumper that was unavailable, he was not above 'borrowing' it. Sam was an accomplished buckjump rider, but he was as rough as guts. His idea of taking the sting out of a bad horse was to leap into the saddle, order the gates open and disappear with a roar and a bellow across whatever terrain happened to be about. When he rode in his show, however, he was professional. He often rode a buckjumper he knew and played the mouth organ in the process—and at times he rode blindfolded.

Sam married Dorrie Zeller in Mitchell in 1920. The couple had four children: three girls—Mabel, Dorrie, and Phillis—and Sam Jnr, the second eldest, who was born in 1925. Mabel died as a result of injuries received in a five-in-hand accident near Dalby. Phillis, Dorrie and young Sam are all now also deceased.

It's probably true to say that Sam Fuller Snr was far from the ideal family man. The lure of the bush and the buckjump show could not be denied. Out there was freedom and excitement, and, above all, buck-jumpers. Always on the lookout for horses that he could back to throw anyone, he picked up a horse he called Send Em. Horses that will continue to buck whenever it is asked of them are rare. In Send Em, Sam had a champion. The horse's name became a household word wherever Fuller's show had entertained the public. Sam pensioned off Send Em in New South Wales after taking a mob down there. When I was with him, he had two top buckjumpers, Depot Glen and Wait and See; they were dam and daughter, and a formidable pair.

Later Sam had a little grey horse he called Sugar. The grey would let kids ride him around bareback, but put a saddle and flank girth on him and it was a very different story. It was about this time that the song 'Sugar in the Morning' hit the airwaves. Sam gave that song hell. He sometimes sang another song when I was with him; someone had written it and given the words to him. I'd forgotten it, but while interviewing his son, Sam Jnr, in Mitchell recently, he mentioned the ditty, and after thinking about it for a while, Sam remembered the words. It went like this:

> There's hessian walls and a sawdust floor,
> With Sam Fuller spruiking at the door,
> Pointing the way for us to go
> So we found ourselves at the buckjump show.
> There's not a seat, for the tent is bare,
> But Sam gives a cooee so we don't care.
> The side of the hessian wall comes down
> And in comes a grey with a mighty bound.
> There's prizes for riders here, you know,
> For this is Fuller's Buckjump Show.

The very worst thing that can happen in a buckjump show is for a top buckjumper to be ridden right out. This often causes a horse to throw in bucking, making the horse a liability rather than an asset. All showmen are adept at using the long flank rope; if a rider from the crowd looked like riding one of Sam's horses, he usually managed to unseat him by the covert use of this rope. If one of his own men were riding, it was an unwritten law that the rider left the horse before it stopped bucking. I remember Banjo Hunt having some great tussles with the two brown mares.

The morning after Sam put on his buckjump show, Banjo and I were in the bar of the Central Hotel. Banjo had just finished for the season, having been in charge of a packhorse plant of Sam's, and Jimmy Charles and I had been with the other one, using a five-in-hand wagonette. Sam had been at the hotel entertaining the drinkers with the mouth organ and when he left the crowd had thinned out a bit. We were talking over a quiet beer when out of the blue Banjo looked at me and said, 'How about going down to the Rocky rodeo?'

I was thinking about the suggestion when the barman said, 'You're a bit late. There isn't any accommodation left in Rockhampton, it's the Australian championships, you know.'

Banjo looked at him. 'What! None at all?'

'Nope, not for the public, anyway. I believe they still have some reservations for competitors.'

'Right,' said Banjo, 'Come on, Simmo, we'll nominate.'

'Like hell,' I said. 'I'm no rodeo rider.'

'It's no bloody different. Come on, mate, we'll get a grandstand view of things.'

Banjo could be very persuasive. In the end I agreed and we caught the mail train. In Rockhampton I was to find that Sam Fuller's name could open many doors. As soon as we arrived, we headed for the rodeo office. Rex Pilbeen, the city mayor, was the rodeo boss. He greeted us with: 'What can I do for you chaps?'

Banjo grinned, 'We're here to nominate.'

Pilbeen shook his head. 'Sorry, nominations closed yesterday, and we're not taking late ones.'

Banjo scratched his head. 'Well, we've come all the way from Longreach—we've been with Sam Fuller—and they tell us there's no accommodation left in town.'

Rex's expression changed. 'Oh! You've been with Fuller, eh? Well, I'll tell you what we can do. We're short of a couple of blokes to saddle up on the chutes. It's worth a bit of money plus a room at a pub. Are you interested?'

Were we interested? We both said yes at the same time.

After booking in at the pub, I told Banjo I was going to find a dentist. The rodeo was on next morning and I had a top wisdom tooth that was giving me hell. I reckoned it was best to get it out first. I spent about two hours in the dentist's chair; the tooth broke off and the dentist had to lance the gum to extract the bloody thing. I never got much sleep that night, for it never stopped bleeding. I'd heard George Huntly was the shute boss, so next morning I asked Banjo to tell George I may be a bit late as I was going back to the dentist to get the gum stitched up.

I arrived at the rodeo grounds via a taxi and went straight to the yards. George, who was a big, gruff character, saw me and roared, 'You're late, aren't you supposed to be saddling up here?'

Before I could answer, a chap standing by chipped in, 'He's one of Fuller's men, George.' Again Sam's name worked like magic, and the attitude of the shute boss transformed. He told me I was on chute six and walked off.

I enjoyed the job, for I had a box seat. People pay money and never get as close to the action as Banjo and I were.

I saddled up for Johnny Roberts in the final of the buckjumping. After he was thrown, I witnessed one of the all time great rides; Tom Willoughby won the championship on a big brown horse called Wombi. Both Banjo and I knew we had Sam Fuller to thank for the memorable time we had together in Rockhampton.

After his first wife died, Sam Fuller married again. He wed Ivy Wager in Longreach and the couple were together until Sam's death. The union was blessed with nine children.

Sam Fuller was a living legend of the outback, one of those colourful, larger than life characters that the Australian bush sometimes produces. Love him or hate him, when Sam departed this mortal coil he left a vacuum that has not been filled. Sam died in 1973 and was buried at Longreach.

A Toast to Sam Fuller

Bush horsemen come charge a glass and drink a toast with me,
Though Sam has gone, his name will live, here's to his memory.
His name was known in every camp across this sunlit state,
For all the West was home to Sam, and every man was mate.

Buckjumpers were Sam's very life, his outlaws were his pride,
The eager crowds in countless shows have seen Sam Fuller ride.
How often have we heard him shout, with all the Fuller zest,
There's prizes here for riders, lads, and busters for the rest.

Wherever bushmen's fires are lit beneath a starry sky,
The legend that Sam Fuller left behind will never die.
Whenever horsemen crowd the rails to watch a battle grim
Between an outlaw and a man, they'll think again of him.

A horseman of the old hard school, a showman to the end,
A diamond rough, no doubt, and yet, he never failed a friend.
So horsemen all where'er you are, come drink a toast with me,
Though Sam has gone, his name will live, here's to his memory.

THE TAKE DOWN

It was just after the horse muster there had begun
That a new chum arrived at the Jabiru run.
From the mail truck he stepped in a bored kind of way
With 'Morning my man' to the boss's 'Good day'.
He was dressed to the nines with immaculate care
From his pigeon-toed feet to his pomaded hair.

From the station's head office in London he came,
And Hector Smythe-Smithers we learnt was his name.
That night after tea for an hour or more
The new chum held forth till our eardrums were sore,
He told of his triumphs at English showgrounds
And of scrub-dashing efforts while 'following hounds'.

He spoke of buckjumpers he'd tamed for a bet
And the rep that he'd won with the show jumping set.
'I suppose they root here,' he remarked, 'but, of course,
A bush nag can't buck like a thoroughbred horse.'
Then the horse breaker said in a muttered aside,
'It's as plain as a pikestaff this dummy can't ride.

'We'll kid him on Blister and drop him a peg,
He's a cert to get thrown if he doesn't renege.'
Now Blister we'd mustered that very same day,
He could buck, twist and spin like a whirlwind at play.
We'd packed him and loaded the packbags with sand,
But the outlaw bucked on till he near threw his brand.

So the head stockman said, 'If you feel like a ride,
We've got a roan horse here that's never been tried,
You could back yourself, sonny, and make a few bob
For they'll bet on a dog fight, this mustering mob.'
The plan was approved by our friend from the town
And we gleefully covered the notes he put down.

For action next morning Smythe-Smithers was keen,
And the clobber he wore was the queerest we'd seen,
He was decked out in jodhpurs and stylish tweed coat
With a polo-necked jumper protecting his throat.
His tall boots, we noted, had heels that were flat
And for head wear he sported a smart bowler hat.

He slapped a smart thigh with a light riding crop
As he strolled to his fate like a chook to the chop.
Then we sat on the rails and prepared for the show
As the horse breaker saddled up Blister below.
He held out the reins as the Pommy climbed down
And walked round the roan like a vaudeville clown.

But he reined up the horse in a manner quite cool
Then quickly and lightly he swung to the 'stool'.
When the air cleared a little to give us a view
Smythe-Smithers was still there, and spurring him too,
We sat round the yard like figures of stone
As the Englishman's yells drowned the squeals of the roan.

For, Pommy or not, he could flaming well ride,
He hit the roan cyclone where'er he saw hide.
His boots raked the dust as the bucking horse chopped
But he sat quite at home till the display had stopped.
Then calmly he picked up the slack of the rein
And stepped to the ground with an air of disdain.

But a horseman's a horseman, no matter how flash,
So we all shook his hand as we paid up the cash,
And the horse breaker said as loudly he sighed
'Young feller, it's true you can certainly ride
And you've taught us a lesson of men and of mounts,
When you're judging a book, it's the story that counts.'

ROUGHRIDERS OF THE BUSH

AUSTRALIAN BUSH HORSEMEN have always been regarded as the best in the world. Certainly the length of time that bad horses were used for stockwork was far longer than in any other country. Australian stockmen had a style of riding that was uniquely their own, a style born of long hours in the saddle, which was easy on both horse and rider. Bush horsemen favoured what was called the forward seat; that is, the rider's legs were forward of the girth. They tended to slouch forward, as well, which put their centre of gravity over the horse's wither, the pivotal point when a horse is bucking. This is quite different to the seat of show riders and present-day rodeo riders.

The gun horsemen of the stations and stockroutes were virtually unknown outside the areas in which they worked. They rode horses equally as bad as the worst rodeo horses, and not only did they ride these horses and work them, they did so without pick-up men and ambulances standing by. Back in the days when the pastoral industry depended exclusively on horses, large stations often had four or five hundred

*A typical foreward seat favoured by Australian
bushmen on rough horses.*

broken-in stockhorses. Stockmen, or ringers, as they were called, were given a string of five or six to work, and the whole horse plant, sometimes more than 100 head, was changed a number of times during the stock season. Most of these horses would buck when fresh after a spell. Some would never give up the habit and would test a stockman's skill at any time.

When stockmen yarned around the fire at night, the talk invariably turned to buckjumping horses and the top horsemen of the day. It was an environment that produced numbers of good roughriders, for young chaps endeavoured to emulate the feats of the top men. I first became interested in recording the names of the bush roughriders when I was working in the Gulf. Frank Uhr had written to the *North Queensland Register* listing the best men he had met during his life in the outback. As a lad, I had known Frank Uhr. He must have been a little over 70 years of age then, but still looked every inch a horseman when mounted. From that point I gathered names of gun horsemen from the old timers I met. During the 1940s and 1950s I worked with some outstanding men myself, and was determined, like Frank Uhr, to one day record their names for posterity. For information about many of the men in the list that follows, I have had to depend on the word of others; however, I have complete confidence in their expertise.

Few, if any, of the buckjump riders who stayed in the bush ever received any publicity or recognition. As a result, gathering information on them has been a challenge. Quite a few bush riders did take up rodeo riding, and most of these men are well known. With few exceptions, this chapter concentrates on the unknown bush riders, although I have included some bushmen who rode in the early buckjump shows and were taken under the wing of men like Lance Skuthorpe. As every bushman knows, not all top roughriders were good all-round horsemen, while there are many fine horsemen who were not above their peers when it came to riding buckjumpers. The criteria I have used here is the recognised ability of a man to master really bad buckjumpers, regardless of anything else. Regrettably many fine all-round horsemen have been omitted as a result. To avoid comparison between many horsemen still living, I have restricted the register to the first half of this century and earlier. I recognise this eliminates many fine roughriders, Luke McCall among them. Luke once worked for me and loved all horses, no matter how bad they were. The following register of roughriders is largely of men from Queensland and the Northern Territory as my appeal for information on horsemen from other States was unfortunately very disappointing; however, I thank those few people who did send me information.

The list of roughriders set out below is neither as complete nor as detailed as I would wish; I believe the job was well worth doing, though. This chapter may not make engrossing reading for city dwellers, but it will create interest, and possibly heated debate, amongst all those who at one time have thrown a saddle on a stockhorse. Any resulting discussion can only throw more light on this long-neglected subject.

Set out below is H.G. 'Frank' Uhr's letter that appeared in the *North Queensland Register* some 50 years ago.

Mr H.F. Uhr writes: Some time back I noticed in the 'Track' a request for the names of outstanding horsemen, probably you will require the names of professional riders, but I am submitting a list of some whom I have personally contacted during my career as a bushman. These men although not professionals in so far as competition riding is concerned were, nevertheless, first-class horsemen, who could or would ride anything that would stand up, and they were local celebrities in this respect.

Firstly I introduce myself as Herbert George Uhr, now known as Frank Uhr, born at Llewellyn, on the Parramatta River (N.S.W.) on the 8th of March 1858. I came to Queensland in 1876 as a jackaroo on Rannes Station, Rockhampton, with Michael Cunningham. Since then I have travelled all over Queensland and the Northern Territory station country, working in different capacities, I did quite a lot of droving and station stocking, and during my career I managed three stations. It was during this time that I came to know H.A. Redford, the well-known fictitious character of Captain Starlight in 'Robbery Under Arms'. I helped him stock Brunette Downs in the Northern Territory, then belonging to McDonald, Smith and Co. On one occasion my brother and I started from Goulburn with 500 head of stud heifers, travelling them to Cape York Peninsula. We were five months on the road without losing a single beast. Many and varied are my experiences of the cattle country, including wild country, wild horses and cattle, wild men and wild natives. I gave up station work in 1907 settling in Finch Hatton, where I have since resided. It is only six months ago that I gave up riding, for the sole reason that I could not get on a horse without being aided. I can assure you that this hurt me very deeply, as I like horses.

Here is my list of first-class riders: **W. and J. CLAYTON** (Chatsworth Station), **M. LALLY** (Mt. Merlin), **C. TOBIN** (Nornsides), **T. RICHARDSON** (Wickton), **J. DILLON** (St. Fort Cooper), **J. MARSHALL** (Lake Elphinstone), **J. GILLIAM** (Eaglefield), **E. GILLIAM** (Blenheim), **T. STERTCH** and **T. McNEIL** (Wellshot), **A. CHICK** (Fanning Downs), **A. TRIVITON** (Hornetbank), **F. DALEY** (Reedy Springs), **J. DALEY** (Broadwater), **H. WALKER** (St. Helens), **JOE ATKINSON** (Travelling Troupe), **J. BRIDGES** (Riverlee), **P. HEGARTY** (Goolsborough), **D. CRONIN** (Newmarket Sales Yard), **G. GROGGIN** (Sesbania), **W. BAILEY SNR.** (Havilah), **P. SYNOTT**, half caste (Corella Downs), **A. WATT**, blackboy (N.T.), **M. McCALL** (Oxford Downs), **H. ROSS** (Creswell Downs), **J. ROLFE** (Wellshot), **C. ROBSON** (Manuka), **D. BLACK** (Sonoma), **W. BATHAM** (Strathmore), **A. ANDERSON** (Ayrshire).

The names of the bush roughriders below are listed alphabetically, not in order of ability.

AH WON, JOHNNY Top horseman from the Northern Territory.

BALDWIN, SNOWY Recognised roughrider in the days of the early buck-jump shows.

BANNAH, TOM Top old-time horseman from Charters Towers.

BARBER, J. Recognised as a gun man in the Gulf.

BARGO, BILLY An Aborigine from North Queensland. A top roughrider who later joined the early buckjump shows.

BARRON, JACK A top man around the turn of the century, reported to have ridden Dargan's Grey at Clermont in 1906.

BRADY, 'BOOMERANG' JACK A renowned roughrider in Queensland and the Northern Territory, Brady is buried beside the stockroute on Eva Downs.

BELL, 'PINCHER' A top Gulf horseman, said to have ridden a station outlaw without disturbing coins placed between his boots and the stirrups irons.

BIGNELL, PADDY A great roughrider, who worked on Dalgonally.

BRENNAN, JIMMY A top buckjumper from the Cooper.

BUTTERWORTH, ALF A top man on a bad horse, from the Nebo district.

BUSSY, CHARLIE Well-known roughrider in the Nebo area.

BUSTARD, BOB A great horseman from Croydon area before the turn of the nineteenth century.

BUTTON, BOB A great roughrider and pioneer of the Kimberley region. In 1884 managed Ord River for Nat Buchanan.

CAMILLERI, PAUL A top horseman from North Eton.

CANT, SAMMY A horse breaker and good buckjump rider.

CASEY, LEO Casey broke-in on A.P. Company stations for many years, a good man on a bad horse.

CATON, PADDY, BILLY AND JIM Were all members of a well-known family in the early days in the Stanthorpe district. They had the reputation of being able to ride anything wrapped in hide and often rode the best horses in travelling buckjump shows. Jim, the last of the roughriding family to pass away, served in both world wars.

CLARK, SANDY A top horseman from the Mitchell area.

CLEARY, CAMMY Recognised as the best buckjump rider of his day, Cammy was a balance rider. I worked with him on Alexandria Station, and he was pretty to see on a bad horse.

Cammy Cleary.

CLINES, JOHNNY Clines was reputed to be a top roughrider and horse breaker.

CLUB, JACK A top buckjump rider, Jack was an Aborigine and worked on Ardmore and Oban Stations in the Mount Isa area.

COLEMAN, CHARLEY A highly regarded Queensland buckjump rider.

COMBANGO, HENRY An Aborigine and a great roughrider of the early days. He worked around Surat.

COOMBER, ROD Coomber had the reputation of being a top man on a bad horse.

COTTON, JACKY Also known as 'Yellow Jacky', Cotton was an Aborigine who worked on Brunette for many years.

COWAN, VIC A fine bushman and roughrider from Leongatha, Victoria. He worked on stations in New South Wales and Queensland, and rode in buckjump shows in the 1920s.

COYE, ANDY Well known around Dimbulah as a top rider.

CRAIGIE, JOE A top man from the Channel Country.

CRISP, MICK Regarded by all as a fine roughrider.

CURLEY, BOB A fine roughrider from the Gulf Country.

CUSACK, PADDY Well known in the Cloncurry district as a top man on a bad horse.

DALE, SPLINTER A well-known horseman of the Central West.

DALLY, JACK Regarded as a fine roughrider in the early part of the twentieth century. He worked in both Queensland and the Northern Territory.

DALY An Aborigine who worked on Humbert River Station. According to the late Charlie Schultz, Daly was unthrowable.

DARCY, CHARLIE Darcy was a great horseman who owned Koonbook Station on Skull Creek in the Kimberley.

DAVIDSON, CECIL A top horseman, Davidson was a head stockman on Gulf stations for many years.

DAVIDSON, RAY A well-known horseman from Charters Towers.

DAVIS, FRANK A top roughrider, he rode an outlaw on Iniskillen Station in 1945 in a saddle without kneepads.

DAWSON, FREDDY A renowned buckjump rider, Dawson was an Aborigine from the Taroom district.

DIAMOND, MICK An Aboriginal man, Mick tracked and found alive a small boy who had been lost for two days on Riverslea Station. Mick worked in the Gulf Country, and according to Les Huddy, a top man himself, Mick was not thrown in the 30 years he knew him.

DIXON, JACK A top horseman from the Channel Country.

DODD, TOMMY A highly respected Aborigine and a top horseman, well known in the Territory.

DOUGLAS, FRANK (SNR) Well known in the Cloncurry district.

DOWLING, 'LOOKING GLASS' JOE A top man on a bad horse, Looking Glass worked in the Gulf Country and was later a Northern Territory boss drover.

DOYLE, BARTLE A top horseman and buckjump rider, well known on many Gulf stations.

DRENIN, TOMMY A good man on a bad horse, Drenin was head stockman in the Tambo district.

DUNCAN, ALEX A good man on a bad horse, from the Mitchell district.

DUNCAN, COLIN Alex's brother and a top man on a buckjumper.

EMMERSON, BILLY Listed by Gregory Mitchell as a top man.

FARBER, HARRY Farber was born near St Laurence in Queensland in 1879. His father was from Morocco. Farber worked for a number of years on Waverley Station at Broadsound, earning the reputation of being a fine horseman who was virtually unthrowable when riding bareback. He rode many of the best buckjump show horses using this method. In 1911 he helped overland a mob of 250 horses from the Queensland Gulf to Derby in the Kimberley. There he followed horse

Frank Douglas Snr.

'Looking Glass' Joe Dowling.

Mrs Ada Devereaux

breaking and later went droving with a plant of mules. Farber's reputation as a roughrider was enhanced by his work in the West.

FINDLAY, 'FIN' A top all-round horseman, well known in the Camooweal district.

FINLAY, ROSS Top rider, from the Thargomindah area.

FORTUNE, 'MONKEY' Fortune had the reputation in the North-West of being a good man on a bad horse.

FOWLER, JIM Fowler was head stockman on Alexandria, where he once rode a notorious station outlaw. Later owned and ran the Rankine store.

FULLER, SAM (SNR) A legendary buckjump rider and showman, known throughout Queensland.

GAITER, BOB Well-known horseman of the Central West.

GREY, PHILLIP A top horseman from Manilla, New South Wales, broke in horses for 'Bluey' Buchanan in 1880.

GROOM, JIM A top man who worked on Dalgonally and Lake Nash.

HARRIS, DOUG A good roughrider and the best all-round horseman I worked with.

HARRISON, JOHN Reputed to be a top man on a bad horse.

HAWKINS, 'QUEENSLAND HARRY' An Aborigine and a top roughrider, Harry later travelled with Skuthorpe.

HAYDEN, ALEX Often described as the best of all Aboriginal horsemen. Born at Chinchilla, Hayden won many buckjump championships. He was accidentally killed in the cattle camp on Auburn Station. He was just 34 years old.

HAYES, JACK Said by many to be a good roughrider.

HILL, BILLY According to men I have spoken to, Hill was a top rider.

HILL, SAMMY Looked after Herbert Downs for many years, few men better on a bad horse.

HORRIGAN, JACK Jack was head stockman on Kyabra Station in the 1870s. A top roughrider in his youth.

HUEY, JOHN Well known around Kynuna, Huey rode the outlaw Windamere Whirlwind.

HUGHS, ALEX A top horseman, reputed to have undone both saddle girth and bridle while riding a buckjumper.

HUTCHING, BOB Said to be an excellent roughrider. He worked in the Croydon district as horse breaker.

HUTLEY, JACK Well-known Gulf horseman.

HYLAND, TOM Listed by Gregory Mitchell as a top man.

ISLES, BILL, GEORGE AND LLOYD Members of a well-known Central West Queensland family, all top horsemen.

JOHNSON, WATTY A top man, he managed Bulloo Downs.

JONES, 'GALLOPING JACK' Well-known Gulf identity and top horseman, a wild character and notorious poddy dodger.

JUNGUALLA I worked on Alexandria when Jungualla was a child. He later worked on other Tableland stations and was regarded as a top roughrider.

KELLY, PAT A well-known horseman who worked in the Barcaldine area of Queensland.

KERRY, JACK A top man on a rough horse, from the Central West of Queensland.

KING, DICK A top rider and head stockman in the Queensland Gulf.

KIRKMAN, ARTHUR One of the best roughriders in the Gulf Country, he was head stockman on Dalgonally for many years before World War II. After war service he did not return to the North.

LAWTON, FRED A top man from the Dawson River area.

LAWTON, GEORGE A top roughrider, and a member of the Lawton family from Dawson Valley.

LAWTON, TED Another of the Lawtons from Juanda Run in the Dawson Valley, Ted was a top horseman and cattleman.

LEDGERWOOD, JIM Renowned buckjump rider, well known in the Territory.

LEWIS, ELMORE Head stockman on Newcastle Waters, and a good rough-rider, Lewis was a strong man and a grip rider.

LEWIS, GEORGE 'SPEAR GRASS' Head stockman on Brunette Downs for many years, and later managed Victoria River Downs. Top all-round horseman.

LLOYD, LEO AND TOM (JNR) Sons of Tom Senior's second marriage. Both were champion buckjump riders who joined Thorpe McConville's troupe of roughriders.

LLOYD, NED A son of Tom Lloyd and Margaret, Ned Lloyd was regarded as Australia's best buckjump rider in his day. He represented Australia in England in 1911 and later he was with McConville's buckjump show.

LLOYD, TOM (SNR) Tom Lloyd was a cousin of the Kellys and a great horseman in the early days in Victoria. He enjoyed a long and fruitful relationship with Margaret, Kelly's sister after her marriage broke up. Years later, after Margaret died, he married Steve Hart's sister.

LONG, GEORGE Long was an Aborigine and a top man on a bad horse. He worked in Western Queensland.

LONGWELL, RAY A top horseman who worked in the Central West after World War II. He rode a station outlaw at Oondoroo.

McCALL, AINSLIE 'CHUM' A top man on a bad horse, well known in the Nebo District. 'Chum' was a nephew of Martin McCall, who was listed by Frank Uhr.

McCORMAC, BILLY An Aborigine born at Chatsworth Station, north of Boulia. A top man on a bad horse, Billy later worked as a teamster. He once took a wagon team to Longreach and while there rode every

Mrs Lola Rowe

Tom Lloyd Jnr.

horse in a buckjump show. Billy died at Kajabbi, Queensland in the mid-1920s.

McHUGH, JIM Jim had the reputation of being a fine roughrider. He worked on Clive Station, Marlborough.

McHUGH, MICK Like his brother Jim, Mick was recognised as a top man on a bad horse.

McMILLAN, LES A fine horseman and buckjump rider from the Dawson Valley, McMillan represented Australia overseas.

Mrs Lola Rowe

Tom Lloyd Snr.

Linda Craig

Ainslie 'Chum' McCall.

Jim McHugh.

McPHEE, HARRY A top horseman from Scone, ex-POW.

MAHER, CLARRIE 'CHIPS' A top horseman from the Barcaldine district.

MAN FONG, GEORGE A fine horseman from the Top End.

MINAGUE, PADDY A famous horseman in the Gulf Country prior to the turn of the nineteenth century.

MOREY, TED A fine all-round horseman and roughrider. Later a well-known member of the Northern Territory mounted police.

MORRISSEY, JACK Jack came from Grafton in New South Wales, a top bush buckjump rider. With other Australians he rode at Crystal Palace, England in 1911. He travelled with Thorpe McConville.

MURRAY, JACK A top horseman in the early days, Murray travelled with Thorpe McConville's buckjump shows.

NAGEE, TOM A top man from the Beaudesert area.

NATHAN, BYRON Born on Carrandotta, where his father was speared by Aborigines, Byron had the reputation of being not only good on a bad horse, but a fine all-round horseman. He worked in both Queensland and the Northern Territory. An Aborigine and expert tracker, he once tracked a pair of cattle duffers for the police. This did not enhance his popularity with his peers.

NICHOLSON, DON A top rider who worked in the Hughenden and Maxwelton districts during the 1920s.

NINUS, JOHN A top rider, he was head stockman on Mount Howard.

NOBLE, BOBBY A top horseman who worked on Caldervale and other Western Queensland stations.

NOBLE, PADDY Brother of Bobby Noble and also a good man on a bad horse.

NORMAN, TOMMY An Aborigine who worked on Nockatunga and many other stations in the area, Norman was regarded as one of the best buckjump riders in the Channel Country.

Byron Nathan.

Mick Bailey

Tommy Norman.

PATTELL, NORM Recognised as a top man on a bad horse, he worked in the Cloncurry/Julia Creek area.

PATTERSON, JOHN An Aborigine and a top horseman, he did a lot of horse breaking on Gulf Country runs.

PENDERGAST, JACK An early roughrider from New South Wales.

PENDERGAST, 'SPLINTER' A top man on a bad horse, well known as a Northern Territory drover.

PIDGIN, ROY A well-known buckjump rider from Queensland.

PRIMUS, NOEL A very good man on a bad horse. I knew Noel when he was head stockman on Chatsworth Station, Boulia.

PROSSER, TOMMY Well known for years in the Mount Isa area as a good man on a bad horse.

RICHARDSON, LES Reputed to be a top man on a bad horse.

RIDEOUT, JACK A famous buckjump rider from the Dawson Valley.

ROSE, JOE Rose, an Aborigine, was born and reared on Tobermorie Station near Unandangie, Queensland. He was a fine roughrider and rode Strike, an outlaw, in a travelling buckjump show.

ROY, TOMMY A fine roughrider, Roy was killed when a horse fell with him.

RUDD, LES Reputed to be a good buckjump rider, Rudd worked in the Gulf Country.

RYDER, JACK A top horseman from the Injune district. Ryder once rode an outlaw—a chestnut horse that had thrown many top professional riders—in the Mitchell showgrounds. He gave the £30 he won to the ambulance.

SALTNER, NELSON A well-known horseman from the Dawson River, Nelson broke in mounts for the light horse during World War I.

SHERWIN, JACK Jack was head stockman on Millungera for many years. He tied his irons on a bad horse.

SIMPSON, DON A top horseman who worked in the Dawson Valley, Simpson later ran camps at Carpentaria Downs and Forrest Home. At a remount depot in England during World War I, he rode an outlaw in a bare military saddle.

SIMPSON, TOM A top horse breaker and rider from the Hunter River District.

SNIEDER, CHARLIE Reputed to be a good man on a bad horse.

SNOWY An Aborigine from Humbert River and a top man on a bad horse, a brother of Daly.

SOUTHEE, BOB A fine roughrider from the Darling Downs, said to have ridden Queenslander, a horse with a big reputation, in a buckjump show.

SPEEDY, MICK (SNR) A very smart old-time buckjump rider and athlete from Central West Queensland.

STACE, OCTAVIUS A good roughrider, Stace worked on stations on Cape York Peninsula during the 1920s and 1930s.

STRATON, WALLY Straton possibly originally came from South Australia, and worked on stations in Western Queensland. While on Riverdale Station, he rode a black station outlaw. Bob Isles witnessed the display. A top horseman himself, Bob said it was one of the best rides he had ever seen.

STREAK, JACK Reported to be a top buckjump rider.

SULLIVAN, JACK (SNR) One of the best buckjump riders in the Top End. It is said that there was $4000 for any man who could produce a horse that could throw Sullivan.

SYMES, DARKY A well-known horseman in the Cloncurry/Boulia areas, Symes worked on Warenda as both horse breaker and head stockman. Later was a boss drover.

TAYLOR, LOU Worked in the Cloncurry district in the 1930s. A great horseman.

THOMAS, BEN A good roughrider, Thomas managed Ticlara.

THOMAS, BILLY 'THE GALLOPING GHAN' A well-known character in Western Queensland, a very good horseman.

TIMMINS, GEORGE A good man on a bad horse and a top man with wild cattle.

TREFFETT, TED A top roughrider from the Julia Creek district.

TRIMBLE, LOUIS Worked in the Einasleigh district during the 1920s. A top man on a bad horse.

VICTOR An Aborigine from the famous Elsey Station, Victor was a top buckjump rider and a very smart man with a bad beast.

VITNAL, JACK A good roughrider, Vitnal worked in Queensland and the Northern Territory. A grip rider, he was a good man with a bad beast.

WAITE, BILLY An Aborigine originally from the Gulf Country, he was one of the smartest horsemen and showmen of his day. Waite became Skuthorpe's right-hand man and represented Australia more than once in both England and America.

WATSON, JACK An Aborigine from Gatton in Queensland, Watson was a top buckjump rider who won a world championship in Sydney in 1924. He later travelled overseas with Skuthorpe.

WEIBER, JACK 'HOOT' Reputed to be a very good man on a bad horse.

WERRIBAN, JACK Originally from New South Wales, he was a very smart all-round horseman. Another fine Aboriginal buckjump rider and an expert with scrub cattle. Well known around Surat.

WILLIAMS, JOHNNY Known as 'Yellow Johnny', he was one of the smartest horsemen in Western Queensland. Williams was born at Davenport Station and worked on many outback runs.

WILSON, JIM A top rider from the St George district.

WILSON, STAN An outstanding horseman from Central Queensland.

WOLFE, ROY Originally from Wellshot in Queensland, Wolfe worked in the Northern Territory. A very good man on a rough horse.

The above horsemen were the cream of Australia's bush buckjump riders. Few of them ever sought publicity, yet they were perhaps the best roughriders in the world. We should remember them with pride.

Rod Bellette

Stan Wilson.

MICK CASEY

Mick Casey was a drover bloke way out at Whistle Stop
Who never knew the price of meat in any butcher's shop;
For Casey scorned the flaccid steak upon the butcher's shelf
And from the Gillgai Station herd he simply helped himself.
The Gillgai herd was rolling fat—and Gillgai rump was sweet,
Mick Casey and his mates in town were never short of meat,
He always got his beef at night, long practice lent him speed,
The stars alone looked down and saw Mick Casey do the deed.

To cattlemen and police alike Mick Casey was a thief,
But many thought it not a crime to dine on station beef.
The Gillgai run was English owned and runs like this it's true
Have long been used by larrikins to boost their revenue.
A sergeant came to Whistle Stop, a cunning sort of bird,
He learnt of Casey's barbecues and fumed at what he heard;
He made a promise then and there that justice would prevail,
And loudly swore he wouldn't rest till Casey was in jail.

Mick Casey laughed at idle threats, not bothered in the least
He sharpened up his butcher's knives to kill another beast.
And just to show he held no grudge towards the local law
He left a juicy sirloin roast beside the sergeant's door.
The status quo remained intact, as days and weeks went by
With Casey eating fillet steak—the sergeant, humble pie.
For Casey kept his fridge well stocked as he was wont to do,
Till fickle fate and carelessness brought on his waterloo.

One night he killed by Gillgai Creek and after he had gone
He cursed himself, remembering he'd left the earmark on,
That in itself was bad enough, then driving back through town
Just as the dawn began to break, his trusty ute broke down.
When evening came to Whistle Stop and light began to fail
The sergeant's fridge was full of meat, with Casey out on bail.
They found the carcass with the head and quickly cut it loose,
This Gillgai head, the sergeant said, will really cook his goose.

They placed it in a drum of brine behind the station cells,
To pickle it until the trial and neutralise the smells.
Mick Casey kept his spirits up, despite the loss of face,
But sausages were all the go for meals at Casey's place.
The breaker came to town one night, he laughed when he was told,
'Some action here is what you need, a simple plan and bold,
I reckon I can help you mate, because I know you well
For twenty quid I'll pinch the head and blow the case to hell.'

The deal was struck, the money paid, the breaker grabbed a sack.
'Go down the creek and dig a hole, wait there till I get back.
There's shelter there, so light a fire, and take some Bundy rum,
I'll signal you if all is clear, I'll whistle as I come.'
The breaker travelled through the dark avoiding any light,
His movements were as furtive as kadaicha men at night.
He reached the lock-up fence at last, he froze at every sound,
Then silently he crossed the yard, his belly to the ground.

The breaker slid the cover back and reaching through the scum
He grasped a horn and slowly drew the head out of the drum.
He heaved the bag onto his back returning without pause,
Mick Casey saw him coming like an outback Santa Claus.
They buried deep the evidence in hope that crime might pay,
Then Casey opened up the rum and threw the cork away.
On Friday Casey faced the court but Casey's step was light,
No longer did the threat of jail hang o'er him like a blight.

A magistrate to hear the case from down the line was brought,
And all of Whistle Shop turned out when Casey went to court.
They lugged inside the heavy drum and with it came as well
The subtle scent of Casey's crime—a faint accusing smell.
But Casey stood there in the dock quite certain of his fate,
When asked to plead he gave a grin. 'I didn't do it mate.'
The sergeant gave the facts, then said, 'Your Worship, if I may,
Draw your attention to the drum that's marked "Exhibit A".

'It holds the Crown's best evidence, a most important clue,
For in it rests a bullock's head—the one that Casey slew.'
The sergeant walked up to the drum, he drew the cover off,
Mick Casey made a strangled sound, that ended as a cough.
The sergeant rolled his shirt sleeves up, he paused as show men do,
Then plunged his bare arms elbow deep into the sluggish brew.
He fished around inside awhile, the court was hushed with dread,
Then from the drum he lifted high a Gillgai bullock's head.

This sergeant was a wily bird, when all is said and done,
It's common knowledge that two heads are better than just one.
He'd checked the drum the day before, but nothing had been said,
He simply shot another beast and got another head.
Mick Casey looked across the court in utter disbelief,
And realised the police had sent a thief to catch a thief.
'I'll change me plea,' Mick Casey groaned. 'And cop what comes me way,
For there's a smarter rogue than me in this here court today.'
Though Casey sweats in durance vile to pay for what he did,
The thing that galls him most of all is wasting twenty quid.

CHARACTERS AND
HARD CASES

THE ECCENTRIC BEHAVIOUR and idiosyncrasies of outback charac-ters have seldom raised an eyebrow; nevertheless, I remember a few cases whose bizarre habits placed them in a class of their own.

Years ago an elderly character known as Sully was employed as a station cook on Sudan, an outstation of Alexandria. As the stockcamp was out on the run most of the time, Sully acted as caretaker as well as cook, a dual role that he relished. It must be said that Sully took his responsibilities very seriously and this, coupled with an intense dislike of his fellow man, caused the welcome he extended to visitors to be rather less than that demanded by bush hospitality.

Sully's constant companion was a half-naked cockatoo that appeared to be permanently fixed to his left shoulder. On meeting Sully for the first time, a keen observer might arrive at two conclusions: firstly, the cockatoo always faced the front; and secondly, Sully seldom if ever changed his shirt—the back of the garment was thickly encrusted with cockatoo droppings. Although Sully was entirely without teeth, he constantly chewed tobacco. You needed to be on your toes when you were around him, for he expelled the juice from his pursed lips with more velocity than accuracy. Like the cockatoo, Sully was a bit thin on top and what hair he did have he cropped short, giving him the appearance of an old lag.

Sully had his own method of discouraging outside visitors. He would emerge from the kitchen with a skinning knife in one hand, a butcher's steel in the other, and the cockatoo on his shoulder. Both he and the bird would fix the stranger with an unblinking stare, then, gently caressing the steel with the knife, Sully would ask in a hoarse whisper, 'Did anyone see you come here?'

No matter what the visitor said in reply, Sully's rejoinder was always the same: 'Well, no one is going to see you leave.'

It invariably worked; Sully and the cockatoo would return to the kitchen in triumph as the caller departed in a cloud of dust.

Years ago a well-known Gulf station was managed by a colourful figure who at times got a bee in his bonnet and sacked the whole station staff. At that time the mail truck ran down the Leichhardt River to

Burketown on one day and returned the next. One morning when the mail was due and all hands were in at the homestead, the manager walked into the men's dining room at breakfast time and sacked everyone, including the cook. They got their cheques from the bookkeeper and in due course climbed onto the mail truck.

That evening the manager and the bookkeeper sat down to a frugal repast prepared by the bookkeeper. After the meal, the bookkeeper leaned back in his chair. 'Well, Mr . . ., there's only you and me left now.'

'That's true,' replied the manager, 'and after the mail truck leaves tomorrow, there will only be me.'

One old-time Territory drover, who was well liked and respected by his peers, was very hard on himself. He had a violent temper, but he seldom directed his spleen at anyone but himself. He usually had a large wagonette on the road with him and used the vehicle in a unique way to punish himself for perceived mistakes. Removing his hat, he would stand back and then charge head-down into a wagonette wheel. After he had regained his feet, he would replace his hat and declare, 'Well, that will knock a bit of sense into you.'

The wagonette was a large one, enabling the drover to carry packs in case of the vehicle breaking down. On one occasion he reached camp to find he had lost one of a pair of water canteens. A packsaddle carries one canteen on each side, to balance the load. One canteen, then, is as useful as a hip pocket in a singlet. The drover roared and raged, then, unable to restrain himself any longer, he grabbed the camp axe and laid into the odd canteen. He had just finished belting it into a mass of twisted metal when a station vehicle pulled by the camp with its missing mate. Once again the drover was left with an odd canteen. It was just too much. Roaring and swinging the axe, he charged the second canteen as the startled motorist leapt behind the wheel of his vehicle and fled. After the drover had disembowelled the object of his wrath, he pulled off his hat and gave the wagonette wheel a touch up.

The indigenous people of the Northern Territory have suffered greatly from diseases introduced by Macassar seafarers and whites. During World War II the influx of both American and Australian forces to the Northern Territory caused a serious increase in venereal disease. This outbreak proved to be as big a threat to the white 'combos' (white men who lived with Aboriginal women) as it did to the Aborigines. However, penicillin, the magic bullet, soon had the disease under control, and the combos took the malady in their stride. There was actually a joke among these hardened sinners that a man had to have suffered from what they called 'the pox' before he made the grade. One old reprobate I knew used to introduce himself with these words: 'They say a bloke has to have had the pox once before he's a man. Well, shake hands with Superman.'

In the days when the horse was still king, outback cooks were an eccentric lot who were sometimes rather unreliable. A fine exponent of camp-oven cuisine was a character known as Barefoot Bob. As the name implies, he never wore boots, and his feet had calluses on them like those of a camel. Barefoot Bob cooked for me on one droving trip and I found him one of the best packhorse cooks I'd struck; nothing was any trouble for Barefoot Bob. Most cooks on the road will only pack the horse carrying the cooked tucker pack. Barefoot Bob, though, would get stuck into throwing on as many packs as the horsetailer. When working around the fire, he sometimes stood on a live coal; someone would have to tell him, for the smell of burning skin pervaded the camp long before Barefoot Bob felt any pain.

I first met the barefooted cook when I was working on Alexandria. Bob was doing the cooking and got on well with us all. During a few days' spell at the Rankine, someone dared Barefoot Bob to walk across a huge pile of broken bottles at the back of the place. Fortifying himself with OP rum, he faced up to the challenge, then marched across singing 'Onward Christian Soldiers'. He did not suffer as much as a scratch.

That night Barefoot Bob, flushed with victory and rum, fell asleep by the open campfire. I'm not sure what woke me, but I looked up to see our cook ablaze from the knees down. Leaping out of my swag, I threw a handy bucket of water over him. Next morning Barefoot Bob seemed more concerned about his ruined trousers than about any burns he had suffered.

There was one character who had worked on the same Gulf Country station for many years. Sometimes he was employed as the station cook and at other times he did the cowboy's job; that is, milk the cows and chop the wood, etc. This character, who we will call Jim, had a great weakness for rum and often, to the manager's chagrin, became a real nuisance. One Anzac eve Jim and a mate secured a bottle of Bundy from sources unknown and proceeded to make the station buildings echo with their revelry. No one had a chance of getting any sleep, and about midnight the manager decided that enough was enough and strode down to the men's quarters. He threw open the door of Jim's room to see the pair standing to attention as the Last Post was played at the midnight service. Disregarding the show of patriotism, the manager tore a strip off them both, and sacked Jim on the spot.

Next morning the head stockman was at the horseyards. He had heard the night's barney from the next room and was surprised to see Jim, as usual, milking a cow, his head buried in her flank. He strolled over and addressed the hungover cowboy.

'I thought you got the sack last night.'

'Oh,' replied Jim, 'if I took any notice of that baldy-headed bastard I'd never have a job.'

There was a stockman known as 'Ding Dong' Bell who worked on stations over quite a lot of Queensland. Ding Dong was a bit of a character, and a bit of a nutcase as well. He often complained about entities he called 'Nigly Aglies' that hassled him. Despite this aberration, Ding Dong was an excellent stockman. I never worked with him myself, but more than once have had a drink with him. He did at times, however, do some crazy things, including burning down his mother's house. Ding Dong finally overstepped the boundary of eccentricity when he decapitated a chap with a cane knife.

The greatest group of hard cases to ride north to the Territory was, without doubt, the notorious Ragged Thirteen. Their exploits have become part of the folklore of the North, and time may well have enhanced their reputation for devilry. Nevertheless, the thirteen were a formidable lot who made free with the stock and property of those unlucky enough to be in the wrong place at the wrong time. The Ragged Thirteen didn't embrace any romantic notions about robbing from the rich to give to the poor, but no one left their camp hungry. Despite their depredations, Territorians never really regarded the Ragged Thirteen as criminals. Whenever I heard them mentioned, it was more with admiration than antipathy. The group apparently got its name from one of their number, 'Tommy The Rag'. According to legend, Rag's thirteen was corrupted to become the 'Ragged Thirteen'.

They were tough men in a land where only the tough survived. All good horsemen, most of them would just as soon have a fight as a feed. The group rode through the Territory heading for the goldfields around Hall's Creek. Some struck it lucky and some didn't. I was privileged to meet a few of them in later life. The leader of the Ragged Thirteen, Tom Nugent, changed his name and established Banka Station, north of Tennant Creek. Another, Bob Anderson, battled droughts and low prices on Tobermory, a run over the border fence, west of Boulia. Anderson is buried on Tobermory and the station is still owned by the family. The rest of them scattered to the four winds, but the legend of the Ragged Thirteen remains.

Otto Khan was a rather benign character who kept a drovers' store at Urandangie. What set him apart from his fellows was his race. Otto was an Afghan, a cameleer who, like his countrymen, turned his hand to other things when the humble camel had had its day. He had a lively sense of humour and wasn't above having a joke with the stockmen and drovers. He met his match when he greeted Jimmy Carr with the words: 'Ah! Jimmy Carr, all the same as motor car.'

'Yes,' replied Jimmy, 'and you're Otto Khan, black as a billy can.'

Otto Khan liked to get fresh meat from the drovers whenever they killed close to the town. However, his religion forbade the eating of meat unless the beast was killed in a manner dictated by the code of Islam. Anyone could shoot the selected beast, but they then had to stand back while Otto Khan bled the carcass and offered up a halal prayer. That done, the meat was cut from the carcass and Otto went off happily with his share.

James Francis 'Gidgea' Taylor was one of the great characters of Winton in outback Queensland. Born in 1905, he suffered from poor eyesight and a slight disability, whether from birth or from a childhood disease like measles is not recorded. Whatever the cause, Gidgea did not let it bother him. He went on to become a much loved character of the town. From a very young age Gidgea was the mascot of the Winton Rugby League team, leading the players on to the field at every home and away game. His memory of past matches was phenomenal. He could quote results and scores of football games going back many years, and could name the winners of any major horse race. Because of his eyes, he never learnt to read or write. Nature must have compensated for this by giving him an almost infallible memory. He only had to hear some detail and it stayed with him forever.

Another of Gidgea Taylor's claims to fame was that he was probably the last town crier in Queensland. Bill Evert, who owned the Royal Theatre, paid Gidgea a retainer to act as a town crier to advertise coming attractions. Gidgea, complete with bell, patrolled the streets of Winton. His description and commentary on the expected movies was at times more entertaining than the films. Gidgea often rode a bike when running messages for the Winton Hotel, where he was an odd job man. It was a common sight to see him pedalling back to the pub with parcels balanced on his head. At age 18 he is reported to have won a bravery award for rescuing a lad from drowning in the Winton dam. In the early 1950s Gidgea Taylor was presented with a Winton Rugby League blazer in honour of his service to the club.

As he grew older and his eyesight became worse, he gave up the bike and walked everywhere. He learned to recognise people by their voices: once heard never forgotten. Gidgea could recognise anyone who had previously spoken to him. Gidgea Taylor died in 1965 and was buried in his football blazer. He is remembered by those who knew him as a great character and a true blue Aussie.

Brian Riaz really was a hard case. He was a big, genial character with an infectious chuckle and an acknowledged weakness for strong drink. After working on wages as a stockman for some time, Brian had a stroke of luck. His uncle, a well-respected drover, gave Brian a complete droving plant to start him off on a career as a boss drover. Brian did a couple of trips, then got on the grog at the Urandangie pub. He drank his cheque then started on the plant. Saddles, horses and packs were all sold, and the money went over the bar. What his uncle thought of this is not known. Having liquidated his assets, Brian was forced to go back working for wages. He ended up cooking in the Channel Country stockcamps. Brian's specialty was cooking fritters, called 'Burdekin Ducks' in the bush; Brian called his 'Riaz's' scrumpducks', although the scrumptious prefix was open to debate. Brian passed on well before his time. He was on a spree in Winton and went to sleep on the lawn between two pubs. He never woke up. For a man who had drunk a whole droving plant, it was an apt place to depart for the last muster.

Albert James 'Tie Wire' Edwards was not so much a hard case as a hard man. When a boss drover, he was refused water from a station owner when the mob he was in charge of were badly in need of a drink. Edwards offered to pay for the water but again met with a blunt refusal. Now, a boss drover is judged by the condition of the cattle he delivers, and Edwards was not about to jeopardise his reputation. Grabbing the station manager by the scruff of the neck, Edwards took him over to a tree, where he effected the immobilisation of his captive by tying him to the tree with a piece of tie wire across the bridge of his nose. Having neutralised the opposition, Edwards proceeded to water his mob. In due course he released the blaspheming owner, who swore he'd have Edwards's guts for gaiters.

He did sue the drover, and the case went to court. There must have been some good cattlemen on the jury, for Edwards was acquitted. From

Blue Ellis

The Glengyle mustering camp at Pulchera yard on the Mulligan River, early 1920s. A.J. 'Tie Wire' Edwards is in white with arms folded.

then on he was known as 'Tie Wire' Edwards. He later became a manager for Kidman.

Thomas Anzac Burrows was an outstanding character. It was not that Tom was an eccentric or a ratbag; he was simply a character, and a likeable and unique one at that. As a teenager he suffered terrible injuries when a horse fell with him. After weeks in a coma, he regained consciousness and left hospital to face life with a serious handicap. To say that Tom overcame that handicap would be an understatement. His sheer guts and determination won him respect and a large number of friends. Tom never lost his sense of waggish humour. More than once I have seen him turn a situation that was about to become serious into one of laughter.

Tom was on the road droving with me not long after his accident. On the way out to pick up cattle, we ran into a rat plague. That night we camped at a government bore and hung all the packs and packbags up in trees to prevent the rats devouring them. It looked like being a sleepless night, but Tom had other ideas.

'Sleep in your swags,' he told us. 'I'll guard the camp tonight.'

We wondered what he was up to, but soon all was revealed. Getting a long length of number eight wire from the fence around the bore, he doubled it then twisted the two halves together.

'This', he said, swishing it about, 'is what I call Tom's tranquilliser. No rodent will enter this camp tonight.'

We unrolled our swags and watched with interest. Tom built up a large fire, threw out a piece of corned meat as bait, then sat down with his tranquilliser across his knees. The action was not long in coming; throughout the night our sleep was broken by the sounds of swish, whack, 'cop that', swish, thunk, 'gotcha, you bastard'.

When daylight broke, the camp resembled a battleground. Tom, bleary eyed but happy, gave us the score: Burrows, 125; the rats, nil.

In more recent years Tom lived at Alice Springs, where he had his own small residence at Ted Egan's 'Sinkatinny Downs'. When Ted was away, Tom acted as caretaker, but always had a few irons in the fire himself. At one time he bred and sold poultry. These he kept in a very large fenced area behind his house. His method of doing business was simple: he took the money and let the buyer run down the purchased birds himself.

Tommy Burrows and mates in Camooweal, 1960.
Left to right: *Alan Simpson, Tommy Burrows,*
Ernie McCarthy and Noel Willetts.

I sometimes visited Tom, and one of my most vivid memories is of a portly cafe proprietor vainly pursuing a fleet-footed turkey, while Tom drank a beer and shouted encouragement.

Tom also had an early morning rubbish contract. In his small red truck, he went around the Alice Springs business houses picking up cartons and other dry rubbish. He got going before the shops opened and the traffic started. This was just as well, for Tom tended to rewrite the traffic code as he went. He knew just about everyone, and his cheerful shouted greetings to the early risers used to echo down the almost empty streets. I have travelled with Tom on these runs; it is an experience I will never forget.

Thomas Anzac Burrows died on 15 February 1999. He was a great Australian whose life story is undeniable proof of the supremacy of the human spirit over adversity.

THE BURROWS MORNING RUN

The tourists come to Alice Springs, they come from near and far,
Some travellers come in aeroplanes, and some by motor car.
There's some who like to ride the rails and catch the famous Ghan,
Some hitch a ride and get there by whatever means they can.
They come to Alice Springs because there's much to see and do,
Some take a trip to Simpson's Gap and some climb Uluru.

They travel out to Alice Springs from many climes and lands
To see the famous masters games or Henley on the sands.
A lot buy prints and artefacts to take back overseas,
And if they don't find value here, they're pretty hard to please.
Some tourists like historic sites and photograph the 'spring',
But most prefer to have a beer and hear Ted Egan sing.

The tourists come to Alice Springs, they come by day and night,
The pious and the pagan, and the sober and the tight.
Of all the sights that they will see, when all is said and done,
There's none can hold a candle to the Burrows morning run.
And fortunate indeed are they, those travellers who have been
Beside a living legend in his famous red machine.

THE DACHSHUND-PONY CROSS

Just twelve months ago tomorrow, I recall the fact with sorrow,
I signed the pledge teetotal and renounced all alcohol.
No greater soak existed till the 'Salvos' got me listed,
But the tale of my salvation is, I fear, a trifle droll.
I had come in with a drover all the way from 'Sanded Over',
For two weary months of boredom we had sweated day and night,
And our skins were fairly cracking from the moisture content lacking
When we struck a Western township by the name of Sandy-blight.

Now our cheques were nice and healthy, we were feeling rather wealthy,
So we started on a bender that extended for a week.
Oh! we made the grog look silly, for we drank it from a billy,
And I ended in the horrors at our camp upon the creek.
In the DTs I was running brumby mobs whose native cunning
Wasn't equalled by the rodents of a well-known public place,
For their speed was hackle raising, their sagacity amazing
As we crossed the creeks and ridges at a denny-hazer pace.

For six days and nights I chased 'em, though I never once outpaced 'em
And the West lay far behind us as the farmlands came in view.
Over fence and field I followed, past the sties where porkers wallowed,
For I swore that I would wheel 'em if they went to Timbuktu.
Then the nag that I was riding seemed to shorten in his striding
As we passed a cocky's farmlet in a belt of gooseberry trees,
And for that I soon accounted, for I found when I dismounted
That his legs from ceaseless riding were all worn off to the knees.

Well, that rang the final curtain on the brumby hunt for certain,
But in my drunken nightmare I conceived a grand idea.
I could see my wallet swelling as I sought the cocky's dwelling
With my erstwhile brumby runner pussy-footing in the rear.
Now the farmer bloke seemed chary when I met him in the dairy,
But I raised my old Akubra and politely called him 'boss'.
Oh! my luck was never better, for my plan worked to the letter
And I sold my stumpy charger as a dachshund-pony cross.

But when the daylight found me with the dead marines around me
I swore with deadly fervour that I'd never drink again,
While my cobbers thought me balmy, that same day I joined the 'army'
For worse times or for better, I signed up with shaking pen.
Though I sometimes get to thinking that I'd like a bout of drinking,
I can't regard its absence from my lifestyle as a loss,
For my spirits still are daunted and nocturnally I'm haunted
By the sawn-off apparition of the dachshund-pony cross.

THE RIDING OF THE DEBIL

(As told by Murranji Mick. With apologies to the late Will Ogilvie.)

Now, you youngsters think you're riders when you break a colt or two,
Why you wouldn't make offsiders for the breakers that I knew;
I have listened to your blowin' and the flamin' blatherskite
Of your ridin' and your throwin' every flamin' day and night.
Your tongues are always waggin' of some harmless flamin' moke,
But you never hear me braggin' of the outlaws that I broke.

I was never one for glory, as I've often said before,
But I'll tell a dinkum story if you'll hold your flamin' jaw.
It was some time in November, and the year was thirty-four,
I was breakin', I remember, on a run called Bullgalore;
That was in the Never Never near the town of Shantyview
On the Bullmakanka River where the crockagaters chew.

Well, one day we heard a rumour from the mailman passing through,
And although it was a boomer he was certain it was true,
For it seemed old Jock McGrilly up at Grabagrogangrin
Had a flamin' outlaw filly that he wanted broken in.
She would buck and kick and trample and she'd killed a dozen men,
Oh! she was a fair example of the nags we handled then.

Yes, she was a real humdinger and McGrilly said he'd pay
A tenner to the ringer who could tame her in a day.
Well, those days I liked to gamble so I ran me horses in
And I started at an amble up to Grabagrogangrin.
I unpacked and boiled me billy where I camped beside the yard,
And I saw the outlaw filly a sorta lookin' at me hard.

Now the Debil they had named her and the ringers in the huts
Said the flamin' man who tamed her would be needin' tons of guts.
All her victims had been recent but no man could ever say
That they didn't do things decent up the Bullmakanka way;
For they made a cemetery where they laid 'em nice and neat,
At their heads a conkaberry and the goat yard at their feet.

Jimmy Bunion came to ride her, he had just come off a spree,
But he said that once astride her he would be a sight to see.
Though his skill was quite outstandin', he was buried in an hour,
For he broke his neck in landin' on the flamin' windmill tower.
Dunno why they buried Bunion, he'd have kept till Kingdom come
He was pickled like an onion from his bouts on shanty rum.

Then along came Billy Gundy, of Gulf riders he was best,
But they laid him one black Monday by the goat yard with the rest.
Next a ringer called Moskeeta from the Booraloola side
Rode three hundred miles to beat her, and they said that he could ride.
With his big toe in the stirrup and a six or eight inch grin
He could stick like golden syrup to a hungry piccanin.

In a high unnervin' treble he'd corroboree as he swayed,
But his swan song on the Debil never made the hit parade.
Well, I had a reputation and I thought about the cash,
So I told them at the station that I'd like to have a lash.
It was early when I caught her as the dawn began to break,
I was windy of her sorta, but I reckoned I'd be jake.

It was just light when I mounted, but the sun shone in me eye
On the third buck that I counted, for she rooted pretty high.
Talk about acceleration, like a bullet from a gun
She departed from the station and lit out across the run.
She was buckin' hell-for-leather and the gibbers flew like chaff
When we left the ground together and she cut a cloud in half.

We had reached the flamin' river with me senses pretty blurred
When I felt the Debil quiver but she took it like a bird,
And there was a mile of clearance 'bove the coolibahs, I swear,
From the pigmy-like appearance of a swaggie fishin' there.
Well, I rode her like a hero till we came to Shantyview
And I waved me old sombrero to some fellers that I knew.

Then the Debil gave a nicker and she cartwheeled off one hoof
And she threw me in a flicker through the flamin' lock-up roof.
Then the sergeant, to me sorrow, came and said, 'How are you mate,
You'll appear some time tomorrow up before our magistrate.'
Well, you should have seen the guiver when I fronted up next day,
To be fined a flamin' fiver or a week in Fannie Bay.

Now the magistrate was rugged in a boozy Top End way,
And I knew me case was buggered, still I thought I'd have me say,
Oh! I knew I was a goner, I was handcuffed to the sarge,
But I said look here, your honour, what the flamin' hell's the charge?
Well, his voice rose to a bellow, 'Don't bung on you didn't know,
We aint found your plane yet, fellow, but the charge was flyin' low.'

BRUMBY GEORGE IN THE CITY

I'm down in this here town at last and hell, writes Brumby George,
The flaming people swarm like ants, the streets are like a gorge.
It's sorta opened up me eyes, but I can tell you mate
I aim to hold me own down here although I've started late.
I know that I'm behind the times and been up North too long
And if a feller called me slow I wouldn't call him wrong.
But I am settling in down here and learning city ways,
And I can see the wicked waste of all me younger days.

I ain't the mug some fellers think and I ain't bought no shares
In statues or in swimming pools or city parks and squares.
The traffic, though, I reckon mate has sorta got me beat
I'd rather face a scrubber bull than cross the flaming street.
The city blokes all go like hell as though they're running late
So they've got lights on corners here to draft the bludgers mate,
These lights will block the flaming lead and string the city push
They work the cars and trucks down here like cattle in the bush.

These city blokes fly for the grog like bullocks round a float,
One night I wanders in a pub to pour one down me throat,
I elbows in to get a rum and just gets to the trough
When some big jackaroo sings out: 'I'm sorry gents it's off.'
'Ho! Is it off?' I says to him, 'you ruddy rouseabout
Just fill them glasses round the bar for this is Brumby's shout.'
He stands and looks at me awhile, agaping like a cod,
And then he grabs the flaming phone and rings the vicious squad.

I'd heard about this vicious squad, they're pretty tough to meet,
And so I downs the barman bloke and hits out up the street.
By crikey mate the pubs is flash, there's carpet here like grass,
They've even got a water spout to clean your flaming arse.
The tucker here's a bushie's dream all wrote out on a list,
First day I strolls in sober like, me quart pot in me fist.
I looks around to find a chair and has no luck at all,
And so I squats down on me heels, me back agin the wall.

I dunno what I done or said to cause a flaming stir,
A little waitress ambles up and says, 'Excuse me Sir.'
I ain't no sir I says to her, me name is Brumby Jones
Just boil me quart and make it strong and grill a few rib bones.
But they have got me broken now to eat like humans ought,
One waitress here has worked out West, she ain't a bad old sort.
I took her out the other night, I tell you it was grand
The way she sorta looked at me and held me flaming hand.

Me name ain't Brumby Jones no more, reluctantly I owns,
I sorta like the idea now of being Mr Jones.
Me flaming eyes is opened like and I can tell you mate
I'll mix it with this city push although I've started late.
I'm settling in down here I am and learning city ways,
And I can see the wicked waste of all me younger days.
I dunno when I'm shooting through, but it's a certain bet
That I'll be back at Grasstree by the finish of the wet.
I'll be there when the muster starts up far off Rocky gorge
But until then I'll live it up, your old mate Brumby George.

BRISBANE OR THE BUSH

I SPENT MOST of my working life in the bush. Twice I took on jobs in the city for a time, but the bush always called me back. On the first of these sojourns in the big smoke I ended up working at a meatworks. Having decided to get a job in Brisbane, I soon realised I had little or no idea of how to go about achieving my ambition. My credentials, first rate in the bush, were of no value whatever in the city. I made a few inquiries, called on some business houses and got nowhere at all. I was feeling pretty browned off and ready to give the idea away when I got a lucky break.

I was staying at the Shandon private hotel in upper Edward Street at the time; I usually stayed there when on holidays in Brisbane. The Shandon was owned and run by a Mrs Hall, a grand old lady who took a motherly interest in her guests and of course knew everyone's business. The good lady was aware of my plight and decided to have a heart to heart talk to me over the breakfast table one morning.

She listened to my story of rejection, then said, 'Young man, why don't you try working behind the counter in a shop. You don't need special training for that.'

The idea was anathema to me, and I said no. The resident taxi driver, who was also at the table, spread butter liberally on a piece of toast and, avoiding Mrs Hall's critical look, put in his two bob's worth. 'Why don't you try the meatworks?'

I brightened up at once. Working at a meatworks appealed to me straight away; I'd be around cattle again, even if most of them were carcasses. My spirits, however, were soon dashed.

'Of course,' said the resident taxi driver, 'you would have to join the union. The Australian Meat Industry Employees Union controls the workforce and I believe it's almost a closed shop.'

I had nothing against unions. I'd always been a member of the AWU, although in all my time in stockcamps I'd only seen one organiser visit the ringers. I thanked the taxi driver and decided to follow up the meatworks idea. Next day I found out that the AMIEU had its offices in the Trades Hall, not far down Edwards Street from the Shandon. I located the office without trouble and walked in. A heavily built man behind a desk looked me over.

'Are you a union member?'

'No, but I'd like to join.'

'Would you? So would a lot of people. Have you had any experience in the industry?'

I told him I could slaughter a beast. I didn't say that I'd done the job in the bush and on the ground rather than on a gallows. I also thought it unnecessary to inform him that the beast had often belonged to someone else.

The man behind the desk thought for a moment. 'Do you know anyone in the union?'

I shook my head, and that seemed to please him. 'Well, you'll have to be nominated and seconded by two union members who know you. Here's the forms.'

As I left the union office I had the distinct impression the man behind the desk did not expect to see me again. It was obvious to me that the AMIEU was not at that time conducting a membership drive. Nevertheless, I was happy. I had cleared the first hurdle. All I had to do now was to find two union members who would provide me with an entree to the union. Although my funds were perilously low, I walked on down to Queen Street, strolled into the Australian Hotel and celebrated with a couple of beers.

As the Shandon was a bed and breakfast establishment, I did not see my advisers until the next morning. At breakfast I told them of my progress and asked their advice on where to find union members. Mrs Hall thought I should try butcher's shops, but the resident taxi driver gave her a pitying look and, reaching for the marmalade, spoke with conviction. 'No, I'll tell you where to go. Slip out to the Cannon Hill saleyards. The place is full of broken down stockmen; they'll fix you up.'

I thanked him and realised the truth of the old saying, 'If you want to know anything ask a taxi driver.' I finished breakfast and set out for Cannon Hill. By luck I arrived as the men were starting their smoko break. I spotted a wiry character squatting on his heels against a yard post. It is a position favoured by stockmen who have to make do without chairs. He looked every inch a horseman, so I strolled over, introduced myself and found I was talking to Colin Bell, an outstanding horseman of his day. We yarned for a while and shortly after he organised the two signatures I needed. I drew a blank when I approached the office about a job there, but left in high spirits. Another obstacle had been overcome.

When I returned to the city, I called into the union office and handed in the application papers. I also paid my union dues. The man behind the desk, looking somewhat surprised, asked, 'Do these men know you?'

I nodded. 'Yes, like me they're from the bush.' It wasn't really a lie, they did know me, if only for a few hours.

'What happens now?' I asked the man behind the desk.

'Well, there will be a union meeting on Monday night at eight. A vote will be taken then to decide if we are going to accept any new members.'

I had to be satisfied with that. I walked up to the Shandon. It was Friday and the prospect of a Brisbane weekend without adequate funds was never rosy; however, I would have to amuse myself as best I could. I spent some time on a verse I was writing, lazed around in the Botanical Gardens and listened to the Salvation Army band on Sunday night in lower Edward Street.

Finally Monday night came and I went down to the Trades Hall and found the room where the meeting was being held. I noticed two chaps sitting outside the room, but went in and sat down inside. After a fair amount of general business the time came to vote on the fate of the aspiring members. The names of the two other applicants and myself were read out, together with the details on the tendered forms. When the vote was taken, my hand was amongst the first to go up. The decision was made—I was in. After the meeting the union officials called the two men in from outside. As I was already in, I waited in the aisle to join them.

It was then that the man from behind the desk spotted me. He glared balefully at me.

'Have you been in the meeting?' he hissed.

'Yes, you told me there was to be a meeting tonight.'

'A meeting for bloody members,' he replied in a hoarse undertone. 'You were supposed to wait outside. Your presence could have made the whole proceedings unconstitutional.'

There is something ridiculous about a man delivering a diatribe *sotto voce*. I suppressed the urge to laugh and apologised with as much grace as I could muster. I had, after all, been in the wrong place at the wrong time.

Somewhat mollified by my contrite manner, the man from behind the desk proceeded to enlighten us on the benefits of unionism and in particular on what the AMIEU would do for us. We were told the union would get us jobs. All we had to do was to wait in the car park each morning; at seven o'clock the union officials would select men for the day's vacancies.

I went back to the Shandon satisfied with the night's work. There was now only one hurdle left—getting a job, and the union, it seemed, would provide me with that.

At six next morning I jogged down to the Trades Hall to find some 30 hopefuls queued up there before me. Within the next half hour there were as many more behind me. A little after seven a union official arrived and selected 10 men from the first dozen or so. The rest of us were advised to go home and try again on the morrow. Wednesday and Thursday mornings were much the same, although I had managed to get near the front both times. I began to depair of ever getting a job.

Back at the Shandon, I was gloomily breakfasting on tea and toast when the resident taxi driver walked in. 'Have you seen today's paper?' he asked.

I shook my head. 'Why, has war been declared?'

'No, but there's a job there for you.' He tossed over the paper.

Sure enough, there it was. An advertisement for a stockman at Borthwick's meatworks. You bloody beaut! But had it been filled? I almost ran to the phone, rang the number given and asked for the manager. After what seemed like an eternity he came on the line. He asked me what experience I'd had with cattle and checked that I was a union member. The vacancy, he told me, had not been filled but was not of a permanent nature. I could start on Monday morning at eight if I wanted the job. Did I want the job? My bloody oath I did! I told the manager I'd be there Monday morning and hung up the phone. I went back to the breakfast table, shook the taxi driver's hand and told him taxi drivers should be running the country. He agreed and said I could buy him a ticket in the golden casket.

Later that day I thought it would be a courtesy to advise the union of my success. At the Trades Hall I strolled into the office and told the man behind the desk of my good fortune. He stood up and for a second I thought he was going to have a stroke.

'The union gets jobs for its members,' he stormed. 'You're not allowed to look for work outside the union.'

I'd had a gutful of the man behind the desk. For the first time, I believed I had the whip hand. Resisting the temptation to call him an arrogant bastard, I spoke slowly and clearly. 'Shut up for a moment and listen to me. I'm no scab; this job was advertised for union members only. I'm a member of your damn union, I've got the job and I'm bloody well going to keep it.'

I turned and walked out of the office, leaving him standing open mouthed behind his desk. I thought my actions may perhaps have precipitated an industrial dispute; however, on Monday morning when

I arrived at Borthwicks I was relieved to find no sign of a picket line. The yard boss showed me what my duties were. All I had to do was to keep the cattle moving up the elevated race to the killing pen. Some sensitive souls may have found the job distasteful, but as far as I was concerned bullocks were bred to be slaughtered, and I had a job again with cattle. The bloke I had replaced was off with a broken leg. My job would last until he returned to work. For the next three weeks I enjoyed myself immensely. The work was easy and it was great to be in the company of stockmen again.

When the injured man returned to work, the management decided rather than let me go they would use me as a spare man. If anyone was away from any one of the many gangs, I would stand in for them. I found myself on hides one day, hooves the next and horns the day after. A week after leaving the stockwork, I was given a week on the digesters. This was where the bones, stripped of meat in the boning room below, were ground up for bonemeal. When I started there the foreman showed me the ropes. The bones came up from the boning room in hoppers. My job was to throw the bones down the digester shute then press a button that returned the empty hopper while bringing up another full one. It seemed a rather simple job to me. When the foreman had departed, a chap from the boning room came to see me. I had noticed two large steel cabinets standing by the wall, and the man from the boning room put me in the picture. Occasionally, he told me, a cut of meat may come up with the bones. Would I mind putting it in one of the cabinets?

I thought for a moment, then agreed. The management knew the cabinets were there, and they seemed to have no other function.

The job was rather boring. The only distraction was the steady stream of fillets and rumps that came up with the bones. By the end of the shift, both cabinets were chock-a-block. I had trouble shutting the doors. As the whistle blew at four o'clock, up came the boners. The cabinets were flung open, and in less time than it takes to tell, the meat was stowed away in lunch bags. Meat workers who came to work swinging those bags went home weighed down by them. They walked as though suffering from some strange and sporadic spine affliction. Now and again I carried a prime rump steak home to the admirable Mrs Hall.

The money was good at the works, but living at the Shandon had its drawbacks. It only provided bed and breakfast and I found having to buy lunch and dinner expensive as well as a nuisance. It was also a long way from the New Farm ferry. So when a room-mate who worked in the

Valley suggested we look for full board and lodging, I readily agreed, providing we found a place closer to the ferry.

I left it in his hands and on the following weekend he gave me the good news that he had found a place at a very reasonable figure. As he had only spoken to the lady on the phone, we both hopped on a tram to look the place over. It was quite close to the ferry, we found, and looked OK from the street. On our ringing the doorbell, a large formidable female appeared and advised us in no uncertain terms that she believed that door-to-door salesmen should go to blazes. As she was about to slam the door in our faces, I managed to tell her we were there about the room.

'Well, why didn't you say so,' she snapped, 'instead of standing there wasting my time. Come in, then, but I can tell you right now I won't stand for no boozing or hanky-panky in this house.'

We looked at one another, then shrugged and followed her into the dwelling. The room she showed us was quite comfortable and roomy, so when we were alone we talked it over and decided that despite our landlady's sour nature we would move in. We were told two sisters had rented the room before us. One thing that struck me was the large notices she had stuck up behind the bedroom door, in the hall, and just about everywhere else. They warned guests not to do this, and told them that they must do that, all couched in very direct terms. We were given a guided tour of the bathroom, with our landlady verbally reinforcing the messages printed on the signs adorning the walls. By the bath stood a sinister-looking gas heater. Its welfare, we were told, was of great importance. I took it for granted that anyone unlucky enough to misuse the thing would bring her wrath down upon his head.

My mate and I caught a tram back to the city, said our goodbyes to Mrs Hall and enlisted the help of the resident taxi driver to move us into our new lodgings. To bring a bit of masculinity to the room, I dug my whip and spurs out and hung them up on the curtain rods, an act for which I was later to be severely chastised. When the dinner bell went that night, we went into the dining room to find that there were two other guests in the establishment.

One was a rather anaemic girl who was extremely timid. She never lifted her face from her plate during the meal, and when finished she scuttled off like a startled rabbit. The other guest was something else entirely. He could have been 70 or more, a grizzled veteran of life's hard knocks. He looked as though he had seen better days, but the shaggy brows could not hide the gleam in his eyes. I decided there was life in the old dog yet. After the meal, our landlady sat back and spoke.

'I like to know something about my guests.' She fixed her unblinking gaze on me. 'Now, young man, just what do you do for a living?'

'Well,' I said, 'I'm a bushman, but at the moment I'm working at a meatworks.'

'Great,' said the grizzled veteran, 'then perhaps you can bring home some decent meat for a change.'

To my surprise, the lady ignored him and turned her attention to the salesman from the Valley. Apart from having him as a room-mate at the Shandon, I knew very little about him myself. He was a solid individual of medium height with closely cropped hair and a ginger moustache. He tended to surround himself with what I believed was carefully feigned mystery. I sat back and waited.

In reply to her question the salesman gave a cheeky grin and said, 'Oh! I sell things.'

'Do you?' our landlady said. 'What sort of things?'

'Oh! This and that, bits and pieces, one thing and another.'

Our hostess was not impressed. 'Not a very suitable career, I'm afraid. A man should have a trade. My late husband, God rest him, had a trade until he fell under the influence of the demon drink.'

'What trade did he follow?' I asked innocently.

Before she could reply, the grizzled veteran spoke. 'My sister,' he said, establishing his position in the menage, 'is a bit sensitive about that. George was a farrier, and a good one. He worked for a brewery and could shoe a draughthorse while some blokes were thinking about it. But the drink got him. Employing George at a brewery was like putting a cannibal in charge of a creche. At the end I reckon George would drink the piss from a brewer's horse.'

The landlady rose to her feet. 'Bill, I will not have you talk like that. Please leave the table.'

We left and followed Bill out of the room. We passed him chuckling to himself in the hall. I suspected that he had been subjected to petticoat discipline for years and finding himself with a male audience had gone to his head a bit. He certainly took the opportunity to get a bit of his own back.

On the following Monday I was put in the freezers for the week. We were in for 30 minutes then relieved for the same length of time, to allow us to thaw out. I didn't mind the job, but was happy, the following week, to join the gall gang. I found this rather interesting. The gall was collected from the gall bladder of the animals killed and put into huge vats. Large paddles kept the gall moving while the heated vats gradually reduced it to a treacle-like consistency. Finally the gall was put into 44 gallon (200 litre) drums and sold—overseas, I believe. There is not a lot of a beast that is wasted, believe me. The blokes used to say that the only thing they missed was the bullock's bellow.

With money to spare, I was now enjoying myself in the city. I went to the races each Saturday and was a regular at the fights at the old Brisbane stadium. The main attraction at the races was the horses. I had never been a gambler and my habit of having the occasional bet had been dampened when I had had a punt on the Caulfield Cup the previous year.

A few of us were in Camooweal for a few days, and were enjoying ourselves in the bar on the Saturday when the local SP bookie arrived. Without knowing the horses, I had a quid on Royal Gem to win. He entered the wager in a tattered notebook, but did not give me a ticket. I promptly forgot about the bet, and it was not until that night that I realised I had backed the winner.

I ran the bookie to earth and asked for my money. He looked at me blankly and told me the bet on Royal Gem had been collected by a fencer. I found it useless to argue with him. In the end he told me that if I wanted my winnings I would have to see the fencer.

I managed to retrieve the money, then returned to the bar, where I shouted for my mates. Backing horses, I told them, was a mug's game. They told me they knew how I felt, as it was written all over my face.

After another two weeks relieving on various gangs, I was put in charge of the lard room. Not a big promotion, as it was a one man job, although I was promised an offsider. It was then that disaster struck at our lodgings. The gas heater in the bathroom had been playing up for some time. The pilot light went out at times and I refused to use the damned contraption. As a cool spell had hit Brisbane, the salesman from the Valley decided to take a hot bath. I walked past the bathroom as he was endeavouring, stark naked, to light the brute of a thing.

'This bloody thing won't go,' he complained.

I explained he would have to use a match and gave him a box of mine. What I hadn't realised was that he still had the gas going.

I hadn't gone five paces when a thunderous explosion shook the building. I raced back to find the bathroom door off its hinges and my room-mate standing with his body hair singed, and covered in black soot.

The gas heater was on the floor still aflame and looking for all the world like a scaled-down version of a plane crash.

I turned the gas and water taps off just as our landlady burst into the room.

'What have you done?' she screeched.

'I've done nothing,' my scorched room-mate cried, reaching for a towel. 'But this thing has nearly DONE for me.'

'I'll sue you,' the virago roared. 'I'll sue for damages.'

At that the salesman fell to the floor.

'Quick, phone the ambulance. This man could be badly hurt,' I told her.

As she left I walked over to the salesman. He looked up at me and winked. 'How was that for a dive?'

'Bloody feeble,' I told him, 'you broke your fall with your hands.'

Things finally settled down. My room-mate's injuries were superficial, and within a week a new electric water heater had been installed in the bathroom. Life at the boarding house returned to what could loosely be termed as normal.

I enjoyed my new job in the lard room. The lard or dripping came up to me as solid blocks weighing 56 pounds (25 kilograms). A wire frame was used to cut the lard into rough pats, which were weighed to 1 pound (450 grams) and finally wrapped. The pats were never cut accurately, and lard had to be either added or removed. To help me in this arduous activity, the powers that be gave me an offsider as promised. I often wished they hadn't, for he was a gangling youth and the most uncoordinated individual I have ever known. His clumsiness had to be seen to be believed. I thought he must improve, but he never did. Finally I did my block and called him a hopeless bloody malingerer who was as useless as tits on a boar pig. He didn't take umbrage at my abuse, nor did he improve.

On Saturday, as was my custom, I went to the fights. A five round preliminary bout was announced and, to my amazement, my clumsy offsider climbed through the ropes and sat down in the blue corner. Opposite him in the red corner sat a rough character who looked strong enough to hold a bull out to piddle. I sat back and waited for the carnage to start, and start it did, as soon as the bell went. My bumbling offsider slipped out of his corner and proceeded to belt the stuffing out of the neanderthal type from the red corner. Pat Hill, the referee, stopped the fight in the second round. After the fights I made my way thoughtfully home, vowing to be a little more circumspect when addressing my offsider in future.

I had been working in the lard room for about a month when the chap I had relieved returned from holidays. I was back relieving on the various yard gangs for a few weeks, when one Saturday morning I met a couple of ringers I knew in the Australian Hotel. We had a few beers and talked generally for a while, then one of them asked how long I'd been on holiday. I explained I was living and working in Brisbane.

He looked at me in disbelief. 'Working down here! You must be bloody mad. There's grass girth high out back.'

'It's been a good season then,' I said.

'Good season! There's clover on the Cooper, they say.'

Clover on the Cooper, I thought, clover on the bloody Cooper. That did it. On Monday morning I gave notice at Borthwicks. The call of the bush could not be denied.

THE BUSHMAN FROM THE BURKE

The rugged bushman rolled his swag, he'd come from off the Burke,
He knew the sprawling stations there would soon be starting work.
He'd had his fill of city life, the time had come to go,
He caught a cab to Roma Street, a station bushmen know.
He threw his swag upon the train and found himself a seat
Beside a girl with golden hair and features pure and sweet.
She gave our friend a timid smile, a greeting tinged with fear,
The bushman said some words to her that no one else could hear.

In startled fright the lass sprang up, hell bent upon escape
And 'Rape,' she screamed out as she ran, 'Help me! Attempted rape!'
The bushman looked in shocked surprise. 'Hey, what's your little game?'
Then from the platform just outside a charging policeman came.
He grabbed the bushman by the arm. 'Right, what have you to say?
That girl just said you threatened rape, that's why she ran away.'
'I told her where I'm going to, I swear that's all I said
And then she flamin' ups and goes right off her flamin' head.'

'I know your type,' the policeman said. 'A deviate and pest
It plainly is my duty now to make a quick arrest.'
'It seems to me,' the bushman growled, 'you won't let me explain
And I will do you grievous harm if I don't catch this train.'
He took the cursing bushman to the station master's den,
A jaded sergeant came and asked, 'What are the charges then?'
'Attempted rape,' the policeman crowed. 'The evidence is clear,
He tried to rape a passenger, she's traumatised with fear.'

'You've set me up,' the bushman cried, 'but I have read about
You city push that prey upon us blokes from further out,
I never tried to rape no one, it's like I said before
I told her where I'm going to, just that and nothing more,
I tried to be real friendly like, I even raised me hat
And told her where I'm going to, there ain't no crime in that.'
'Hang on! Hang on!' the sergeant said. 'Why did she run in fright?
How could the place you're going to cause panic-stricken flight?

'I cannot see from what you say just why the woman fled
So tell me slowly word for word precisely WHAT you said.'
'Well, I said I'm goin' to Bullya and then she goes berserk,
Youse musta heard of Bullya town, old Bullya on the Burke,
I wish I'd stayed in Bullya now and dodged the likes of youse
And had me spree at Bullya pub and shopped at Donahues.'
The weary sergeant groaned aloud. 'You still can catch that train
So go to flaming Boulia, Sir, and don't come back again.'

Ringer's Farewell

The city now seems dull and stale—
The lights have lost their lustre,
We miss the bush mates rough and hale—
The branding and the muster.
We've had our fun with reckless glee,
Cards, women, wine and singing,
It's high time now to end the spree
And once more go back ringing.

With blasé smile we've done it grand,
Gone paddock at the races,
Made merry in the way we'd planned
In dives and other places.
But when from bar to outback plain
Nostalgia takes us winging,
It's time to roll the swag again
And once more go back ringing.

We've dined in state and tête-à-tête,
Of parties had our ration,
It seems a century since we ate
In careless stockcamp fashion.
For further out we've shown the flag
And set a few hearts singing,
It's high time now to roll the swag
And once more go back ringing.

It's raining now through neon glare,
Though lawns could not be greener,
We wonder if they've had their share
Out on the far Georgina.
A good west wind came with the rain
A hint of gidgee bringing.
It's time to catch the outback train
And once more go back ringing.

WILD MEN AND WINDLASSES

BRENNEN REINED IN his horse on the side of the ridge and, with eyes narrowed, surveyed the landscape beyond. His lead packhorse drew up beside him, rubbing his head on Brennen's leg to gain relief from the bush flies. The rider pushed him away with a curse and checked that the saddle bag hanging from his saddle dees was still there. Brennen grunted with relief; in that saddle were gems, the result of a month of solitary hard work. Brennen was a loner. The location of his opal mine was known to none but this secretive, and often unsociable, hermit from the hills south-west of Kynuna, and he took great care that his mine should never be found. He never camped close to where he was working and shifted camp regularly, choosing a different route to the mine each time so that no one would be able to follow his tracks.

Brennen had a thinly disguised contempt for the opal gougers who worked the Kynuna field south of where he mined the precious gems. Most of them were on government money, an idea that was anathema to him.

An opal buyer who paid regular visits to Kynuna was due on the mail on the morrow. He knew Brennen's opal and the loner was confident of getting a fair deal. The only time Brennan was ever seen in Kynuna was when the buyer was in town. Brennen was a man who aroused a lot of curiosity, a taciturn character with a secret mine that produced the finest quality opal.

Brennen knocked the ashes from his pipe on a kneepad. He spat, then checked the time by the sun. There were cattle pads running into water at the end of the ridge. He would ride down those pads shortly, and cattle walking out to feed would wipe out his tracks. Later he would take a roundabout route into Kynuna. No one was going to backtrack Brennen to his mine. He would camp down on the bank of the Diamantina that night. But he would not sleep. Men had been murdered for less than he had in that saddlebag. He would douse his fire and sit awake cradling a Winchester rifle until daylight.

Brennen sold his opal next day, after haggling for some time with the buyer. Not altogether satisfied with the deal, he made his way to the post office and banked the notes. Then he headed for the pub to have a few drinks. He had time to spare, for he would not start back before dark. Brennen drank alone, making it plain he wanted no company. There was a group of noisy shearers in the bar, and one of their number was drinking next to him. Somehow or other a sixpence fell to the floor between them. Both men claimed it and a brawl started. Brennen went down, striking his head a sickening blow. The injury proved fatal. Brennen, the man with the richest claim in the whole area, died fighting over a sixpenny piece.

After his death, interest continued to grow in Brennen's opal mine. It had to be out there somewhere, and many attempts were made to locate it. The dead man had covered his tracks well, however. Good prospectors, like Mick Cheadle and my brother Jeff, spent weeks combing the area without success. They did find another mine that had been lost for many years, one that had been worked by a chap named Peter Karfe, but Brennen's mine remains lost in the rough country south-west of Kynuna.

Opal is nature's greatest treasure. When found it needs no faceting: from a nick in its surface, its vivid colours blaze forth. Men who fall under its spell seldom, if ever, get over their love affair with the most beautiful of gems.

Opal was formed millions of years ago by water that leeched down through deposits of sedimentary sandstone to form hydro-silica—a mixture of water and silica. For many years the reason for opal's prismatic capability remained a mystery, until the electron microscope finally unmasked its secrets. Gem-quality opal is made up of neatly stacked plates cemented together by hydro-silica. This gives the stone the ability to break up white light like a rainbow. In potch, or common opal, these plates are not uniform and do not have the prismatic capacity of gem opal. In Queensland, opal is found in boulders and in sandstone that is close to an ironstone band.

Hard on the heels of the overlanders and settlers who opened up the outback were the packhorse prospectors. These hardy characters were interested only in what might be secreted deep beneath the inhospitable landscape of the interior. Despite having to rely on horses, they missed very little, as their modern counterparts can vouch for. Many a prospector in a four-wheel drive vehicle has arrived at what he thought was new ground, miles from water, to find evidence of the activities of the old-time packhorse brigade.

During the 1970s most of the prospecting and mining was done in the pre-Cambrian landforms around Cloncurry, an area rich in copper and other minerals. The country further south, being non-metalliferous, was far less promising, and had been inundated over millions of years by the long dry inland sea. Covering most of inland Australia, it is what geologists call desert sandstone country. Its topography is mixed, being made up of creek and river flats together with low ridges and rough, flat-topped hills. The sedimentary deposits of this area were laid down during the Cretaceous era, and hidden deep in its sandstone layers are opals.

The first gem-quality opal found in Queensland was in 1883 at Bull Creek, west of Quilpie in the far west of the state. Two years later opal was found at the Alladin mine, north-west of Eromanga, and a company was formed to market the gems, which it did with some success. In 1887 a tough bushman named Cragg arrived at the Mayne River, a tributary of the Diamantina, and started prospecting. It is not known if Cragg had worked on the opal fields to the south, but he appeared to know what he was looking for. He found opal and his mine became known simply as Cragg's mine.

The country up along the Mayne is very rugged indeed. In the late 1950s I drove a mob of Territory bullocks up the Mayne and over the range at its headwaters. There was next to no grass and, as a cattleman, I decided that the Mayne River area was next to worthless. When I was taking the plant back after delivering the mob, I spent a little time with the Martyr family at Mayneside Station. On talking with Mrs Martyr, I realised the place was steeped in history.

By 1888 Cragg was producing good quality opal and interest in the area grew. He was camped on a waterhole below the junction of Horse Creek and Hyde Park Creek; these two join to form the Mayne River. The waterhole was close to Mayneside Station, and became the camping ground for newly arrived opal gougers. These men began prospecting up the tributaries of the Mayne, including New Year Creek. Soon other mines were producing opal, including Carlisles and the Poison claim.

At this time the outback was enjoying a period of rapid growth. Stations were being taken up and townships were being developed, with wagons and coaches raising the dust on newly made roads that linked the runs and embryo settlements of the far west. By 1880 the police had a strong presence in the Winton and Boulia districts. Winton boasted a sergeant and two constables, while Sub-Inspector Eglington was stationed at Boulia with a squad of native police. There were also native police at Tulma barracks on the Diamantina River. By 1883 Winton had a greatly enlarged police force, a magistrate and a courthouse, where district court sittings were held.

Mrs Martyr Snr in front of the old store at Mayneside.

The Goa tribe of Winton and the Pitta Pittas of Boulia, unlike their northern neighbours, the Kalkadoons, were regarded by the newcomers as more of a nuisance than a threat. Their presence was never a problem to the opal miners; however, in 1882 a part-owner of Warnambool Station, a man named Young, was speared to death at the Old Station waterhole, and the Goas raided a wagon loaded with provisions en route to Warnambool. The Aborigines carried off a great deal of the supplies, including a consignment of kerosene soap. Knowing no better, they decided the soap must be tucker and hoed into it. A police party caught up with the culprits at Skull Hole, where they were 'dispersed'. When one considers the effect soap has on the digestive system, the unfortunate Aborigines would not have been hard to track.

The Goas were soon subdued and became fringe dwellers around stations and townships. The authorities hung brass plates around the neck of selected older Aborigines; these half moon shapes nominated the bearers as King so-and-so of such-and-such a tribe. It was an insult to their culture and a grotesque parody of English royalty.

The mining activity on the Mayne did not go unnoticed by commercial interests. A man named Pegler and his wife opened a store to cater for the needs of the miners, choosing a site close to the Mayneside Station homestead. Pegler, in his hastily erected building, was soon in business, but quickly won a reputation as a man who cheated the gougers, and came to be regarded by everyone as a poor type. One day when Pegler and his wife were away in Winton, a man whom the storekeeper had wronged arrived at the store. He gave Pegler's sister-in-law five minutes to get out, then set fire to the store and watched as it burnt to the ground.

In due course the police from Winton arrived to investigate the arson and began questioning the opal miners camped at the waterhole. One suspect was either frightened that an earlier sin would come to light, or was just sick of living, for after being questioned he returned to his claim and shot himself. This threw the police investigation into chaos. After dealing with the suicide and clearing the dead man of arson, they resumed questioning the opal gougers and finally arrested the culprit at his claim on New Year Creek.

All shafts put down in the early days of opal mining were put down by pick and shovel. These shafts were slightly rectangular in shape and many of them were quite deep. During the sinking, the overburden was brought to the surface with buckets and ropes attached to a windlass made from bush timber. The trunk of a small tree was usually employed as the barrel of the windlass; the barrel was supported on two forks, and a winding handle was attached to an iron bar driven into one end of it. Usually two men worked a claim: one down below loading the buckets, and the other on top, raising the dirt with the windlass. Roughly made ladders were also used in working shafts.

Mining development continued at the Mayne opal field, with new mines coming into production, including the Echo, Biddies and the White Cow. A new store was built close to the Mayneside homestead. It was constructed by a man named Lancashire, who had the mail run from Winton. The building had a bullock-hide floor and was later used as a storeroom by Jim Martyr and his family when they took over the station in 1925.

The most famous of all opal mines in the area of the Mayne was the Yellow Jimmy. According to the old timers, the Yellow Jimmy was a producer of beautiful gemstones. The claim was near Horse Creek, and was owned by two men who were still working it when World War I broke out. Both men went into Winton and enlisted in the AIF. They had thrown their picks and shovels down the shaft of the Yellow Jimmy, they said, and would return when the war was over. Whether or not the pair

Peter Knowls

Present-day tourist area at Opalton.

survived the war is not known, but they never returned to work the Yellow Jimmy.

Efforts were made by gougers to find the mine, which was rapidly gaining legendary qualities, but it was never found, and after World War I activities on the opal fields tapered off. In 1925, when Jim Martyr was on Mayneside, there were only a few old timers still working in the area.

During the period when the Mayne was producing opal, there was some prospecting done in other areas, but for the most part gougers concentrated on the established field on the headwaters of the Mayne River. There are reports, however, that a kangaroo shooter found opal near Mulga Creek; this area was later to become the famous Opalton field. There was no mining done there until 1893 when McLennon pegged the Brilliant Claim. Other finds such as Conways Claim followed in quick succession, and the rush was on. By 1896 there was said to be between 500 and 600 men working claims in the area. The field produced a great deal of gem opal, the value of which can only be guessed at, for little was declared to the authorities. Private deals were seldom recorded, so government figures regarding opal production have always been suspect.

Water for the thriving community was brought from No Name Rockhole and sold for 25 shillings for 100 gallons (455 litres). Good seasons meant there was plenty of grass for the growing number of miners' horses. The now booming town of Opalton soon had two hotels, a store, a police station and two butcher shops. Conway's butcher shop was a no frills affair, just a mulga tree for a gallows and a stump for a butcher's block. In the boom Conway slaughtered nine beasts a week. In 1894 a coach service was started from Longreach to Opalton. Winton now had a mining warden, and in an effort to attract business, a road was built from Warnambool to Opalton.

One of the first opal buyers in the field was a red-bearded character by the name of Clancy, who was in the employ of Wollaston, one of the best known and most influential opal dealers in Australia. Opal gougers are never happy about the price buyers offer for parcels of gemstones, which is mainly because gougers have an inflated idea of the value of their opal, and they ignore the fact that buyers do have to allow a margin for profit. The miners at Opalton made such a stir about prices that the government sent out H.L. Hyde, a valuer. Hyde found that Clancy was an honest man whose prices were fair. Other southern buyers on the field were Fairfax and Roberts, and a local buyer, John Hotton, was also active.

Peter Knowls

Remains of the baker's oven, Opalton.

One of the greatest opal robberies of all time took place at Opalton. Two Germans sank a shaft down to 80 feet (25 metres), then abandoned it when they found no opal. Two gougers, Dick Shillington and a chap named Johnson, went down the shaft out of curiosity; on the way back up, they knocked off the end of a stone projecting from the wall of the shaft and discovered it was part of an opalised tree containing gem-quality opal. The pair broke up the huge stone after it was raised to the surface and the pieces are reported to have filled a wooden beer case. Castledine, the Opalton policeman, was away at Mayneside and had left the station keys with one of the publicans. That night the box of opal was locked in the jail for safekeeping.

Next morning, to the consternation of the miners, the opal was missing. Its value in today's currency would be in the millions. The police from Winton were notified and arrived soon after to investigate the disappearance of the opal. They questioned the Opalton miners and the publican, and searched the camps, but did not elicit any useful information. The case was never solved, but for months after, miners searched old shafts, hollow logs and any other likely hiding spots in hope of finding the cache. All Shillington and Johnson got out of the find were the chips and small pieces of opal that were the result of breaking up the big stone.

The story of the Opalton robbery closely resembles one told by Ion Idriess in his book *Lightning Ridge*, but the location given by Idriess was Lightning Ridge. I have found it impossible to check the story, as records are non-existent. It is possible that Idriess, in writing his book, had heard about, and borrowed, the story.

I was first told the story of the robbery by Fred Holm at Winton in 1963. Fred was born at Windorah on 15 June 1880 and spent most of his life in the Winton district following horse breaking work and stockwork. Fred was over 80 when he talked with me, but his memory of the Opalton robbery was clear and concise. A fine horseman, Fred was quick to embrace motorised transport and in 1908 owned one of the first motor-bikes in the area. He was very proud of the performance of his iron horse. Fred was always accurate when dealing with historical facts, but was not above spinning a yarn to his grandchildren.

Once, he told them, he rode his motorbike out to a station. When he got there he checked the oil and found it needed to be topped up. He asked the station's bookkeeper if any was available and was handed oil in an unlabelled bottle. He used about half and returned the bottle to the

Brian Holm

Fred Holm at the age of 92 in Winton.

Larry Holm

Fred Holm at Vindex Station, June 1907.

bookkeeper. On the way home he passed a drover with a pack of dogs; the dogs flew out and attacked the strange machine with gusto. When the melee was over, Fred found himself on the ground. Looking around for his bike, he was surprised to find it up a tree. Fred told the kids he had a lot of trouble getting the bike down out of that tree, but eventually, although puzzled by its behaviour, he continued on his trip. The next time he visited the station he asked the bookkeeper what sort of oil he had been given.

'Oh,' said the man, 'that was goanna oil.'

Fred Holm passed away on 21 May 1975, a few weeks short of his 96th birthday. His grave is in the Winton cemetery.

The Opalton field and Conways slumped in production at a time when opal prices were low, so the miners drifted away to new finds on Horse Creek. Trooper Castledine was transferred to the Duchess, the police barracks were purchased by George Cragg, and the hotels were removed and re-erected elsewhere. The last publican to leave was a man named Neal; he was later shot at Devoncourt Station near Cloncurry.

The Mayne fields continued to produce opal after Opalton's demise and a hotel was built at Mayne junction prior to the turn of the century. The site chosen was where the road from Mayneside met the Winton to Diamantina Lakes road near the junction of the two rivers. It had a rather chequered history, and the last licensee, a man named Edwards, is buried near the hotel. In the late 1940s the pub was pulled down and the material was used to help build the Mundurin homestead.

Opal was found at the Kynuna field around the turn of the nineteenth century and a number of gougers were digging there before World War I. The opal was not far beneath the surface, but the quality and production level was nowhere like that of Mayneside or Opalton. At one time the gougers were paid by the government to keep the field going.

Around the turn of the nineteenth century Charlie Rigby was employed as a dogger (dingo trapper) on Woodstock Station. The run was then owned by a man named Ellis, who also owned a small hotel on the place that catered for the coach passengers en route to Boulia and beyond. Also working on Woodstock was Harry Macrossan, who did a bit of prospecting for opal on the property. He had no real success, but dug a few holes around the station and picked up a bit of potch at Opal Lagoon. After Macrossan left Woodstock, Rigby became interested enough to do a bit of gouging in Macrossan's workings. He had no luck, although he did dig up a bit of potch at Opal Lagoon.

Peter Knowls

IN
LOVING MEMORY
OF
MINNIE
DEARLY BELOVED DAUGHTER
OF
CHARLES & HARRIET BAMPFIELD
DIED OCTOBER 4TH 1899
AGED 30 YEARS

A SUDDEN CHANGE IN A MOMENT FELL
I HAD NO TIME TO BID MY FRIENDS FAREWELL
THINK NOT THIS STRANGE DEATH HAPPENS UNTO ALL
THIS DAY IS MINE TO MORROW YOU MAY FALL

*Headstone on grave of a young girl close to
site of the old Mayne Junction Hotel.*

In about 1905 a man named Banning purchased Woodstock from Ellis and put a bore down near Bulbi Creek some time around 1911. Rigby, who had previously camped on the creek, moved to Bulbi bore. On a small hill that ran off the range beyond the bore, Rigby saw an eroded opal band. In his spare time he put down a couple of holes on the hill, without result, then dug a small open cut mine in the side of a gully that ran beside the hill. He is supposed to have found some opal in this open cut, but never continued working there. Rigby left Woodstock during the 1930s and retired to Charters Towers.

The mining of opal then virtually ceased in the areas around Winton for over 30 years. The Opalton and Windsor mineral fields were deserted, save for weekend fossickers looking for opal chips lost when the gougers were knapping stones. One man, Tom Pether, did dig for opal matrix (a mixture of stone and opal) on Carisbrook Station and Trevor Cluff also unearthed shallow boulder opal on his station, Franklin. It was no more than a hobby for Trevor, however. As a result of the inactivity on the opal fields, the mining warden at Winton was transferred. The Opalton mining area fell under the control of the Longreach warden, and Cloncurry was responsible for administering any mining in the Windsor mining field.

In 1961 four men set out from Kynuna to locate Rigby's diggings near Bulbi. In the party were Mick Cheadle, a stockman and prospector; Graham McKerrow, a grazier who had worked on Woodstock and knew the location of the mine; Rick Wallduck, a mate of Cheadle's; and Christy Black, an old timer from Kynuna who had been involved in opal mining in the early days. Two vehicles were taken: an ex-army blitz buggy owned by Mick, and Graham's ex-army jeep. The group first located Peter Karfe's old workings, where there were a couple of deep shafts and some shallow ones that had almost fallen in. Some good opal chips were found and it was obvious that good quality stones had been found there.

Above Kynuna the Diamantina River comes in from the south-west. South of the river the country is exceedingly rough, with creeks like Glen George and Glen Urquhart running north to join the Diamantina. Despite having four-wheel drive vehicles, the going was very rough and some of the creeks tested the skill of the drivers and the quality of the vehicles. En route to Rigby's old mine the party visited the old Kynuna diggings; these shallow mines proved to be of little interest to the party, who then went on and camped on Glen Urquhart Creek. Next morning they found their way down the range that divided the watershed and arrived at Rigby's workings.

There was not a lot to be seen. The shallow holes on the hill were mostly fallen in and the small open cut was also badly eroded, but some faded chips of opal were found near the open cut. After looking around, the four men had lunch by the small creek that ran past the end of the hill. Graham was having generator trouble with the jeep so they decided to return via Woodstock Station, avoiding the rough country over the range.

Graham McKerrow wasn't interested in opal mining and returned to McKinlay, having played his part. Christy Black was too old to go gouging, but Mick Cheadle had caught the opal bug. Rigby's workings were to become the 'Red Flash' mining lease, the first mine to be worked full time since the collapse of the mining activities years before. The Red Flash produced gem-quality opal, and I was to become deeply involved in the mine.

THE OPAL GOUGER'S LAMENT

(Sung to the tune of the 'Girl I Left Behind Me')

I've left the rat race far behind,
good luck to those who foller,
For I am down this flamin' shaft
a-gouging for a dollar.
The good life is for others now,
but I do not begrudge it,
For like a wombat underground,
I do not have a budget.

We work like hell upon this ridge,
for tucker to sustain us,
I've tightened up the windlass pipe
with washers from my anus.
We have no fridge upon this ridge,
the air is filled with thunder,
The food is rough and bad enough
to make a kelpie chunder.

The reds and blues of opal hues,
seduce me like a vision,
My duds and shirt are full of dirt,
thank God for circumcision.
There could be opal just ahead,
the thought is always nagging,
So I will strive to dig this drive
although my bottom's dragging.

To work like this without reward
a man must be a wanker,
I'm soaking wet with flamin' sweat,
my cheeks they run a banker.
But I am deep down underground
where the tax man cannot find me,
There's opal dirt on every side
and opal dirt behind me.

I've left the rat race far behind
and never wash my collar,
And I am starving slowly here
a-gouging for a dollar.
But when I climb this bloody shaft
at the nearest pub you'll find me.
There I'll have a beer and shed a tear
for the good life far behind me.

THE RED FLASH

BY EARLY 1963 the saddle repair shop I had established in Winton was doing well. I had not as yet sold my droving plant, but held no aspirations of returning to the stockroutes. Droving had been good to me, but with the trucks gaining an ever-increasing share of stock transport, the writing was on the wall. Besides, I was 39 years of age, and like most men I wanted some day to get married and have a family; the stockroutes were no place for a woman.

I had rented a shop opposite the council swimming pool from Gaynor Brushe and Sons, the plumbers. It had previously been the doctor's surgery and I often wondered about the privacy of consultations, for when Gaynor and his sons were building rainwater tanks, I had to shout to make myself heard. There could not have been too many medical secrets in Winton in those days. A Dr Ram had been the last medico to practise in the old surgery. There happened to be a spate of twin births in the little town during his time and the town wags used to go around chanting, 'Dr Ram will bring your lamb, two for the price of one.'

I used the back room, which had been the surgery, as a workroom, while in the waiting room I placed a counter and displayed some stock. One morning I was hard at work, when I heard someone enter the front of the shop. I went out to find a curly haired character of medium height holding a saddle. He heaved it onto the counter and said, 'Do you know what that is?'

I looked at him in surprise. 'Well,' I replied, 'it looks remarkably like a saddle.'

'Yeah, yeah, any bloody fool knows that. But what sort is it?'

I looked at his saddle carefully. 'Well, I'd say it's a Tim Carr, and without examining it I'd say it had a broken tree.'

The owner of the Carr saddle looked at me with grudging respect. 'OK, you know your saddles, but can you fix it?'

'No worries,' I told him, 'but I'll have to send away for a tree, and rasp a fair bit of it away to get it to fit.'

The curly headed ringer agreed and introduced himself as Mick Cheadle. He told me he had been running the camp on Yelvertoft Station near Mount Isa, but was now at Kynuna. He departed after telling me he would pick up the saddle in three weeks time. It was a rather inauspicious beginning to a lasting friendship and business relationship.

I obtained a tree and repaired the Carr saddle, but time went by and there was no sign of Mick Cheadle. Finally he strolled into my shop one day, ran his eyes over the saddle and paused. Then he said, 'I don't suppose you would take some opal for repairing it?'

I shook my head. 'Sorry, Mick . . . Where did you get the opal?'

He snorted. 'You don't expect me to tell you that do you?'

'You mean you dug it yourself?'

'Bloody oath! I'm onto a good show.'

I thought for a while; opal had always fascinated me. I knew there had been no mining done around Winton for years and I was intrigued by Cheadle's remarks. 'Look, Mick, I may be able to help you later. Give me half the cost of repairing the saddle now, and I might look at some of your opal later.'

Mick Cheadle, stockman and opal gouger,
at the Red Flash mine, 1964.

Mick went away rather relieved. I guessed he was finding opal mining a strain on his finances. I gave little more thought to Mick and his opal until he arrived at the shop a fortnight later. He showed me a parcel of rough opal. There was sand in some of the stones but the colour was excellent. I knew very little about opal at that time, but nevertheless I was impressed. Mick told me he was in half shares in the mine with Ron Brenton, but neither of them had any experience at marketing the opal. They had been selling large milk tins of poor quality rough to Harold Hurst, the Kynuna storekeeper, as tourist stones. This provided a bit of tucker money, but Harold wasn't interested in parcels of better quality opal. Mick said he and Ron felt they were not in a position to get a fair price for the gem-quality stones. After getting my assurance that anything he told me was confidential, Mick related to me the short history of the mine they were working.

After visiting Rigby's old claim with Graham McKerrow, he managed to get Ron Brenton interested in joining him in a mining venture. Ron was the Julia Creek to Kynuna mailman. Mick also enlisted the help of his mate, Rick Wallduck. After careful inspection of the old mine, Ron registered three mining leases, the Blue Speck, Opal Den and the Red Flash. The latter lease covered most of the old workings and was to be the one that would produce gem-quality opal. The group built a hut on the Blue Speck lease, constructed a windlass and started putting down a shaft on the hill. A primitive type of whip was also built using the old lever and fulcrum system: a long pole is placed in a fork set in the ground; on the long end of this pole a lighter perpendicular pole is attached, to which the bucket is fastened; a rope on the short end allowed the bucket to be lowered, raised and swung to one side at the shaft head. One man worked the whip or windlass while his mate worked underground filling the bucket. These whips can still be seen in use in third world countries. Ladders were also used in working the Red Flash. As there was inadequate surface water available close to the Red Flash, 44 gallon drums were used to carry water up from the Bulbi bore.

Mick asked me if I would be interested in either buying the opal or alternatively acting as marketing agent for him and Ron. I told Mick I would like to see the mine and would give him a decision later. The following day Mick and I drove out through Woodstock Station to the Red Flash. There was not a lot to see but I was impressed by Mick's enthusiasm; I agreed to meet both partners in Winton to discuss a deal.

The meeting duly took place and I was offered a third share of production to market the opal. Mick, Ron and I were partners. Rick Wallduck was still working with Mick, and apparently they had some financial arrangement worked out between them. The first thing I did was to send the rough opal to Brisbane, where I had found a cutter willing to cut and polish the rough opal. When the cut stones came back they looked great to my uneducated eyes. Some were quite big, as heavy as 10 carats; I soon found out, however, that I had a lot to learn about the opal business.

Opals should be cut to a standard size, ranging from one to three or four carats, so that setting the stones could be done at a reasonable cost. Only top quality gems warrant individual settings. Rather disillusioned, I sent the cut parcel to my brother Jeff, who was at that time working in Sydney. I had done a bit of homework and was aware that Sydney was the headquarters of the opal trade in Australia. It didn't take long for Jeff and I to find out just how hard it was to break into the business of selling opal. We talked on the phone and agreed that the stones should be cut again into regulation sizes. He was fortunate to obtain the services of a top cutter who was working for one of the biggest dealers in Sydney. He cut our opal in his spare time.

The freshly cut parcel was sold, although the price was a bit disappointing. Despite that, Mick and Ron were pleased; at last they had

General area around the Red Flash mine.

The Red Flash mine, with the whip in right foreground.

an outlet for their gem opal. Jeff played an important part in the marketing from that point on. Being in Sydney was a great advantage. By mid-year the mine was producing well and sales were being made overseas. I decided to register a company name to give our operations a more professional image, and the Capricornian Opal Company was duly registered at the Winton courthouse.

In August the Winton rodeo was held. The town was full of rodeo riders, station people and stockmen. Mick was in town, of course, as was Clive Teece, a mate of both Mick and mine.

Once the rodeo was over, someone organised a party out on Mistake Creek. Mick persuaded Clive to lend him his car and headed out. Mick loved a party, and it didn't bother him how rough it got. During the evening Mick and a rodeo rider had words, then got stuck into one another. Mick was no slouch with his fists, and to get a better view of proceedings some of the rodeo riders used Clive's car as a grandstand.

I knew nothing of this until next morning when an irate Clive found me at the Central Hotel. He invited me to inspect the roof of his car. I did so and commented that it looked as though a mob of billy goats had been dancing on it.

'It wasn't bloody billy goats, it was rodeo riders.'

He told me the story, and said Mick was too busy at the time to see who the culprits were. I felt sorry for Clive, for a generous gesture to a mate was going to cost him money, but I did not see what he wanted of me. I was soon to learn.

'I'm going to find the bastards that did this, and I need your help. You know most of these rodeo blokes—we'll go round the pubs and question them.'

I knew it would be a futile exercise, but Clive was a mate of mine, so we set out on a search-and-destroy mission. It was, as I had suspected, a waste of time. Nobody knew anything, or if they did they weren't saying. Clive, who was usually a good natured chap, was getting progressively more hostile.

Finally I suggested to him that we give it away. He reluctantly agreed, but first we would have one more drink at the Australian Hotel. Like most of the pubs, the bar was crowded and Clive elbowed his way to the bar. As he reached it, he bumped against a chap in a black leather jacket, who turned to Clive and told him to f... off. Coming on top of the failed investigation, it was the last straw. Clive felled him like an ox.

The man in the leather jacket lay as though dead on the floor by the bar. On reaching for his beer, Clive almost fell over him.

'A man comes in for a quiet beer,' he complained, 'and he has to put up with bastards lying all over the place.' He turned to the barmaid. 'Why don't you get someone to drag the bludger out of here?'

He got short shrift from her. 'You knocked him down, drag him out yourself.'

We had another drink and left. As Clive drove me home I could see his humour had improved considerably. He hadn't found the culprits, but he'd had a victory of sorts.

I thought he would let the matter rest, but I could not have been more wrong. Next morning Clive turned up again, ready to continue the inquiry. I pointed out that it was a waste of time for us both, but Clive was adamant we could find the villains. He was a good mate so in the end I agreed to accompany him. As I expected, we had no more luck than on the previous day. At 11 o'clock Clive agreed it was hopeless and we dropped in to the North Gregory Hotel for a last drink before heading home.

Those days the North Gregory was a top hotel. It was owned by the Winton Council and managed by John Heads. We walked into the bar and ordered beers. By some twist of fate Clive found himself standing beside the man he had floored the day before. The man was minus the leather jacket, but was recognisable by his damaged face. Clive must have felt he had to say something.

'How are you going today?' he asked the man politely.

'Not bad, but I'd be a lot better if I could find the mongrel who king hit me yesterday,' was the reply.

'Oh, you would, eh? Well, your luck's in, you've found him.'

It was on again. The bar floor was tiled and Clive, who was wearing riding boots, slipped over. Sitting on the tiles, he pulled off a boot and flung it away. It headed straight for a glass shelf holding numerous bottles of spirits. John Heads leapt high and pulled off a spectacular one-handed catch. It would have extended Mark Taylor to the limit. By the time Clive had the other boot off, the situation was under control. Clive settled down, we drank our beers and departed. The investigation was over. Clive discovered his insurance would repair the car and everyone was happy.

The mining and marketing arrangements continued to work well until October 1963, when Ron Brenton, who had business interests elsewhere, sold me his half share in the Red Flash together with all the mining equipment. The leases had always been registered in Ron's name. From that point on the three leases—Nos. 5636, 5637 and 5667—were held in mine.

Mick and Rick carried on working the Red Flash mine, and production was steady. We now had a forwarding agent in Sydney to handle the parcels of opals we were exporting. Jeff took holidays from his job and was keen to get involved in mining the gemstones he had handled in Sydney. He came up to Winton and went out to the mine. He soon became an expert opal gouger.

By December the heat made mining difficult and the operation was shut down until after the wet. Jeff returned to Sydney and continued with marketing the opal. I planned to get married later in 1964, but at that time I was still in residence at the Central Hotel. I spent a rather boisterous festive season, but in preparation for my marriage I bought a block of land in Allen Street, and engaged Bobby Mann, a local carpenter, to build a modest home on the site.

Once weather conditions allowed, the mine started production again, Mick working on the open cut with some success. In May 1964 he asked me to buy his share of the Red Flash and Blue Spec leases. The Red Flash was the only lease of the three to produce opal. Mick kept a share in the Opal Den lease, and Ron retained his shares in both the Blue Spec and in Opal Den. It was more to remain involved than anything else; those leases had never shown signs of being worth working—holes drilled with the extended auger had drawn a blank. As a result, their sale price was virtually nil.

Jeff now left his job in Sydney, as contacts with buyers were well established. He joined Mick in working the Red Flash on a share of opal produced. By then Rick had given the opal gouging away and returned to stockwork.

Jeff and Mick got on very well together. A good working relationship is absolutely essential when two men are thrown together in an isolated situation. Mick had then been working at the Red Flash for over 12 months, and Jeff and I were aware he was getting itchy feet. Mick is a born prospector, always eager to see what is over the next hill. To ease the monotony of mining, the pair would go off prospecting for a day or two. The Red Flash was not far from where Brennen's claim must have been and the fact that the long lost mine may well be close was a constant challenge to Mick.

Sometimes if money was late arriving from buyers, I made an advance from my bank account to cover costs. On these occasions, Mick, who had

Brian Holm

Windlass on shaft at the Red Flash mine.

a lively sense of humour, used to call me 'Mr Big'. He would inspect the depleted tucker box, turn to Jeff and say, 'I fear we must go to town and put the fangs into Mr Big.'

It was about this time that Mick and Jeff received a visit from a rather odd character. He was driving an almost brand new LandRover and informed them he was a dogger employed by the council. He raved on about firearms and showed the pair a .44 automatic pistol he had planted under the seat of the vehicle. After he had departed, Mick decided they would need to keep an eye on the dogger, declaring, 'That bastard could knock us off for our opals.'

It wasn't an outlandish statement. The Red Flash was in an isolated spot, miles from anywhere. Jeff agreed, and the next time the dogger drove up to the mine Mick met him on his own.

'Where's your mate?' asked the visitor.

'You can't see him,' replied Mick. 'But he's over there with a rifle pointed at your guts.'

The dogger did not wait around. He put the LandRover into gear and departed at great speed. Mick, who always saw the funny side of things, thought it was a great joke.

They only saw the dogger once more. There was a rough road down the range behind the mine. One morning Mick and Jeff heard an engine at full revs, and over the top of the range, well away from the road, came the dogger. The LandRover was ricocheting from rock to rock and colliding into trees, and before the eyes of the startled pair, it began to shed bits and pieces as it tore down the descent. The dogger was thrown about like a rag doll, but was still clinging to the wheel of the battered vehicle when it hit the bottom. The LandRover was hardly recognisable. The hood was gone and the mudguards were hanging loose. Without a glance at the opal miners, the dogger accelerated away, shedding parts of the vehicle as he went.

The pair worked the mine almost up to Christmas, then spent the festive season in Kynuna, and then, rather the worse for wear, returned to the mine. The wet season brought them into Winton for a well-earned respite. Production from the Red Flash had been good, new shafts had been put down and the old open cut had yielded some very good opals. We were now forwarding parcels of rough opal to overseas destinations on a fairly regular basis.

The government's policy on levying sales tax on opal left me wondering about the collective brain power of politicians. Australia is the only

Opals from the Red Flash mine.

country in the world that produces gem-quality opal that will stand cutting. To sell a cut stone, however, 25 per cent sales tax must be added, while as much rough opal as you wish can be sent overseas tax free. It's much the same with most of our primary industries. Instead of encouraging the adding of value to what we produce, we ship it abroad for others to make money out of by processing the raw materials. We then commit an even greater folly by buying back the finished products.

While in Winton Jeff bought a Willy's jeep tray body truck, and as soon as the weather allowed he returned to the mine. Mick stayed on working the Red Flash under a new agreement for some months, after which Jeff mined it on his own until the end of the year. I cannot say I was all that keen on the idea, but Jeff wasn't at all worried about it. To be truthful, being newly married, I was not keen to join him, besides I had my hands full at the shop, a business that could, if required, provide financial support for the mining venture. My brother is one of those unusual characters who can work quite well with others, but is in his element when operating on his own.

A lot of station owners and managers resent the presence of prospectors and miners on their property. We were fortunate that the manager of Woodstock, Alex Logan, was a gentleman. Realising the mine was in an isolated location, he did everything possible to help. I knew Alex quite well, as he was one of the stalwarts of the Diamantina Devils Cricket Club.

Jeff produced some very good parcels of opals during 1965. By the end of the year, though, Jeff and I decided to cease full-time work at the Red Flash. Over the previous three years the mine had produced a lot of top quality opal, but in Jeff's opinion more ground would have to be opened up to maintain production. We agreed we were in no position to carry out expansion at that time.

During the early part of 1966 Brian Holm and his mate Ron Norris did weekend share mining at the Red Flash. On some occasions, Brian's grandfather, Fred Holm, accompanied them. Fred had been on the Opalton diggings in the field's heyday. Clive Edmonstone and Ron McKenzie also did a bit of work at the mine. In May 1966 I sold a major interest in the three leases to Ron.

The mining boom began soon after and the stock exchange went berserk. A company was floated in the South with nothing more than an authority to prospect over a large area around the old Opalton field. A parcel of shares was allocated to the local people, but I refused to subscribe to a company that could offer no more than a map of an ATP

Brian Holm

Fred Holm inspecting opal-bearing sandstone at the Red Flash mine.

Brian Holm

Brian Holm at the top of the old shaft at the Red Flash mine.

area. The shares went onto the market at a high price and a lot of people made a quick quid. The poor devils who bought shares and held them got their fingers burnt; the company folded without putting a hole down. I could have made money at someone else's expense, but my principles will probably keep me poor until the day I die.

Towards the end of the mining boom, Ron and I were approached by a group with an offer to buy the Red Flash. They planned to float a company called I.B.I.S. Mining NL. The proposed company had plans to lease other promising areas, and seemed genuinely interested in long-term opal mining. I knew some of the people involved in the company and was fully satisfied with their bona fides.

By the time the company was ready to float, however, the boom was over and mining shares were no longer the flavour of the month; as a result, the float was under-subscribed. I.B.I.S., unlike its namesake, never got off the ground.

The Red Flash was the first opal mine to be worked full-time in the area for many years. More importantly, it revived interest in the old opal diggings around Winton. Before I left Winton I sold my remaining interest in the mine to the late Vince Evert. Vince went on to become one of the pioneers of the new opal boom. Within a few short years Mayne Side and Opalton were again hives of industry.

ON THE BANKS OF THE OUTER BARCOO

Today is the Sabbath, the last in the week,
A day of devotion and rest.
But there's no morning service and no 'Salvo' band
For the toilers who work in the West.
Down in the city they're off to the beach
Or have taken the kids to the zoo.
There are no like attractions around about here
On the banks of the outer Barcoo.

Now sport is ideal for passing the time,
Thus putting in part of the day,
But when one had neither opponents nor gear
It's a bit hard to know what to play.
We couldn't play cricket or tennis or bowls,
We've neither a draught board nor cue,
And never a golf club or caddy we've seen
On the banks of the outer Barcoo.

Now shooting, they say, is a very fine sport,
With that we are forced to agree,
But the only firearm that we have in the camp
Was made in the last century.
The barrel's cut short and its blasting report
Can be heard from here to the Loo,
And a most lethal shock is got from the stock
If one shoots on the outer Barcoo.

We've tried our hand fishing down by the big bend,
For a big feed of fish would be nice,
But never a word from the fish have we heard
Though we've dropped them a line once or twice.
We've sat on our tail never seeing a scale,
Though the mossies were biting, it's true,
But the fish don't approve of the bait that we use
On the banks of the outer Barcoo.

Now down in the city when Sunday comes round
And you're off to the footie or club,
Give a second's thought then to the poor working men
Who are stuck away out in the scrub.
When it's all said and done it isn't much fun,
Though whingeing with us is taboo,
But hop on your bike and see what it's like
On the banks of the outer Barcoo.

BUSH ENTERTAINMENT

MY MATE BRUCE HANSON and I once took a couple of girls to the pictures in Camooweal. The 'theatre' was no more than a rectangular galvanised iron fence with a fibro screen erected at one end and a projection box at the other. The projector was turned by hand, and as the projectionist's arm grew tired, action in the film would slow then jerk and speed up as he changed hands. But it was somewhere to go, so in we went and sat down on the canvas-covered deckchairs that were placed in rows on the stony ground. The film was a run of the mill affair, with cowboys and Indians chasing one another across the screen. Then came the part where the immigrant train circled the wagons against an impending Indian attack. The braves were shown lined up on a nearby hill, then the chief rode forward and the camera zoomed in to give a close up of him sitting arrogantly on his horse. At that moment a hard case in the audience bent down and, picking up a stone, threw it with unerring aim at the screen. The missile took the chief's head clean off his shoulders, and left a hole the size of a basketball in the fibro screen. The offender was hustled out amid laughter, boos and whistles; for me it was the highlight of the evening.

The introduction of television and videos to the bush radically changed the social life of its people. Moviegoing was once one of the main sources of entertainment. Every town had its picture theatre; many of the outback ones were open air shows, but that was of little consequence as it seldom rained out there and when it did it was always welcome. Few of these theatres have survived the invasion of technology. One that has is the Royal Theatre in Winton. A partly open air building, it has been owned and operated by the Evert family for three generations. During its early days it survived a fire, and doubled for a boxing ring and a skating rink. Of late it has become the popular venue for 'The Poets' Breakfast' during the Winton festivals. The Royal Theatre still puts on two shows a week during the tourist season. Long may it defy the idiot box.

Once when I was trucking bullocks in Dajarra, I found the Australian Inland Mission vehicle had arrived in the little trucking town. Word spread that the padre would put on a picture show that night, and the town kids were delighted. Rather than drink at the pub, I decided to join them at the show. The projector was set up in the street, with the side of the galvanised iron storeroom acting as the screen, and everyone brought along their own chairs. I forget what the picture was, but I thoroughly enjoyed myself; the kids did too. They were fascinated by the way the actors made their undulating way across the corrugated iron screen.

In the days before couch potatoes and push button entertainment, people had to amuse themselves. This was even more critical in the bush; city people have always had the edge on their country cousins where entertainment is concerned. The denizens of the bush managed to amuse themselves quite adequately, however, and they did so for the most part without the aid of strong drink—the ubiquitous stubby had not then become an Australian icon. Unmarried stockmen and drovers did drink, of course, but for the most part this was a short spree after months in the bush.

When I was a youngster, family picnics were always popular. I have vivid recollections of picnics on Cattle Creek with my family friends. Our respective parents would recline on rugs spread under the paperbarks and talk of whatever parents discussed in those days. Meanwhile, we kids would swim in the clear waters, sail makeshift boats and play 'make believe' games in the scrub that bordered the sandy reaches.

Children back then had to rely more on themselves for amusement, and as a result they learned to use their imagination rather than to depend on provided diversions. A child's imagination is a treasure house, a veritable fantasy land. Children who utilise the gift of youthful imagination are seldom bored.

Tennis has always been played in the country. There was a lot of small bush schools about in the past and most of them had a court, usually built from an ant bed. This was collected from white ant nests and puddled to provide an excellent playing surface. Most of the school courts were home to adult tennis clubs and as a result the school became the hub of local social life. Many of the bigger stations, particularly in the sheep country, had their own courts and station tennis afternoons were popular social occasions.

Everyone could dance in the days before television and every little town had a hall of some sort where the local dances were held. The country state schools were also pressed into service for these events. Most were on high stumps, and when a dance was planned, the desks and forms were taken underneath, the cracks in the floorboards were filled with candle grease, and a mixture of sawdust and kero was broadcast. The result was a satisfactorily fast surface. I rode to many of those dances as

Don Simpson

Tennis in the Outback, 1920s style.

a youth and enjoyed myself immensely. The girls would sit along one wall while their mothers played euchre in the supper room, with one eye on their cards, the other on their daughters. Getting musicians for these dances was never a problem—the country seemed to be full of them. One could dance with a girl then and whisper sweet nothings in her ear if one desired; to converse with your partner at today's discos, a man would need semaphore flags or a megaphone.

Country dances ranged from the schoolroom hops to the grand race and woolshed balls of the outback. Those balls were splendid affairs at which the ladies would be resplendent in ball gowns, with up-to-date hairstyles. These functions were good news for the business houses in the Western towns. Graziers had money back then and the local dress shops and hairdressers welcomed the ball season. Unfortunately, class distinction was alive and well years ago in the sheep country. At one town, at least, a rope was put across the hall at the balls, the grazing fraternity dancing in splendid isolation at one end of the hall, and the townsfolk and workers at the other.

Happily, this obnoxious practice has disappeared from the West. I organised a rather remarkable dance once in Camooweal. My mate Bruce Hanson and I were waiting for the season to break in 1952, so a couple of girls we knew persuaded us to put on a dance. We agreed and

Social gathering at Isis Woolshed, 1920.

Bruce left the arrangements to me. I booked the shire hall at the council office and found a lady who played the piano and a ringer who could play the drums. The big night came and, as there was no door charge, a good crowd was soon dancing to lively music. Shortly after 10 o'clock the local sergeant of police came into the hall. He must have asked who was in charge, for he came over to me. The sergeant was a well-liked bloke and I wondered what the trouble was.

He drew me to one side and said, 'I'm afraid you'll have to stop the dance.'

'Stop the dance! It's just getting warmed up. Why?'

He pushed his cap back and scratched his head. 'Well, I've just got word that King George the Sixth has died. I think you had better stop as a mark of respect.'

I reluctantly agreed, although I doubt if Buckingham Palace would have worried too much about our activities. I went over and told the musicians to stop playing, then announced the news to the assembled dancers. They accepted the closure with good grace, although I suspected some were more upset about the cancellation of the dance than about the death of their monarch. Bruce and I turned off the lights and closed the hall doors on a memorable evening.

At one time hotels in the country had billiard rooms with a permanently employed billiard marker to look after them. The bush produced some outstanding players at both billiards and snooker as a result, and Jack Howard of Boulia is reputed to have been a player almost as skilled as the great Walter Lindrum. Most mothers warned their sons about these billiard rooms, calling them dens of iniquity, no doubt in response to the illegal gambling that went on in them. This was a matter for the local police to control, of course, and raids were sometimes made, but the results were never spectacular.

Usually one man ran the gambling in the billiard rooms, and games like crown and anchor, inns and outs and two-up, or swy, were favourites. In Winton the man who ran the gambling school was Wicky Taylor. Wicky was a respected character of the town. He could fight like a thrashing machine and his wits were as fast as his fists. He usually ran a game of two-up on Sunday mornings, the venue a spot behind Elliot's dairy, just behind the present Waltzing Matilda Centre. Being careful of his reputation, Wicky always employed the services of a cockatoo, or look-out. On one particular morning the game was progressing in a satisfactory manner, the heads of the crowd raising and lowering as eyes followed the flight of the pennies. Unfortunately the look-out must have been dozing, for Wicky looked up to see the police almost upon him.

'Quick! Pick up your money,' Wicky hissed. In one quick movement he slipped the kip and pennies into his pocket and pulled out a dog-eared bible.

'Raise up your eyes to the Lord, brothers,' he cried, at the same time throwing his arm in the air.

'Now let us pray.' Wicky lowered his head and the crowd did likewise.

As the police arrived, Wicky held out a hand. 'Welcome to our little prayer meeting. Brother Bates will be taking the hat around in a minute, please give generously.'

It was a masterful performance. The baffled police left before the hat reached them and the game continued.

The racing game has always had a large following in the outback. Meetings ranged from the corn-fed meetings in the larger towns to picnic races in smaller ones, where grass-fed horses carried the colours of their owners. Bookmakers usually attended these meetings, but the odds they offered were nothing to write home about. Two of these bush race meetings, Brunette and Birdsville, have become notable successes. The

Brunette races have retained much of their original character, but the Birdsville meeting has unfortunately become a venue for yuppies.

Problems with race fixing, doping and other dubious practices have been a common feature of the racing game worldwide, and the outback has never been any different. At a meeting in the Gulf years ago the jockey on the favourite was told to pull the horse—that is, prevent it from winning. The horse's connections had put a large wager on another starter and hoped to make a killing.

The jockey followed orders, but the horse had other ideas. It came down the home straight lengths in front of the field, almost pulling its rider's arms out of their sockets in the process. Realising that his mount could not be beaten, the jockey promptly dropped the reins and fell off. The horse was of course disqualified, the connections won the money and all was well.

For those punters who followed the sport of kings from afar, there were always SP bookies in every town to cater for their habit. Although this type of betting was illegal, little was ever done to stamp out the practice.

Rodeos were also popular annual events in the bush. I was associated with the sport for some time in Winton, acting as shute boss and later as judge. Those days the buckjumpers were brought up from stations like Springvale; most of them would buck a town down and their style was quite unpredictable. They spun, bucked high, shoulder bucked and chopped. They were a real test of a horseman's ability.

Mount Isa was the last major rodeo in Queensland to buck its own horses. Under pressure from rodeo 'cowboys', though, the committee will now be using contract stock only. The horses provided by these contractors are known to the riders and have only one style of bucking—straight ahead while kicking up. Rodeos have certainly changed. Horsemen have become 'cowboys' who ride in big American saddles, and buckjumpers are now 'broncos'. Give me the old days when men who looked like Australians rode really bad horses in small Australian saddles.

Stockmen who worked in the cattle camps years ago had to rely entirely on their initiative for entertainment. There were no radios in those days and newspapers were virtually unknown in the camps. Sports were held and even after a hard day's branding, ringers lined up for broad jumping, backwards jumping and various other athletic diversions. Other contests were held, too, such as one which involved toeing the line and, with one hand on the ground, placing a match box out as far as possible with the other. A variation of this was to place the matchbox between the teeth while balancing on the hands with the knees placed on the elbows. We had some weird and wonderful events, but they helped to pass the time. At night we yarned, recited and played mouth organs, the only musical instrument we could carry in a swag. At times we played cards—poker mostly, for matches, as we had little cash with us.

At times we played a game called 'yarding the bull'. Like noughts and crosses, it was a game that usually ended without result; however, it could be won if one of the players lost concentration. It was usually played with the game board scratched on the ground in this fashion:

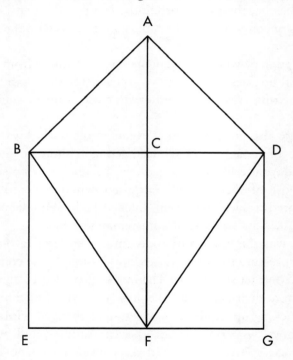

The idea was to yard the bull to position A, with the horsemen at positions B, C and D. The game starts with the bull at position C and the horsemen at positions E, F and G. The bull must move first. The bull can either be yarded or can escape by reaching any of the positions marked E, F or G.

The Aboriginal stockmen used to play a far more difficult game that needed a lot of mental concentration. A diagram like this was made in the dirt.

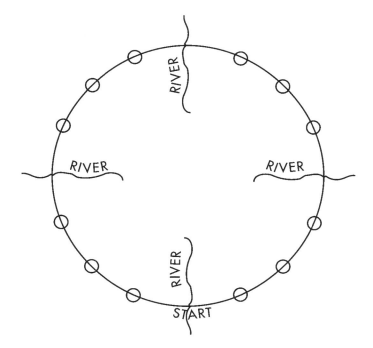

This game is played by having a caller ask the player, who is blind-folded, to nominate each position by asking, 'What's here?'. The player starts by answering, 'river' then 'nothing', 'nothing', 'nothing', 'river', as the caller questions him. When he has gone round the board to the starting river once, he must then put a man on the first 'nothing' space. He then continues putting one man on the next space at each round of the board. When all the positions are manned, he must then remove a man at each round of the board until the 'nothing' spaces are empty again. This goes on until the player makes a mistake.

I have tried this game and it is very challenging indeed. A player must retain a clear mental picture of the game board at all times. I was never as good at it as some of the Aborigines.

There was, of course, a lot of well-organised sport played in the more heavily populated area of the outback. In the sheep country the grazing fraternity played polo, while the less affluent tried their hands at polo-crosse, a game resembling la cross but played on horses. Polocrosse never really prospered as polo did.

Rugby League was always a favourite with both players and spectators. In the Central West, the local competition was a high-profile affair played between the towns of Tambo, Barcaldine, Blackall, Longreach and Winton. Paid players and coaches from the South were engaged regularly, and at times ex-international players schooled the teams. As a result the standard of play was close to that of city clubs.

Travel, although arduous, was never a problem. The team from Tambo and its supporters would leave home early Sunday morning, travel to Winton, play a hard-fought game that afternoon, indulge in a few drinks afterwards and then drive back to Tambo, a round trip of 970 kilometres. Very few city teams could stand that pace. Next day the Tambo lads would be back in the shearing sheds, work that contributed a great deal to their toughness.

I doubt if anything could be further removed from droving than the grand old game of cricket. However, during its heyday as a drovers' town, Camooweal prided itself on having quite a respectable (I use the term loosely) cricket team. Over the summer months when droving was done, I had an occasional game with them, as did others who, like me, had fallen under the spell of the willow in earlier days and in far distant places. As we invariably played in temperatures of around 40°C, the organisers of our games, conscious of the grave dangers of dehydration, were generous in the provision of liquid refreshment. This, of course, was vital for replacing the bodily fluids lost in the pursuit of leather. It was an admirable precaution but made winning the toss imperative, for the life-preserving fluid affected our batting far more than our bowling. If we batted first, we usually put together a respectable total. If, however, unkind fate decreed that we should go to the crease second, a batting collapse was inevitable. It was of no use looking to the lower order to restore our fortunes; the tail never wagged. By the time the tail enders were due to bat, they had difficulty finding their way to the wicket, let alone striking the ball.

To say that the Camooweal cricket ground was rough would be a gross understatement. We did have a concrete pitch, but the outfield was totally devoid of grass and was littered with stones far larger than the ball we used. The ground was dragged before each game, but it made little difference—new stones were unearthed as the top ones were removed. Nothing could get rid of them. The Barkly Tableland Shire Council, at that time based in the drovers' town, admitted defeat. On most cricket fields the course of a cover drive is reasonably predictable. It wasn't like that on the Camooweal ground. There the ball was likely to rear up off a stone and strike the startled fieldsman smartly between the eyes. Fortunately, due to the life-preserving fluids we felt little pain.

GEORGINA TIMES

THE OFFICIAL ORGAN OF THE CAMOOWEAL CRICHET CLUB
VOL.1 ISSUE No 5.

THE GRAND OPENING OF THE CAMOOWEAL CRICKET OVAL

Reports on the opening ceremony and the days
cricket.

The Oval was offically opened by the Chairman of
the Barkly Tablelands Shire Council on Sunday the
23rd October,1955, who congratulated the Cricket Club
on their enterprise in providing the Oval not only for
Cricket but also for general sporting activities.

The first over was bowled by Pop Finlay to Jack
Dawson. No runs nor wickets were taken. The only thing
nearly taken was the wicket keepers head.

A scratch match was played on that day between
teams Captained by Squash Perry and G.Trembath .Squash
won the toss, and elected to bat. The innings was
opened by F.Martin and Doug Milne. Milne was caught by
Tait bowled by Sheehey for a duck. Martin was then
joined by Holt and with the score at 47 Martin retired
after scoring 22 runs. Ormonde was the next batsman but
was out very smartly for another duck. Caught by the
mighty Steene. Bowled Tait. Buchanan then joined Holt
and together they took the score toll0 before Holt was
caught and bowled for 52. Which included 8,4's this wa
the highest score on both sides. Simpson was the new ba
-sman joining Buchanan who was later given out. L.B.W.
to Trembath.(Umpire.J.Ormonde).After this the tail did
its best to wag but the innings closed at 136.

Sheehey and Burke opened for Trembaths 11, where
they scored 43 runs between them before Burke was
caught Perry bowled Holt for 15. Freckleton then joine
Sheehey, but was soon out for 2. bowled by F.Martin.
Tait was the next batsman, but had a change of partner
soon after. Sheehey was bowled by Holt for 29. Trembath
then faced the bowler making 5. Bunny then entered the
wicket and made 6. Steene made 11. Rooke then joined
Tait but only three runs were added before Tait was
caught. F.Martin. Bowled D.Milne 42. runs being made whic
included 2. 6's and 3 4's Rooke made 15. before he was
stumped by Buchanan off Perry. A few more runs were
made by the remaining players before the innings closed giving Trembaths 11 victory by 9 runs.

The Camooweal eleven sometimes travelled to Mount Isa to play social cricket against the teams there. We played on a field at Spear Creek that was later to become the Mount Isa rodeo grounds. On one memorable occasion we played a team from the town's post office. They were a genial bunch who did not take the game too seriously, and as a result the beer flowed like bore water and a good time was had by all.

I forget who won the match; somehow it did not seem all that important at the time. What was unusual was that one of our members who never drank let his head go and became as blind as a bat. It may have been the weather or the lively company, we never found out. When the time came to depart he was legless and had to be helped into a car, where he promptly went to sleep.

On the way back to Camooweal we all pulled up for a comfort stop at Inca Creek. Our drunken mate woke, lurched out and leapt into a muddy waterhole by the road. There he wallowed about like a water buffalo, muttering, 'Gotta sober up or the missus will kill me.' He was finally persuaded to come out, looking more like the creature from the black lagoon than a cricketer. No driver wanted the mud-covered inebriate in his vehicle, but the problem was solved by rolling him up cocoon-like in the long cricket mats. He was snoring loudly when we reached Camooweal. Pulling up at his house, we unrolled him on the front lawn, then waved and sped away as his wife opened the front door.

During the years I spent in Winton I became heavily involved in cricket; the game was enjoying a period of intense popularity in the West. The town teams took part in a three-cornered contest as well as playing social cricket with country sides. Representative teams also played against elevens from Muttaburra, Hughenden and Longreach. These rep games were taken very seriously. The arch enemy was Longreach, against whom we played for the Speed Myers' trophy.

One of the chaps who played with my town team was a rather difficult chap to handle—difficult, that is, on the cricket field or in a brawl. He was a fast bowler who hated batsmen almost as much as he disliked policemen. We shall call him Frank. Frank's bowling was very fast indeed, his speed only being exceeded by his lack of direction. Now and again, however, he bowled the unplayable ball. On one occasion a Winton rep team played an away game at Muttaburra. On inspecting the concrete pitch, we found that it was covered by coir, or coconut matting. Now, coir is quite springy and usually helps spin bowlers, and we found it certainly added pace to Frank's deliveries.

Muttaburra won the toss and decided to bat. When all was ready, the captain tossed the ball to Frank to open the bowling. As he walked back to his mark, the man at mid-off told him the batsman facing up was a policeman. This put the opener in double jeopardy. Frank turned with a light in his eye that was enough to make strong men shudder. I was fielding in the covers, but I never saw the ball Frank bowled, it was so fast. It must have landed just short of a length. It came off the coir like greased lightning, striking the unfortunate batsman on the forehead. He went down as though shot and was carried off unconscious. We apologised for the incident and the game continued. Frank's bowling became normal again, his next ball almost taking first slip's head off, then going screaming to the boundary for four byes.

Of all the social cricket we played, the games I enjoyed most were against the Diamantina Devils, a team of bushmen from the Channel Country stations. They were a great group of sportsmen whose home ground was a huge claypan at Munduran Station. It was almost as hard as concrete, and as fast as a skating rink. If a ball penetrated the field, it went like a flash, not only to the boundary, but seemingly to the horizon. A fieldsman virtually needed a fast horse and a cut lunch to retrieve it. The cricket mats were pegged down straight onto the natural surface, which always stayed firm, and a clump of gidgee trees on the edge of the claypan served as a grandstand, dressing room and bar. The ladies from 'down the river' always put on a slap-up lunch and after the game we ate our fill of good local beef, cooked using a large circular saw blade as a barbecue plate.

After the meal everyone had to take a turn at entertaining the crowd. By popular demand two items never varied at these after-game festivities. Phil Cluff always sang 'The Road to Mandalay', and then he would play a gumleaf while his brother Trevor did a tapdance on the upturned barbecue plate.

Whether true or not, the Diamantina Devils always told us they had a proper constitution. Rule 42 of this document forbade players to engage in sex the night before a game. They also said there used to be a rule 43 advising players not to engage in this pastime after a match. With broad grins, we were told that this rule was struck out as it was found to be unnecessary. Every match against the Diamantina Devils was a memorable affair.

Cricket is the greatest game of all. It is played worldwide by many different people, but no one plays the game with more zest and enjoyment than the 'flannelled fools' of the outback.

THE QUARTPOT MAIDEN

Out further West some time ago when fashion favoured laces,
The day arrived in Quartpot Town to hold the yearly races.
From miles around the bushmen came to pass a friendly greeting
And try to take each other down and clean up on the meeting.
The program was designed to woo the local racing gentry,
And for the 'plum', the maiden plate, there was a record entry,
For nominations numbered four—a mighty field and classy,
From sandhill runs beyond they came—from paddocks lush and grassy.

The bush crowd lined the Quartpot course, a crooked mile and tricky,
A blue-bush swamp just past the turn was sometimes rather sticky.
But little did they care for that, to them it had small meaning,
Nor did they mind the crazy way the judge's box was leaning.
One bookie came to rob the crowd and bribe the leading rider
And from his odds, a crippled goat was scarcely an outsider.
From off a box he laid the field, his voice was far from mellow,
The wire and sapling members' stand vibrated to his bellow.

Now Mulga Lad, a likely colt, was fast though rather tender;
The hoop engaged for Wallaroo was still upon a bender.
The Spider had a chance, some said, a smart and trusted starter,
But favourite for the maiden was a filly known as Garter.
A cunning field they were, no doubt, some 'stung', some dead as Caesar,
The ancient stipe who checked them out could scarce see past his
sneezer.
And while the judge drank twenty rums to banish indecision
He read a girlie magazine to fortify his vision.

The field lined up, the starter raised an old and rusted Snider,
The shot he fired to start the race wrote finis to the Spider.
The rest took off along the track o'er stony ground and ridgey,
And soon were lost to public sight behind a clump of gidgee.
Around the turn and up the straight the field was next seen speeding
And by a length, or so it seemed, that Mulga Lad was leading.
In wild abandonment he raced, the dirt and gravel throwing,
His laboured breathing as he rolled was like a grampus blowing.

Now Garter racing close behind, the inside too was hogging,
At every stride her crooked hoop the leader's rump was flogging.
Just then upon the narrow track, his master's oaths unheeding,
There strayed a canine specimen of rather doubtful breeding.
With tail a-jaunt he jogged along, gaze fixed on post and railing;
All efforts to avoid a smash were futile—unavailing,
For Mulga Lad leapt o'er the fence while Garter legged it after,
And Wallaroo bucked through the stand amid the hoots and laughter.

The hound, ignoring totally the havoc he was causing,
Changed his mind and trotted by the post not even pausing.
Then from his box the drunken judge, his bleary eyeballs shadin',
Declared that Mick Malaney's dog had won the Quartpot Maiden.
And still today they tell the tale and never lack a hearing
In public bars, in drovers' camps, in sheds when they are shearing,
For in our outback history an epic never fadin'
Occurred in Quartpot Town the day a sheep dog won the Maiden.

NORTH TO THE GULF

THE BAR OF the Australian Hotel was crowded with bushmen—men who after a year's hard work in the outback were down in Brisbane letting off steam. It was a noisy session as yarns, jokes, exaggerated claims and downright lies floated around the bar. It was a strange place, the old Australian, known to most of us as Mulga Corner. The beer served there was not our favourite drop, yet it drew us all like a magnet. The hotel was on the corner of Queen and Albert streets, but once inside you could have been in any bush pub in the outback.

I was drinking with a mate of mine, Jack Britt. We had worked together in stockcamps and on the road droving. I had run into Jack a few days before, and not having seen him for over two years, we found plenty to talk about. There was a burst of laughter down the bar and I looked over to see Big Jack Stead trying to win the heart of one of the barmaids. Jack was from Quilpie and, like most of us those days, his technique with women was fairly basic; but the girl handled his approaches with the ease and aplomb gained from long experience with amorous bushmen. She was missing a great opportunity, Steady told her, then returned to drinking beer with his mates. I ordered a couple more drinks and when they arrived I told Jack I was thinking of heading back bush. He looked at me. 'Where do you reckon you'll go, back to the Territory?'

I had spent the last two years in the Channel Country and I felt I needed a change. 'I'm not sure, Jack. I've been giving some thought to the Gulf.'

'Well, mate, if you're not certain, the best thing is to toss a coin.'

He picked up a penny from the change on the bar. 'Right, it's heads the Gulf, tails the Territory.' Britty tossed the coin in the air, caught it and, without looking at it, slapped it on his wrist. He removed his hand, and there it was, a head. I would try my luck on the stations in the Gulf of Carpentaria. I was quite happy with the decision-making process. It may seem a bit harum-scarum, but we were a carefree lot those days, quite happy to accept whatever might befall us.

Jack and I had a couple more beers then crossed Queen Street to the Central Cafe. We sat down and ordered a traditional meal of ham and eggs with mashed vegetables. Over lunch Jack and I yarned about the Gulf Country and the best areas to work in. I had already decided to go to Cloncurry and pick up a job ringing there. I was happy about the decision because it would give me an opportunity to see my mother. She was now living in Mackay and I could break my journey there for a few days. I had not seen her for over two years. My youngest brother, Jeff, was still at school, but we three older ones were a footloose lot. I knew my mother worried a lot about us, but it was not until years later, when I had children of my own, that I realised just how many of her grey hairs we must have been responsible for.

After Jack and I finished our meal, we shook hands and wished each other good luck. I then walked down to the tourist bureau and booked a rail ticket to Cloncurry. It would be a long trip, first of all up to Townsville on the Cairns Mail, then out to Cloncurry on the train to Mount Isa. That night I threw my swag into the luggage compartment of the northern mail train and settled back in a seat. It was goodbye to the bright lights and back to work.

I broke my journey at Mackay and after three very pleasant days there I again caught the northbound mail train. Although it was early April, the wet season was not yet over and the rain bucketed down during the night. I expected the Burdekin to be over the bridge, so was pleasantly surprised when the train puffed across with some leeway between the tracks and the rising floodwater. Our good fortune was too good to last, though, and washouts further north brought the train to a lengthy stop. When the Cairns Mail finally pulled in to the station at Townsville it was close to midnight. Cramped from the long journey, I retrieved my swag and waited for the platform to clear.

The train pulled out after a few minutes, and very soon everyone had departed. I shouldered my swag and walked to the end of the roofed platform, where I dropped the swag on the concrete. The rain gleamed in the station lights and lashed down on the railway lines while the wind moaned in the overhead wires and swept down the deserted platform. It was at best a very dismal night. I shivered slightly and rolled my sleeves down, buttoning them at my wrists. This situation didn't bother me for I had my swag and, to a bushman, his swag is virtually his home. Sitting on my haunches, I unbuckled the straps around my swag and unrolled it. The contents were rather basic. A large pocket held my clothes and other gear, and acted as a pillow. The swag contained two well-worn blankets but no mattress. The concrete would be hard, but I had slept on hard surfaces before and was tired enough to sleep on a barbed wire fence. Pulling off my boots, I placed them beside my whip and lay back, pulling my hat over my eyes.

I was almost asleep when I heard an angry voice. 'What do you think you're doing?'

I sat up to see a railway character glaring at me. I glared back. 'I'm trying to catch up on a bit of bloody sleep. What does it look like?'

'Well, you can't sleep here—it's not allowed.'

'Who the hell says so?'

'I do, and if you don't roll that swag up I'll call the police.' He marched off, full of his own importance.

I thought things over. If the petty dictator was right, I didn't have enough money left to waste on a fine, so reluctantly I rolled up my swag and put it on the last seat on the platform. I sat down and, using it as a pillow, I was soon asleep. My tormentor must have checked up on me again, for he was not finished with me yet. I was rudely awakened by a rough hand on my shoulder.

I sat up abruptly to see him standing beside a large policeman. The copper looked me over and turned to my persecutor. 'Is this the trouble-maker?' he asked.

'Yes, that's him! That's him!'

The policeman turned his attention to me again. 'Right, what's your name? And what are you doing here?'

I told him my name and added bitterly that I was hoping to get a bit of sleep. He digested that and then advised me sternly that I should have booked into a hotel. He added that he could provide me with accommodation if necessary.

To hell with it, I thought, attack is always the best defence. I stood up. 'Are the pubs open here in the middle of the bloody night? I just got off the northern mail and I'm catching the train to Cloncurry tomorrow. Lock me up if you want to—as long as I can get away from that officious bastard, I might get some sleep.'

'There,' the railway man said, 'I told you.'

The copper turned to him and told him to shut up. He looked me over again. 'Watch your language. What are you going to do in Cloncurry?'

I said I was going to get a job ringing.

'You don't look like a ringer. Where did you work last?'

I had to admit he had a point. I was in town clothes and a long spell down South had given me the pallor of a city dweller. I told him where I had last worked, and pointed out that I wasn't in a stockcamp at the moment.

'What's the sergeant's name in Boulia?' he fired at me. I thanked God for a good memory and gave him the answer.

'Right, show me your rail ticket and some identification.'

I pulled the ticket out of my back pocket and handed it to him, together with my birth certificate. The railway man was getting fidgety, no doubt waiting impatiently for me to be hauled off to the clink. The policeman handed me back my ticket and certificate. He pushed his cap back and spoke.

'Well, you've got a big day ahead of you tomorrow. If I was you, I'd stretch out on that seat.' He paused. 'And I'd get a blanket out of your swag—it may turn a bit chilly towards morning.'

'But! But!' spluttered the railway man.

The policeman gave him a withering look. 'Don't you have anything better to do than harass a bonafide traveller?' he said coldly, and left us.

I grinned at the discomforted railway man and bade him goodnight.

I did better than pull out a blanket, I unrolled my swag on the seat and slept blissfully until I was awakened by the morning bustle on the platform. Pulling a clean set of clobber out of my swag, I made for the station showers. There for two and sixpence I freshened up, and leaving my swag at the cloakroom, I was ready for breakfast.

A lot has changed with rail travel over the past 50 years, not all for the good. The refreshment room at the Townsville station was the size of a hotel dining room. Crisp white table linen covered the tables, which were set with heavy silverware and china all bearing the QGR brand. A waitress in uniform ambled up, gave me the breakfast menu and took my order.

After a plate of rolled oats followed by steak and eggs, I sat back, rolled a smoke and poured myself another drink of tea from the silver-plated teapot. I was at peace with the world and outside the sun was shining. After paying for the meal, I decided to have a look around the town. The pubs weren't open as yet but the shops were trading and the streets were crowded. I wandered around until 10 o'clock then walked into the first pub I came to.

I ordered a half rum and cast an eye over the clientele. The bar was empty save for an unhappy-looking individual who was leaning on the bar and cradling a half empty rum glass. A battered hat was pulled down over his unshaven features and he had the slightly dishevelled look of a bushman on a spree. I finished my drink and invited him to join me. He looked at me suspiciously, then seeing that I too was drinking rum, he sidled down the bar. I introduced myself and told him I was on my way to Cloncurry. He nodded and said, 'Yeah, not a bad place, the Curry. I wish to Christ I was there now.'

I gave him a hard look, expecting him to put the fangs into me for money. 'What's the trouble?' I asked him.

He pushed his hat back. 'I arrived from the Charters Towers yesterday. I'm booked into one of the pubs here, but I don't remember which bloody one, so I'm on a pub crawl until I find it.'

I asked him where he had spent the night. He grinned ruefully and told me he had got on the piss and the coppers had locked him up for being drunk and disorderly. I laughed and related how I had very nearly joined him. After he had shouted, we strolled up to another pub in search of his room. At the fourth hotel we went into, my companion looked around and shook his head. 'No, this isn't the place,' he said despondently. 'I should have stayed in that bloody stockcamp.'

'Why did you leave?'

'Because of a bloody jackaroo head stockman. I ended up knocking the bastard arse over head and got the sack.'

Just then the publican came over to us. 'I didn't see you at dinner last night, Bill,' he said to my dejected mate.

Bill looked at him in astonishment. 'You mean, I'm booked in here?'

Mine host assured him that he was indeed a guest of the hotel. Bill let out a loud 'You bloody beaut', then, turning to me, said, 'Hang on here. I'll go and have a clean up and then I'll shout you a feed in the dining room.' He was almost to the stairs when he stopped and looked back. 'Hey! What room am I in?'

The publican told him and walked away shaking his head.

After about 20 minutes Bill came downstairs. He was freshly shaven, clad in clean clothes and generally looked like a new man. Lunch proved to be an enjoyable meal. My new-found companion was now in top form and regaled me with the shortcomings of the incompetent head stockman. The meal finished, we strolled outside, where I bade Bill farewell and advised him to sleep in his own bed that night. He grinned broadly.

'I'm going to give the grog away,' he declared. 'And see if I can get on to a sheila.'

Looking at the new Bill, I reckoned he had a chance at that. I sauntered back towards the railway station. As the train did not leave until after four o'clock, I took my time. Passing a stock and station agency, I noticed a sign in the window: 'Stockmen wanted', it proclaimed. I had never had the need to canvas agents for work, but curiosity got the better of me. I walked in and stood at the counter. A youngish chap came over and I told him I had seen the notice in the window. He looked me over. 'Have you done any stockwork?'

I assured him that I had.

'This is cattle work—do you have any references?'

'No, I've never needed references to get a job. Once you're known out further, that's good enough.'

I told him where I had worked and added I was on my way to Cloncurry.

'Well,' he said, 'they are looking for three stockmen on Lorraine, that's between Cloncurry and Burketown. I employed two chaps this morning—you can go out with them.'

He told me I would have to catch the train from the Curry to Dobbyn, then get a ride on the Burketown mail truck. He then got some details from me so he could wire the manager of my impending arrival, and dismissed me. I went away quite happy. I had a job in the Gulf and it meant I would not have to hang about the Curry looking for work.

Arriving at the railway station, I redeemed my swag and bought an Ellery Queen mystery book. I then settled down to a quiet read until the time came to board the western mail train. I noticed two young chaps dressed in ringers' garb on the platform and decided they must be the other two going to Lorraine. They were obviously mates and as they seemed happy in their own company I returned to my book.

I always enjoyed train travel, but being on the western mail was not a new experience, as I had made the trip a number of times when going further west. Despite this, I found myself absorbed in the passing countryside. Those days there were many gangs of fettlers along the length of the Queensland railway lines. Whenever a mail train passed a gang, the men would line up beside the track with cries of 'Paper, Paper'. It was the latest newspapers they were after. Most of the passengers obliged by tossing the papers out of the window. Sometimes if the train was making its way up a gradient you could hand the required reading matter to them personally.

The trip out to Cloncurry was fairly uneventful. Upon leaving the train, which was now heading for Mount Isa, I inquired about the Dobbyn rattler. God willing, I was informed, it would leave the following morning. I got the impression that the staff regarded the Dobbyn train as a bit of a joke. Back on the platform, I ran into the lads who were going to Lorraine with me. We yarned for a while, and I gathered they had never been this far north before. They appeared to be treating the whole thing as a bit of an adventure. I knew it would be an experience that would tax both their ability and their resilience but decided to let them find out for themselves. Picking up my swag, I walked to the nearest pub and booked a bed for the night.

The town of Cloncurry has always interested me. It has had a fascinating and turbulent history. Ernest Henry, who found copper in the area in 1867 and later established the Great Australian mine, has always been regarded as the founder of Cloncurry. The district was rich in minerals, and many mines were soon in operation in the area. These mines included the Gilded Rose, a gold show some 12 kilometres from the town, which was established after a short-lived alluvial rush at Soldier's Cap. Other mines in the district gave rise to towns like Selwyn, Kuridala, Duchess and Dobbyn. Some of these once-booming towns have struggled on and survived due to pastoral activity.

In January 1883 Sub Inspector Beresford was killed by the Kalkadoon tribe, which held sway in the district for some time. At one point there were fears that Cloncurry would be raided by the warlike Kalkadoons. In March 1884 Sub Inspector Frederick Urquhart was appointed to take control of the native police in the area. Widely experienced in dealing with Aborigines, Urquhart soon had the situation under control. The spearing of Powell, a part-owner of Carlton Hills, proved to be the rock on which the Kalkadoons perished. Urquhart, together with graziers like Kennedy, went out and broke the power of the Kalkadoons.

Apart from its mining history, Cloncurry has always been the quintessential cattleman's town. The area contains a lot of rough country, and rough country always produces smart men. Over the years Cloncurry has also been the home of many characters as rough as the terrain—men like Galloping Jones, who regarded cattle duffing as a game rather than a crime. The Kajabbi and Dobbyn district has always had a reputation for lawlessness. Shortly before I started on Lorraine there was a double shooting in the area. The incident was put down to murder/suicide, but many of the locals questioned the verdict.

For many years Cloncurry hosted magnificent horse sales. I have seen hundreds of horses put through the yards, with buyers from many parts of Australia bidding for them. When a site was being sought for the Stockmen's Hall of Fame, Cloncurry threw its collective hat into the ring. I was living in the town then and was a member of a deputation formed to establish its claim. Cloncurry's bid proved to be unsuccessful, with the Hall of Fame going to Longreach, but that was of course years after my going to Lorraine.

In my room at the Leichhardt Hotel I unrolled my swag, emptied the pocket and went through my clothes. It was obvious I needed some new work clobber, and now that I had a job to go to, I could afford the outlay. Going downstairs, I strolled around the town until I found myself at Power's Emporium. When I left that well-known establishment, I had all the gear I needed, together with the information that there was a cattle duffing case in progress at the courthouse. As I was at a loose end, I presented myself at the hall of justice and spent an enthralling few hours there. The defendant, one Billy Mitchell, was on trial for duffing cattle from Coolullah Station. Mitchell had no country of his own, but ran a thriving herd on the Dobbyn common. Les Teece, the head stockman at Coolullah, was giving evidence when I sat down. It was soon evident to me that Mitchell would not be escaping justice as Harry Redford had.

I left Mitchell to his fate in the Cloncurry court house and returned to the Leichhardt Hotel. Next morning, dressed in brand new riding gear, I caught the train to Dobbyn. Dressed as I was, I knew I'd be letting myself in for some baiting at Lorraine. Blokes who turned up to a job in new gear were usually regarded as being as inexperienced as their clothes. Although initiation in the workplace is fairly uncommon in Australia, we've all heard of the new apprentice being sent to get a tin of striped paint. Jokes like that were often played on new chums on stations, but the only serious test of ability was the 'trial horse'—a horse that could buck a little and was used to establish the experience of a new man. The practice was neither company nor managerial policy and depended largely on the personality of the head stockman.

When the three of us arrived at the station, we were greeted in friendly manner by the assembled ringers, but I noticed a few nudges and winks directed towards me. Everyone was going down to the Leichhardt River for a swim. The other two new blokes jumped at the idea, but I decided to do some washing in preparation for work, which was to start the next day. The Lorraine lads seemed disappointed—no doubt they had something in mind for my benefit.

After hanging my clothes out, I strolled down to where the stockcamp lads were having a great time in the river, diving out of a boat made out of the belly tank of an aircraft. I declined the offer to join them and sat down on the bank to await events. I knew sooner or later I was going to end up in the river, but was determined it would be on my terms. One of the other new arrivals asked me to look after a camera he had, so I carefully put my hat over it, surreptitiously slipping my tobacco under the hat as well. Then, taking my boots off, I made a great point of paring my toenails with my pocket knife.

After a few minutes, they showed their hand. The boat edged in to the bank. 'If you can't swim, come for a ride in the boat. We'll look after you.'

I almost laughed. 'Righto,' I said, and stepped into the boat.

I knew they would tip the boat over out in the middle of the hole, and I was not disappointed. They started skylarking, jumping in and out, and finally over she went. I dived off the high side as it tipped and, swimming underwater, headed for the bank. I broke the surface behind a canopy of drooping tea-tree boughs, then sat on the bank and watched as their mirth turned to concern. Very soon concern became blind panic as they dived in an attempt to find my body.

Deciding that the joke had gone far enough, I stood up and went and sat down by my hat. When they finally saw me, one of them whom I had picked out as a smart ringer, swam over to the bank. He stood up and looked at me. 'You bastard! You put it over us.' There was mingled relief and astonishment in his voice.

I grinned at him. 'Yes, I'm not quite as wet behind the ears as you blokes thought.'

He climbed up the bank and sat down beside me. I rolled a smoke and handed it to him, then rolled one for myself and lit them both. He took a drag on the cigarette and declared, 'I reckon you've been around a bit, eh?'

I nodded and told him where I had been. We yarned for a while about the various stations we had worked on, then returned together to the ringers' quarters. He became a good mate of mine; in fact, I got on well with all the ringers. They were a lively lot and it was one of the happiest camps I had ever worked in.

Next morning we were to muster workhorses for the coming cattle work. By keeping my ear to the ground, I had verified that Lorraine did have a trial horse. He was a bay gelding with a blaze face called Crocodile and, sure enough, when we got to the horse yards Crocodile was among our mounts. I half expected to be given him, but apparently I had already established my credentials. Crocodile was given to the tallest of the other new arrivals.

We saddled up and rode off, with the trial horse giving no clue to his real nature. When we had the workhorses mustered later that morning, however, Crocodile was among them and his saddle was empty. I was told that Crocodile was not a bad buckjumper, although quite capable of throwing a novice. Two of the ringers caught and unsaddled Crocodile, then, leading a quiet horse, rode back to find the missing lad. On their way, they came upon a gum tree with a message scratched on its white bark: 'Going down river to try and find station.'

They found the missing lad unharmed, and a red-faced young ringer joined us for the midday meal. That gum tree became known thereafter as Crocodile's tree.

That afternoon the horses were drafted and a string of five was given to each ringer. When two good-looking brown mares came into the pound yard, one, Rosette, was put into my string and the other, a nice-looking mare called Sea Breeze, was given to Keith Campbell. Keith was

Bruce Simpson as a young stockman in Queensland.

a member of a well-known Gulf family, and he and his brothers were all top horsemen.

Once we knew what horses had been allocated to us, we tidied up their tails and started shoeing them. I had just caught Rosette when Keith came over to me. 'What about swapping that brown mare for the one I've got?'

I was a bit surprised, for neither of us knew the horses and I thought Sea Breeze was the better-looking mare. He was keen to trade, though, and I finally agreed to the change.

After we finished shoeing next morning, we all gave our horses a ride in the yard. Most station horses those days would buck or at least pig jump when fresh. We were taking turns to ride them and when Keith saddled up Rosette I watched with interest. The mare pulled away before he could mount her and put on as good a display of buckjumping as I had seen for a long time. I grinned at Keith, but he just shrugged his shoulders, caught the reins and swung into the saddle. He rode her easily in the yard, but once outside on the flat, she started bucking with a vengeance. Keith had no trouble riding her, but I was not sorry I had agreed to the exchange. Soft and out of condition as I was from a spell in the city, I doubt if I could have ridden her outside. I later saddled and rode Sea Breeze. She had a couple of goes at me, but she was not in Rosette's class.

The camp was going out to Cassady's camp next day and the horse plant was let go overnight in the station horse paddock. A grey gelding was put in the yard to use for running them in the next morning, and I was told by the head stockman it would be my job to do so. He also told me not to use a whip when riding the grey. I looked at him in disbelief, the horse paddock was fairly heavily timbered in places and a whip would make the job a lot easier.

'He's never been broken in to a whip?' I asked.

'No, you can't use a whip on him.'

'Well, the bastard will have one used on him tomorrow morning.'

At daylight I caught and saddled the grey, then, throwing my whip over his wither, I mounted and rode to the back of the paddock. I started horses back to the yards as I went and then cantered along the back fence. I swung the whip up and cracked it—and the grey exploded under me. As he hit the ground, I cracked it again. The next moment he went crashing into a tree, splitting my head open. Half blinded by the blood that was streaming down my face, I struggled to stay in the saddle. The grey was now galloping along behind the horse mob. I just made it to the yards, where two of the ringers helped me out of the saddle and over to a patch of lawn. I must have lost a fair amount of blood, as they had to hose down both the horse and my saddle. I was helped over to the quarters, where I wrapped a towel around my head and got out of my clothes, which were growing stiff with dried blood.

I was lying back on my bunk when the head stockman came in. He looked at me. 'Well, are you satisfied?'

I gave a weak grin. 'Oh, you can use a whip on the bastard all right, but you want to bail out f... smartly afterwards.'

I stayed on my bunk all day. The flying doctor, when contacted, advised plenty of fluids. As the stockcamp had departed, I was plied with sweet tea by one of the manager's daughters. My head was never stitched but healed up quite quickly, although I pulled pieces of wood out of my scalp for a number of years afterwards.

A couple of days later I rejoined the camp to a chorus of 'Did you bring your whip with you?'

I enjoyed my time in the Lorraine stockcamp. On occasions when we were in at the head station, a few of us gave an impromptu night-time concert on the flying doctor's network. One chap played the gum leaf, another the comb; I played a mouth organ, and Jack Durham coaxed music out of a rare instrument he made out of an oil can and some tie wire. They were a great bunch of blokes.

Towards the end of the year the mustering finished and the stockcamp moved to the head station. Many of the ringers made plans for the holidays later. Taffy, who had been cooking in the stockcamp, took over the men's kitchen and cooked for us there. Most of us got on well with him. A swarthy-looking individual, Taffy claimed to be a Welshman, and would offer to fight anyone who doubted his word. A week after we got to the station Taffy pulled out and caught the Burketown mail that would connect with the train to Cloncurry.

An hour or so after the mail truck had gone, the manager, George Schultz, came over to me. He asked me if I wanted to go for a drive, explaining that he had to put a parcel on the train. I wondered briefly why he had not put it on the mail truck, but said I'd be happy to go with him as a gate opener.

We arrived at Dobbyn with the Cloncurry train standing at the station. When we walked onto the platform, Taffy was standing there with a rather pregnant-looking swag. As soon as he saw us, he ran over to George, crying, 'I'm sorry, Boss. I didn't mean to take that gear. I don't know what came over me.'

George looked at him and said, 'Right, Taffy, show me what you've got.'

The terrified Taffy went to his swag. He unrolled it and half of the cooking gear from the ringers' kitchen fell out onto the platform. I left Taffy appealing to the manager not to hand him over to the police and carried the assorted kitchenware to the station vehicle. George did not charge Taffy, but he did tell him he'd never get another job in the Gulf. We watched a deflated Taffy depart with an equally deflated swag.

George Schultz was a man who kept his own council. I don't know to this day if we went to Dobbyn because he suspected Taffy. Now and again on the way back to Lorraine George hummed a little tune. It was vaguely familiar, but I could not place it. Then it hit me. He was humming the old nursery rhyme: 'Taffy was a Welshman, Taffy was a thief'.

ALL AMONG THE WOOL

AFTER SPENDING TWO stock seasons in the Gulf, I left Augustus Downs in October. My younger brother and I had arranged to go down South for a holiday. Alan was breaking in horses on a station around Clermont and we planned to meet in Mackay, then, after a few days at home, we would head to Sydney to let off a bit of steam. However, the old adage 'The best laid plans of mice and men . . .' reared its hoary head the day before I left Augustus. I received a telegram from Alan saying he would not be ready for another month. Consequently, I found myself in a difficult situation; I could not afford to sit around spending money while I waited for Alan, and stockwork had all but finished.

I spent a couple of unrewarding days in Cloncurry, then caught a mixed train to Hughenden. This train, affectionately known to the locals as the 'Old Nineteen Down', duly delivered me at my destination. Heaving my swag on my shoulder, I walked up town and booked into a hotel. Hotels were the only accommodation for travellers those days; they made their money over the bar but were compelled by the licensing laws to provide rooms for the weary commercial travellers and others. They did so with no great enthusiasm.

I dragged my swag up the stairs to the room I had been allocated and sat down on one of the beds. The room held two single beds, a large wooden wardrobe with one door askew and a washstand. Washstands were standard bedroom furniture those days. This one had a grimy mirror and a marble top holding a large china wash dish and a tall water pitcher. There was also a drinking glass on the marble top, in case a weary traveller should take the unlikely step of drinking water. Under the washstand was a badly cracked and chipped chamber pot. In the condition it was in, I doubted it would be of any use to any guest with a full bladder.

I found the showers at the end of a hall near the back stairs. The toilets were located in the backyard. The male facility consisted of a galvanised iron shed housing two thunder boxes; the urinal was a concrete drain, and an iron fence provided privacy, but it did not boast a roof. I considered the hazards of reaching the toilets from the bedrooms in the middle of the night, and came to the conclusion that the chamber pot may not yet be redundant.

I had a clean up and wandered down to the bar. It was Friday afternoon and the place was crowded. I ordered a beer, and when I got the chance, I asked the barman about the work situation. He told me there was little stockwork about, but that the shearing sheds were still busy. The opinion I held of sheep and shearing was typical of all cattle-men—sheep were stupid and the only thing dumber than a sheep was a sheepman.

I had a few more beers, then when the dinner bell rang I wandered into the dining room. Though the accommodation in the bush pubs of that era might have been less than desirable, the tucker was first rate. I saddled up to a huge meal of roast mutton plus roast potatoes and pumpkin, garnished by a rich brown gravy. I have never been keen on desserts, but the aroma of the steam pudding and custard almost seduced me.

After dinner I returned to my room to find a battered suitcase under the other bed. Shortly after, my room-mate appeared. He was a rather rotund individual of middle age with a round, cheerful face and greying hair. He said he was a woolroller and that I could call him Blackie. I introduced myself and told him I was looking for stockwork. Blackie made a sympathetic noise then excused himself with: 'I've got to study the form now'. He opened the paper he had been carrying at the racing guide pages and got to work with a pencil.

I lay back on the bed and thought things over. It looked as though I would have to go in further to pick up work. My reverie was broken by my room-mate, who stood up saying, 'I'm going downstairs to get some money on before the price shortens. I'll see you when I get back.'

Blackie duly returned. He sat on his bed and looked at me. 'So you're looking for a job. Why don't you try the shearing sheds?'

I looked at him in surprise. 'I've never seen a sheep at close quarters and I know nothing at all about shearing.'

Blackie looked me over. 'You're young and fit. You'd get a job pick-ing up.'

'Picking up what?' I asked him.

He laughed. 'Picking up fleeces, of course. When a shearer finishes shearing a sheep, he leaves the wool on the shearing board. It's the picker-up's job to gather it and throw it out on the wool table.'

'How the hell do you pick up a heap of wool?'

Blackie looked disgusted. 'Here, I'll show you.' He opened his port and dragged out a none-too-clean towel. 'Now, the fleece is upside down when it comes off,' he said, and threw the towel across the floor in front of him. 'Now, watch what I do.' He straightened the towel a little, put his left foot up to the near side and then, reaching forward, he picked up the far side between the thumb and two fingers of each hand. He then brought both hands back together and picked up the folded towel at his foot.

'That's all there is to picking it up, but now you have to throw it out right side up like this. He walked over and threw it on the bed. He was still holding the edges between thumbs and fingers and this had the effect of flipping the towel over so that it landed with the other side up. He looked at me.

'There you are, there's nothing to it. Here, have a go.'

The towel landed on the floor and I attempted to emulate Blackie's smooth handling of the make-believe fleece. After 20 minutes of practice and advice, I was picking the towel up and throwing it out with confidence. Blackie, obviously pleased with his pupil, told me I'd have no trouble getting a job in the sheds.

'I'll tell you what,' he said after a bit of thought. 'The contractor I work for is looking for a shedhand. I'll give you a break to him tomorrow. I reckon you'll be as right as rain once you get the hang of it.'

True to his word, Blackie introduced me to the shearing contractor on Saturday afternoon. When he heard I was looking for a job, but was inexperienced, he looked me over and said, 'Well, I'll give you a start—if you're willing to learn, you'll be right. We'll pick you up with Blackie tomorrow afternoon.'

Later I asked Blackie if I needed any special gear. 'No,' that worthy replied. 'Just make sure you take sandshoes or gym boots.'

I looked at him in dismay. I owned neither, and the shops were closed.

I learnt from Blackie that I would be picking up for five shearers. The gun, a chap named Matthews, was shearing more than 200 a day, and the others were not too far behind him. I was going to be handicapped by wearing riding boots, but was prepared to give it a go. I was to learn to my dismay, however, that picking up newly shorn fleeces was not as easy as handling Blackie's towel.

Next afternoon I threw my swag onto the contractor's truck, and my life as a rouseabout began. There were a couple of other shedhands on the vehicle, including Blackie. The shearers, apparently, could afford their own transport. At the shearers' quarters I found there was a spare bed in Blackie's room, so I claimed it, keen not to lose contact with my adviser. The evening meal was an eye opener for me. There was a choice of three main courses and two desserts. Afterwards I asked Blackie if Sunday dinner was regarded as a special occasion. My room-mate threw back his head and laughed. 'No, Simmo, that was a bit below the standard of meals during the working week. Shearers are hungry bastards. But they do work hard.'

As we lay on our beds that night Blackie gave me a rundown of the shearing game. It started, he told me, when a grazier and a shearing contractor signed a contract in which the contractor agreed to shear the flock for a set price per head. The contractor then employed shearers who shore for so much per hundred sheep and a wool presser, who agreed to press the clip for so much a bale. The rest of the team were waged or salaried workers. Two of the team were specialists. The wool classer was a semi-professional who graded the wool into various qualities; the expert, another skilled man, kept the shearers' cutters sharp. The other waged men were called rouseabouts and included penners-up, pickers-up, piece-pickers and woolrollers. Then there was the cook. The shearers had a big say in the hiring of the cook and he could be sent packing if they voted him out. The contractor kept an eye on the whole operation. I asked Blackie about the machinery and he explained that an engine-driven shaft ran the length of the shearing board; friction wheels above each shearer's stand drove a flexible enclosed shaft connected to the handpieces used to do the shearing. These friction wheels could be engaged or released by pulling a rope beside each stand. Armed with this knowledge, I went to sleep.

I thought Blackie may have been pulling my leg about the tucker, but after a multi-choice breakfast next morning I was convinced. As we left to go to the shearing shed, Blackie turned to me. 'Have you got your ticket?'

'Ticket! What ticket?'

'Your union ticket, the AWU ticket. You do have one?'

'Yes, it's in my gear somewhere. I'll see if I can find it.'

After rooting around in my swag, I finally found the ticket I had taken out on Augustus. It was just as well I did, for at the shed there was a call for a show of tickets. There was no place for scabs in the sheds those days.

On the job I was more or less under the orders of the wool classer. He was an Irish Australian, and a bit of an old woman. He watched my attempts to pick up the first fleece, then pushed me aside and showed me how I should be doing it. To be honest, I found it extremely difficult to handle the fleece and even harder to throw the damned thing out in the prescribed way on the wool table. It was also part of my job to take a tar pot to any shearer who nicked a sheep and to sweep the loose wool up from the shearing board. For quite a while there was more wool on the board than thrown onto the wool table.

By the end of the first run I was beginning to get the hang of it, although I was often late in getting fleeces out of the way before the shearers started on another sheep. Four of them would kick the fleece to one side so I could get at it, but the man on the far stand shore on top of it, making it a bloody mess. He was a cranky old bastard who had been a gun in his day but was now the slowest of the lot. I cursed him under my breath, swearing I would bide my time and get even.

At the end of the day I was buggered. Ringers are in pretty good nick, but in picking up, a completely different set of muscles are called on. That night I was asleep almost before my head touched the pillow. Next morning I threw my riding boots off and worked in my socks. I found it a lot easier, although I did pick up a few splinters from the shearing board. I threw the last fleece out before smoko and it landed perfectly. Blackie grinned and gave me a thumbs up. I had never had time before to see what happened then, so I watched with interest as Blackie and another chap picked the dags and broken pieces from the fleece then rolled it up for the classer to inspect. The classer gave it the once over and threw it in one of a number of bins denoting quality.

By the end of the third day I felt I was getting on top of the job. Despite a few blisters and splinters, I was beginning to enjoy the bustle and rivalry on the shearing board. That night after a hot shower and a first class meal, Blackie continued with my education. Shearers and rouseabouts had little in common, he said, and this arose because of the different way they were paid. Being on contract, shearers were only paid while they were shearing. If they had to stop because of an engine failure or wet weather the money stopped. Rouseabouts, on the other hand, were on wages and were paid during any hold-up in shearing. Blackie told me that an old Afghan he once knew summed it up in a little ditty he used to sing. It went like this:

> *Shearer man like plenty butter*
> *Moffat comb and Cooper cutter,*
> *Rouseabout like plenty joke*
> *Rain come up and engine broke.*

I asked Blackie about hold-ups due to rain and what the real problem was. He sat up on his bed and rolled a smoke.

'Well,' he replied, 'wet sheep are supposed to give shearers arthritis. If there is any doubt, the shearers vote on it. If they vote wet sheep, then shearing stops. Mind you, a lot depends on how cashed up they are. I've seen 'em vote wet sheep after a heavy dew; I've also seen 'em vote dry when the bloody frogs are jumping out of the fleeces.'

Blackie told me that shearers did not approve of women in the sheds. If a female was seen approaching, the cry of 'Ducks on the pond' went up. He added that shearers were a superstitious bunch, but did not elaborate. Later I was to find out just how true this was.

Matthews was still well ahead on numbers shorn. As a shearer finished a sheep, he pushed it down a shute leading to a pen that held only his shorn sheep. At the end of the day a tally was made, so everyone knew the score. I was now faster at picking up, although the old coot at the far stand still caught me occasionally. He would just look at me and say, 'Well, you'll just have to smarten up a bit.'

At the weekend I went into Hughenden and bought myself a pair of gym boots. Now, I thought to myself, that old bastard is about to get his. I held off until Wednesday, when big strong wethers were being shorn and the old shearer had his hands full. My moment came when he came out of the pen backwards, dragging a big wether. I picked up his last fleece and, crouching down, moved sidewards, leaving my right leg out-stretched. He fell over it backwards and the big wether kicked hell out of him before it escaped. He stood up and glared at me. I glared back and said, 'Well, you'll just have to smarten up a bit,' and left him.

I had now become quite an expert at the job and was growing in confidence. The shearers weren't a bad bunch, but one night an incident occurred that made me question their sanity. I was lying on my bunk after tea and Blackie was occupied elsewhere. I pulled my mouth organ out of the pocket of my swag and started to play it. A few minutes later a commotion started in the quarters; men were shouting and walls were being thumped. I imagined the shearers were engaging in a bit of horseplay, until two irate-looking shearers appeared in my doorway.

'Stop playing that bloody mouth organ,' one of them demanded.

I looked at them in astonishment. 'What the hell are you talking about?'

'Stop playing that blasted thing or we'll jam it down your throat.'

I stood up. 'Will you now?' I said.

Just then Blackie arrived on the scene. 'I'll handle this,' he told them.

After they'd gone Blackie looked at me. 'You never told me you played the mouth organ.'

'So bloody what?'

'Hang on, cool down a bit. You remember me telling you that shearers were a superstitious lot?'

Mystified, I nodded.

'Well, they think that playing the mouth organ will bring rain.'

I looked at Blackie in disbelief. 'You're joking?'

'No, the silly bastards really believe it. You've seen their reaction.'

To me it seemed incredible that grown men could believe such nonsense; it was not only childish but stupid. Next morning the contractor buttonholed me. 'Look, I'm happy with your work, but I'll have to ask you not to play that mouth organ again. I like a happy team and that does upset them.'

I reluctantly agreed, but could not resist having a dig.

'Do you have to put money under their bloody pillows when they lose a tooth?' I asked.

He gave me a hard look then walked off. Later I told Blackie of the encounter. He called me a cheeky bastard and said I was lucky to still have a job.

After two-and-a-half weeks the shed cut out and we were all paid off. Back in Hughenden, Blackie, who seemed to know everything, said he had heard we were going out to another shed. As always he was right, and the following Sunday afternoon the shearing team assembled at the new station. There was a larger flock to shear and the contractor had put on another shearer.

'Christ!' I said to Blackie. 'I'll have to pull my finger out here.' He just laughed and advised me that if six shearers were engaged there had to be two men picking up.

This turned out to be the case. I got on well with the new picker-up, a lad from Charters Towers. With two of us working, it was a breeze. We took turns in working the three far stands and kept racing each other to send the fleeces flying out onto the wool table. However, on one occasion Blackie failed to get out of the way of a fleece thrown by the new lad, and the wool classer threw up his hands in horror. Blackie backed out from under the fleece and said dryly, 'If you young fellows like running so much, I might have a word to the cook about putting some jalap in your tucker.'

We did steady up a bit. I did not want to fall out with my mentor. We finished the first week with Matthews still well ahead on the tally board.

The new shearer, a young chap from New South Wales, put it to him for a while, but then Matthews forged ahead.

I was almost sorry when I heard that the shed would finish up on the Monday two weeks after we had started. On the Friday a young chap who was horse breaking on the place asked me if I was going in to town on the last weekend. I told him I wasn't, as we were due to finish on the Monday. He then asked if I would mind riding out a colt to muster the last of the sheep. He explained he had two freshly broken horses that were now ready for a bit of work. I jumped at the chance to get on a horse again and agreed to meet him at the horse yards after lunch on Sunday.

At two o'clock I strolled down to the yards, where the breaker was mouthing two colts. He seemed relieved to see me, and leaving what he was doing, walked over with me to another yard.

'There they are,' he said. 'You can take your pick. Both are going okay.'

I got a bridle, and walking up to a bay filly, caught her without any trouble. She humped a bit when I girthed her up so I led her around until she relaxed. When breaking in, it is best not to let horses buck. They learn bad habits quickly enough without being encouraged. When the breaker was ready, we both mounted and, after giving our mounts a ride in the yard, joined the musterers. The filly I was riding had a good mouth and seemed quite tractable. It was not a big paddock we were mustering and we soon began putting the sheep together. I noticed a small mob going for their lives in the wrong direction and, seeing it as a chance to give the filly a good gallop, set off after them. I had nearly caught up with them when something flashed by my mount's ears, and a telephone line hit me in the face. It almost dragged me out of the saddle, but I managed to regain my seat and keep the filly under control. My face, however, was a bloody mess. The wire had lifted the skin on the left side of my face from jawline to forehead and I could not see out of my left eye.

I rode back to the mob and later let the filly go at the yards. The young horse breaker was both concerned and apologetic, but I assured him it was not his fault. It was the second time in two years I had been involved in a similar accident, but the first, at Lorraine, had been entirely my own fault because of over confidence. Here, however, I felt the station was guilty of carelessness bordering on criminal negligence. I was leaving the yards when the manager, who had seen something was wrong, stopped me.

'Did that horse throw you?'

I glared at him with my one good eye. 'No, the filly didn't throw me, that bloody phone line of yours nearly took my f... head off.' I then proceeded to give him my opinion of sheep stations in general and his in particular.

'But, but,' he spluttered, 'you went out of your own volition.'

'That's true, but you'll be hearing from my solicitors,' I said and walked off.

It was an idle threat, but it sounded good. I knew as I was not on the station books I could not even get workers' compensation.

When I walked in to my room, Blackie, who was half asleep on his bed, sat up. 'Jesus Christ! What have you done to yourself?'

I explained what had happened and he rabbited around in his suitcase and came up with a battered-looking first aid kit. My left eye was completely closed, but facial injuries always look worse than they are. Blackie patched me up with bandages and sticking plaster and I went to the evening meal looking like the phantom of the opera.

The shed cut out at three o'clock the next day, with Matthews still the gun. We packed up and drove into Hughenden. It was to be my first and last encounter with sheep. There was a letter from Alan for me at the hotel. He had arrived at Mackay and was rearing to go. Three days later I joined him.

GLOSSARY

Babbler short for babbling brook—cook

Bang-tail, to to cut the tassel off the end of a beast's tail as an indication that the beast has been counted

Bang-tail knife knife used for the above

Bang-tail muster muster cattle for the above

Beaver moles a type of moleskin trousers

Belar a type of tree

Board-boss supervisor of the shearing shed

Bogan fleas small, low-growing burrs

Bogis shearer's handpieces (pronounced 'bog eyes')

Blow-out a spree

Blue a fight or argument; also a summons

Bolter's chance no chance at all

Bronco rope a greenhide rope used to catch unbranded calves

Brownie bush cake

Bull's head brand of Victoria River Downs; road mobs from VRD were known as 'Bull's head bullocks'

Bullocks fully grown male cattle that have been castrated as calves

Bum trot sit on a trotting horse without rising in the saddle

Bush a horse turn the horse out for a spell, or for good

Choked down fall into a drunken sleep

Clatter a rattling sound

Cleanskin unbranded cattle

Clumper a heavy type of stockhorse

Curio a famous buckjumper

Dawn patrol a gathering of drinkers served at the back door before the pub opens

Dinner camp a break during the heat of the day

Dogwatch a short watch before the regular watches start and after they finish

Drafting cutting selected beasts out of a mob

Dough roaster a camp cook

Duffer someone who steals branded cattle

Flinders grass a very nutritious native grass

'The Fort' Fort William, just north of Boulia

Founder to break down

Front leg, to to throw a beast by the front leg

Gibber a stone

Gidgee a species of Acacia

Gilgai shallow depression holding water after rain

Goas Aboriginal tribe in the Winton areas

Gooly a stone

Goosenecks spurs

Goose picking short, scattered grass shoots after rain

Greenhide untanned hide

Guyver style

Hand (as in horse height) 4 inches (10 centimetres)

Hip shot standing with the weight off one hind leg

Hobble or **hopple** a chain with two short straps to tie a horse's front legs together; the horse can walk, but it can't stray far

Hobble up the act of putting hobbles on a horse

Holt corruption of the word hold

Horsetailer a ringer or stockman whose job it is to look after the horse plant

Jackaroo a company man sent to the station for experience

Jibs refuses to move

Jillaroo female version of a jackaroo

Jump-up a steep incline leading to a tableland

Killers beasts killed for beef

Knackered exhausted

Knock up become exhausted

Lug or **to lug** to get a firm grip of a horse's ear to mount

Maluka Aboriginal term of respect for a boss or old man (pronounced mul-a-ka)

Mick, micky a young wild bull

Min min light an unexplained phenomenon of the outback

Mitchell grass a nutritious native grass

Monkey strap a short strap on the off (right) side of the saddle sometimes used in mounting a horse

Munjon myall native

Murranji the stockroute between Newcastle Waters and Top Springs (pronounced Murran-jai, to rhyme with 'eye')

Near leg front of hind leg on the left side

Nick, get into get fit

Nighthorse a special horse for nightwork with cattle

North-West usually refers to North-West Queensland and part of the Northern Territory

On the road droving

Packs pack saddles used to transport equipment on packhorses

Peter Pan a winner of the Melbourne Cup back in the 1930s

Pills sheep dung

Pikers big wild scrub cattle

Plant a drover's horses and equipment

Poddy an unbranded calf

Poddy-dodgers someone who steals unbranded calves

Pound a small yard

Pug a boxer

Quart quart pot, a small flat-sided billy carried on the saddle

Reef (at the bit) pull hard on the reins

Reined up pulled on the reins to pull a horse up

Rooter a pig jumper, a horse that does not buck badly

Rouseabout semi-skilled worker in shearing shed

Rush a maddened gallop of cattle, usually at night

Salvos the Salvation Army

Scrubbers wild scrub cattle

Shank a short rope tied to a halter

Sideline a chain fastened to both the front and hind leg of a horse

Silver-leaf box a type of timber

Spayed cows de-sexed female cattle

Store-conditioned not fat

Stores store-conditioned beasts; not fat

Stoush a brawl

Stunner a good sort; an attractive girl

Surcingle a strap that goes over the saddle to secure it

Swinger top notch

Tailing cattle to shepherd or keep under control

Tucker food

Turpentine low scrubby native bush

Turkey nest an earth tank for water storage

Two-pot screamer a cheap drunk

Utility or **ute** a light commercial vehicle

VRD Victoria River Downs

Waler a famous type of Australian cavalry horse exported in large numbers

Watching cattle riding round road cattle at night

Wave Hill route the route west of the Murranji was often called the Wave Hill route

West that part of the Northern Territory that was west of the Murranji, including the East Kimberleys

Windy (of something) afraid

NOTE ON CURRENCY

The following is an approximation of the decimal equivalent of currency mentioned in the text; the actual value of the original currency at the time in question would be considerably higher than that of its decimal equivalent today:

sixpence (or zac)	5 cents
a shilling (or bob)	10 cents
a quid (or pound)	2 dollars

BIBLIOGRAPHY

Books

Armstrong, R.E.M., *The Kalkadoons*, William Brooks & Co. Pty Ltd, Brisbane.

Australian Dictionary of Biography, Vol. 3, Melbourne University Press, 1969.

Bagnell, Fred, *North Queensland Cavalcade*, published by author, Charters Towers, 1979.

Booth, Edwin C., *Australia in the 1870s*, facsimile edition, Uhr Smith, Sydney, c1975.

Buchanan, Bobbie, *In the Tracks of Old Bluey*, Central Queensland University Press, Rockhampton, Qld, 1996.

Buchanan, Gordon, *Packhorse and Waterhole*, Angus and Robertson, Sydney, 1933.

Cole, Tom, *Hell West and Crooked*, William Collins Pty Ltd, Sydney, 1988.

Cotton, Catherine Drummond, *Ludwig Leichhardt*, Angus & Robertson, Sydney, 1938.

Cusack, Thomas, unpublished account of his droving trips in 196–62.

Downer, Sydney, *Patrol Indefinite*, Rigby Ltd, Adelaide, 1963.

Fysh, Hudson, *Taming the North*, Angus and Robertson, Sydney, 2nd edition, 1950.

Green, Jean and Fitzgerald, James, *McLennan's Way*, Hesperian Press, Carlisle, WA, 1994.

Hill, Ernestine, *The Territory*, Angus and Robertson, Sydney, 1951.

Idriess, Ion L., *The Cattle King*, Angus & Robertson, Sydney, 1947.

Kerry Kendall, unpublished account of incidents at Topsy Creek and Keelbottom Creek.

Kerr, Margaret and Colin, *The Overlanders*, Rigby, Adelaide and Brisbane, 1975.

Laffin, Laurence James and Dargush, Marion Joan, *The J.A. Laffin Story*, published by authors, Ipswich, Qld, 1996.

Lamond, G.A., *Tales of the Overland*, Hesperian Press, Victoria Park, WA, 1986.

Linklaker, William and Tapp, Linda, *Gather No Moss*, Macmillan of Australia, 1968.

Mackanes, George and Mackanes Joan S., 'The Wide Brown Land', Angus and Roberston, Sydney, 1954—An anthology.

McConville, Ray, *McConville's Wild Australians*, published by author, Myrtleford, Vic, 1997.

Morey, Ted, article in *Northern Territory Newsletter*, May 1977.

Powell, Alan, *Far Country*, Melbourne University Press, 1982.

Pike, Glenville, *Frontier Territory*, published by author, 1972.

Pike, Glenville, *Round the Campfire*, Pinevale Publications, Mareeba.

Teece, Cecil and Pike, Glenville, *Voice from the Wilderness*, published by authors, 1978.

Newspaper articles and stories

Adelaide Advertiser, 15/11/1883, 16/11/1883, 17/11/1883, 29/11/1883.

Blachall, correspondent of the *Queenslander*, 5/10/1878.

Cairns Post, 27/11/1951, 28/11/1951.

Carr-Boyd, reports in the *Queenslander*, 7/9/1878, 5/4/1879, 12/4/1879, 26/4/1879, 31511879, 17/5/1879.

Clune, Frank, 'Skeletons in the Sand', *Short Story Magazine*, December 1948.

Cronau, E.R., article in *People* magazine, February 1961.

Delhunty, Larry, article *in North Queensland Register*, 22/2/1990.

Evert, Peter, unpublished article on Gidgee Taylor.

Mitchell, Gregory, article in *Hoofs and Horns*, December 1995.

Morey, Ted, article in the *Northern Territory Newsletter*, July 1997.

North Queensland Register, 24/10/1883.

North Queensland Register, 8/1/1917.

North Queensland Register, 10/3/1945.

Northern Territory Times and Gazette, 5/1/1884.

Oldtimer, report in the *Queenslander*, 5/10/1878.

Orme, Les, article in *Man Magazine*, August 1949.

Tatz, Colin, article in *Hoofs and Horns*, July 1996.

The Pastoral Review, May 1905.

The Pastoral Review, August 1929.

The Pastoral Review, September 1929.

Uhr, Frank, letter to the *North Queensland Register*, some 50 years ago.

Interviews

Death on the Barkly

Interviews with Cecil Teece of Normanton, Qld and Peter Treloar of Delaney's Creek, Qld. Phone interview with Ron Easey of Petrie, Qld.

Dangerous Waters

Interviews with the following people: Laurie Hansen of Finch Hatton, Qld; Noel Thompson of D'Aguilar, Qld; Keith Haughton of Narangba, Qld; Bob Isles of Redcliffe, Qld; Colin Campbell of Mitchell, Qld; Bob Howard of Caboolture, Qld; Lucky Forrester of Strathpine, Qld; Eugene Costin of Brunette Downs, NT.

Phone interviews with Jim 'Ringer' Edwards of Gin Gin, WA and Bill Alexander of Marion Downs, Qld.

After Buchanan

Interviews with the following ex-drovers: Bob Isles of Redcliffe, Qld; Noel 'Pic' Willetts of Camooweal, Qld; Herb Heumiller of Barcaldine, Qld; Ian Tait of Koumala, Qld; Jack Gardner of Caloundra, Qld; Bobby McDonald of Barcaldine, Qld; Rodney Mosted of Camooweal, Qld; Noel Thompson of D'Aguilar, Qld; and Peter Isles of Redcliffe, Qld.

Prizes for Riders

Interview with Sam Fuller Jnr.

Rough Riders of the Bush

Information contributed by the following people: Jack Cunningham of Brisbane, Qld; Mrs Lola Rowe of Mildura, Vic; Rod Bellette of Patterson Lakes, Vic; Jim 'Ringer' Edwards of Gin Gin, WA; Merv Rogers of Charters Towers, Qld; Luke McCall of Batlow, NSW; Bob Isles of Redcliffe, Qld; Barry Desailly of North Ward, Qld; Les Huddy of Mt Isa, Qld; Gordon Gaffney of Tamworth, NSW; Ray Webster of Landsborough, Qld; George Booth Jnr of Port Douglas, Qld; Mick Bailey of Broken Hill, NSW; Tidly Treffett of Charters Towers, Qld; Alex Logan of Kumbia, Qld; Ernie McCarthy of Pine Creek, NT; Eddie Hackman of Rockhampton, Qld; Herb Heumiller of Barcaldine, Qld; Ian Tait of Koumala, Qld; Jack Gardner of Caloundra, Qld; Bob Kirk of Herbert Downs, Qld; Mal Debney of Glenormiston Station, Qld; Walter Lloyd of Boulia, Qld; Bob Howard of Caboolture, Qld; Ross Ratcliffe of The Willows, Qld; Jeff Simpson of Stanthorpe, Qld; Merv Thomas of Landsborough, Qld; Mick Thomas of Barcaldine, Qld; Noel Thompson of D'Aguilar, Qld; Barney Bellford of Eukey, Qld; Bobby McDonald of Barcaldine, Qld; Gilbert Macintosh of Mt Isa, Qld; Noel 'Pic' Willetts of Camooweal, Qld; John Chaplain of

Cloncurry, Qld; Jack Drake of Eukey, Qld; Ab Teece of Cloncurry, Qld; Mrs Ada Devereaux of Brisbane, Qld; Colin Campbell of Mitchell, Qld; Ray Gillham of Suttor Creek Station, Qld; Lyn Craig of Eton, Qld; Graham Murchie of Stanthorpe, Qld; Lloyd Linson-Smith of Oakey, Qld; Peter Isles of Redcliffe, Qld; Alex Long of Caboolture, Qld.

Wild Men and Windlasses

Interviews with the following people: Fred Holm of Winton, Qld; Mrs Martyr Snr of Mayneside Station, Winton, Qld; Ron Bates of Gatton, Qld; Bill Moore of Redcliffe, Qld; and Graham McKerrow of Weona Station, Winton, Qld; Ion Idriess, Lightning Ridge, NSW; Brian Holm of Winton, Qld and Matt Masterson of Mareeba, Qld.

The Red Flash

Taped interview with Mick Cheadle of Millungra Station, Qld. A number of long interviews with Jeff Simpson, of Stanthorpe, Qld and Mick Cheadle, Millungra Station, Qld. Interviews with Graham McKerrow of Weona Station, Winton, Qld and Vince Evert of Winton, Qld. Files of the Capricornian Opal Company.

80025 75540